EVERYDAY WAYS TO SAVE OUR PLANET

200+
SUSTAINABLE SWAPS
FOR YOU AND YOUR FAMILY

TV Meteorologist

Laura Tobin

with Melanie Hancill

EVERYDAY WAYS TO SAVE OUR PLANET

200+
SUSTAINABLE SWAPS
FOR YOU AND YOUR FAMILY

TV Meteorologist

Laura Tobin

with Melanie Hancill

MIRROR BOOKS

To Charlotte

MIRROR BOOKS

First published in Great Britain in 2022

@TheMirrorBooks
Mirror Books is a part of Reach PLC Ltd, 5 St Paul's Square, Liverpool, L3 9SJ
One Canada Square, Canary Wharf, London, E15 5AP

Hardback ISBN: 9781913406738

Photographic acknowledgements:
Laura Tobin personal collection, Alamy, UnSplash, Pexels
Cover photo:
Lorna Roach

Written with: Melanie Hancill
Design: Rick Cooke, Adam Ward, Chris Collins
Production / sub-editing: Roy Gilfoyle, Chris Brereton
Cover design: Rick Cooke, Adam Ward

Printed and bound by Bell & Bain Ltd, Glasgow

Every effort has been made to trace copyright.
Any oversight will be rectified in future editions.

CONTENTS

'NO ONE CAN DO EVERYTHING BUT EVERYONE CAN DO SOMETHING'

So go on, tell me… what's the weather like where you are today?

We are a nation obsessed with the weather. Whatever the conditions, Brits have got something to say about it. It's our go-to topic when making small talk, and nine out of 10 of us will mention it at least three times a day. It's not surprising, considering how much it changes. One minute we can be sunning ourselves in our gardens, the next we're dashing inside to escape a torrential downpour. What's not to love about that?

As a broadcast meteorologist and scientist, it will come as no surprise that I LOVE to talk about the weather. I've been forecasting it for 17 years now, but my love affair with the subject started much earlier in life – during a particularly memorable geography lesson when I was just 14 (cue embarrassing photo).

My teacher, Mr Hannant, asked all the boys to stand in one straight line and all the girls to stand in another straight line next to the boys, as though we were about to start two conga lines. Then he told us to run across the classroom as quickly as we could, pushing against each other on the way, until we got to the other side. When we made it, our lines weren't straight any more, they were wiggly. And that, he said, is how weather forms. Confused? Let me explain. What he'd done was create a jet stream in our classroom. The jet stream is a conveyor belt of winds high up in the atmosphere – and it's this that brings weather fronts to our shores. It separates the cold Polar air to our north (which is pushing down), from the warm air coming from the south (which is pushing up). So in our classroom we had the boys (warm air) pushing into the girls (cold air). Who would win? Boys or girls? Warm or cold? This battleground is set every day across the UK, and the weather changes depending on whether the jet stream gets pushed north or south.

From that moment on, I was hooked. I called the Met Office at 14 to ask what exam results I'd need to be a meteorologist (maths and physics GSCEs and A-levels) and the rest, as they say, is history. Now, I'm lucky enough to talk about the weather every day on breakfast TV. And I really do think it's the best job in the world.

In recent years you've probably heard me talking more and more about climate change. After all, it's the major factor affecting the weather that we love to talk about so much in the UK. Our world is heating up at an alarming rate. July 2021 was the hottest month ever recorded for our planet, and the last decade has been our warmest ever recorded. We've seen more extreme weather events than ever before (such as the flooding in Germany and the wildfires across Europe) and it's clear that if we don't make changes now we will reach tipping points when the damage will become irreversible – think melting ice caps, rising sea levels, displacement of communities and the extinction of entire species of animals.

Climate change has gone from something we thought might happen in the future to something that is very much happening right now. People used to ask me, "Is climate change real?" But these days, the two most common questions I get are, "What can I do about climate change?" and, "Will I make a difference?"

My answer, of course, is "Lots" and "Yes!" In the following pages of this book, you'll find more than 200 suggestions on how you can live more sustainably to reduce your impact on the planet. From buying second-hand clothes and singing in the shower (yes, really!) to sending fewer emails and composting your food scraps, so many of the changes in the book are simple – and free!

It's easy to think one person's efforts can't make much difference. But let me tell you, they can! If every person in the UK made just one change from this book, that would be 67 million changes.

I've also included a chapter on the science of climate change because I've always believed that understanding the problem can help us fix it. I explain why the Earth is heating, how we know humans are to blame and what the devastating impacts will be for our planet if we don't act now.

If you've watched the film *Don't Look Up* starring Leonardo DiCaprio and Jennifer Lawrence you might have noticed the parallel between the climate change crisis we are currently facing and the comet that is hurtling towards the Earth in the movie. All the facts are there, the scientists have told us what we need to do and what will happen if we don't – now we need to listen and take action rather than ignore the issue. There's a profound line at the end of the film (spoiler alert!) where Leo says, "We really did have everything, didn't we?" The same is true for us now. We have everything we could possibly need on Earth but we often take it for granted.

Charlotte is one of the main driving forces behind why I want to help the planet

One of my favourite things to do is look at a satellite image of the Earth from space. Our blue marble in all its glory. With so much going on it's easy to forget how amazing our planet is. It's the only one in the entire known universe to harbour life – us and our animal and plant friends. It has given life to everything and everyone we have ever known, but all we have done is take from it.

I often hear people say, "There's no planet B." But the truth is, the Earth will be just fine. It doesn't need another planet – we're the ones who are in danger. The planet will be much better off without us at the rate we are going!

One of my biggest driving forces for speaking out about climate change and writing this book is to leave a better world behind for my beautiful daughter Charlotte. She was born 12 weeks prematurely in 2017, and my little baby had a fight on her hands from day one. And now it's my job to fight to save our planet for her. We are the first generation who are really going to be impacted by climate change, but we almost certainly won't be the last. It upsets me to think there are animals my daughter may never see because they're under threat of extinction, and places she might never get to visit because they'll be under water. When she asks me what I did to help stop climate change, I want to be able to tell her I did everything I could. So for you, Charlotte, I've written a letter, on page 14 of this book.

Charlotte is four now, and as you go through the book, you'll see what a little eco warrior she has become. From her bamboo toothbrush to growing her own veg in our allotment and never throwing anything (and I mean ANYTHING) in the bin. She has a better understanding of our impact on the planet than many people I know. And it's often Charlotte who tells me off for "doing a bad thing" rather than the other way round.

You'll also meet my husband in the chapters of this book. I met him while studying physics at Reading University and let's say he's been dragged along on this journey with me, rather than being a willing participant. He actually lives quite sustainably already. He turns off plug sockets at the wall every night, watches the smart meter like a hawk and takes Charlotte to school on his bike instead of in the car. But NOT because he wants to save the planet… because he is the tightest person on it! You'll hear all about our thermostat wars, how he calls our food-waste bin 'Greta' (after environmental activist Greta Thunberg) and how he "already knows how to save water so doesn't need a lecture on it!" On a weekly basis, he'll roll his eyes and ask, "So, how are you saving the planet THIS week?" But when he realises my planet-saving ideas are also money-saving, he usually gets on board.

And that's the thing. There are so many benefits to living a more sustainable life. One of the biggest things I've learnt is that tackling climate change doesn't have to mean making sacrifices. It's thinking about what you will gain rather than what you will lose.

The biggest benefit of living more sustainably is, of course, that we are helping to save our planet. But as you work through the sections of this book, you'll see that being eco-conscious and having a healthy lifestyle go hand-in-hand. And the best bit – it's often easier on the wallet! (I think I can hear my husband cheering…)

As someone in the public eye, I'm used to receiving criticism for some of the things I do. Earlier this year I posted pictures of me and Charlotte litter-picking in our local area. And while most people thought we were doing a good deed and 'saving the planet', there were others who commented things along the lines of, "What use is litter picking when you fly all the way to the Arctic to forecast the weather?"

What they're referring to is my trip to Svalbard in the Arctic Ocean in September 2021. The irony of flying somewhere – which is bad for the environment – to talk about climate change is not lost on me. But I believe that any negative impact me, my cameraman Ed and producer Ruth made by flying, was far outweighed by the positive impact from showing millions of people the true realities of the climate crisis – and the changes people made as a result. Like I said before, when we understand the problem, it's easier to fix.

Why am I telling you this? Because I think it's important to know that this book and the journey to a more sustainable life is NOT about pointing the finger (unless you're still using single-use plastic bottles – shame on you!). It's about giving you the information you need and then letting you decide what changes will work for you. We are all different and what works for one might not work for another.

My philosophy is that no one can do everything, but everyone can do something.

You don't have to read this book from front to back or all in one go, you can dip in and out of the sections that interest you the most. If you need initial inspiration, you can check out my Top 10 changes at the back of the book. My biggest advice is to take your time. There is no point deciding to never eat meat again, stop using your car altogether and never buy anything in plastic all in one go. You'll be overwhelmed and give up altogether. It's not a race. Remember that the smallest changes can make the biggest difference.

If you do want to keep track of your progress, I've included a checklist at the back of the book (I love a list!) of all the suggestions, plus some blank space for you to add your own ideas too. I know from experience that the more changes you make, the more inspired you'll be to keep going – and to tell others. While writing the book I shared my journey with friends and family, who then told their friends and family and it has a ripple effect. Before you know it, everyone around you is doing their best for the planet.

It reminds me of American mathematician and meteorologist Edward Lorenz's theory of the 'butterfly effect'. He suggests that a small change, such as the flapping of a butterfly's wings, can have a large effect elsewhere, such as on a hurricane on the other side of the world. So can you start a small ripple and create a big wave of change?

I'm guessing that if you've picked up this book, then you're ready to take action now. So what are you waiting for? Together, we can make a world of difference…

MY LETTER TO CHARLOTTE

To Charlotte

They say there are seven wonders of the world, but to me there is only one – you. On this whole amazing planet you are the most special thing of all, in my eyes.

In fact, most of the original wonders aren't 'wonderful' any more because they have been destroyed or left in ruins. Some people are working hard to protect those that are left, but why did we take so long to act? Why didn't we try sooner?

So this letter is to tell you that I will do everything I can to make sure that you can see all the wonders our world has to offer. I want your eyes open wide at all the new things you see and for those memories to last a lifetime.

I'm sad that some things may only be alive in stories, photos or the memories of other people. Will I be able to take you to Svalbard to see the beautiful fjords that stretch as far as the eye can see? Will you see the polar bears and reindeer, or will they be long gone? One thing is for certain – if you stand where I stood, the landscape will look very different. It's already too late to preserve it as it is now, BUT we can do something about just how different it will look, because that will depend on how long we carry on overheating our planet and how much ice melts. It's not too late to rewrite the end of the story and I want to do that for you, so you can see the world in all its glory with all the tiny islands, all the beautiful plants and all the amazing animals.

I'M SORRY...

I'm sorry that we have known for so long that our world is overheating because of our actions. Sorry that we've polluted all of our oceans and all of our skies. Sorry that the ice is melting and the seas are rising. Sorry that millions of people are having to move away from their homes because of the impacts of climate change – because of heatwaves, wildfires and floods. Sorry that we continue to burn fossil fuels and pump them into the atmosphere – the air that you have to breathe. Sorry that in the short span of your life so far our planet is the hottest in human history. Sorry that one in eight animal and plant species are threatened with extinction (that's one million!) and that in the last 50 years we have lost 68% of global wildlife.

I'm sorry that we aren't kinder to our planet and everything on it. Sorry that we think it's okay to dig holes in the ground and fill them with rubbish when so much of what we cover with soil could have been given new life. Sorry that we keep cutting down trees, which act as the lungs of our planet. Sorry that by 2050 all the plastic in the oceans will weigh more than all the fish unless we take urgent action. Sorry that there are tiny low-lying islands that will soon disappear beneath the waves through no fault of their own.

I'm sorry too that Australia has had its worst wildfires in history and that more than one billion animals perished. Sorry that many types of animal – such as the Hawaiian crow and Père David's deer – are already extinct in the wild and can only be seen in zoos and wildlife parks. We share our planet with them but don't give them an equal share!

I'm sorry we think it's okay to throw rubbish on the ground. Sorry I can't answer your question, 'Why did we do that?' because I'm not sure we know ourselves. Laziness? Not caring? Not understanding? I'm sorry we think it's okay to drive to the shop for some milk or bread when often we can easily walk. Sorry that we are not kinder to our planet – it's the only one we have and we should look after it as carefully as I will look after you.

I PROMISE...

I promise that I will do everything I can to save our planet – to encourage everyone to listen to the scientists and take action. I promise that we will slow down and then stop pumping pollution into our atmosphere, to make the air clean again. I promise we will make more use of the wind and sun and tides that are ours for free to give us power. I promise that we will give the Earth's marine life a fighting chance by phasing out the plastic that pollutes our rivers and oceans. I promise that we will live more sustainably so we can save more of the planet's precious resources, that we will think more of others and help developing nations to give their people a better life. I promise that we will let nature flourish – like it did during the pandemic when the world started to heal, the pollution cleared, we could breathe fresh air, hear birdsong – and beaches in Thailand were full of turtles laying eggs because the tourists stayed away. I promise that we will stop taking so much unfair advantage of our planet.

I HOPE...

I hope that the message of this book does not fall on deaf ears. I hope it will inspire lots of people to start making the kind of small but important changes that will give you and your generation of children the most beautiful and unspoilt planet possible. I hope I can take you to see animals that were nearly extinct being reintroduced to the wild and that we can still visit the tiny low-lying islands that are under threat, knowing we helped save them. I hope that more people will stop and appreciate the beautiful world around us and realise that it is worth more than all the 'stuff' we buy. I hope we come to realise in our hearts how much we can achieve if we act together, and that we use all of our knowledge and our power to innovate to make real change. I hope that when you reach my age, perhaps with children of your own, we will have stopped warming the Earth, so you and other people who understand the danger don't have to devote so much time and energy to persuading other people how urgent it is.

Charlotte, I love you and I love our planet. I want to protect you and I want to protect it too. I do all this for you, my Number One Wonder Of The World.

Mummy xx

When I read Charlotte the letter she said, "Mummy, is the planet happy?" and I had to tell her no. She asked if the ice was still melting for the polar bears, and when I said yes, she asked when all the ice would be gone. She also said we must find people who smoke and tell them not to because our planet is too hot! She then said, "We need to save our planet, don't we Mummy?"

I feel like she has a much better comprehension of the damage we are doing to the Earth than most people and she is only four!

WHAT IS CLIMATE CHANGE?

In the 17 years that I've been a meteorologist, I've prepared weather forecasts for local councils, the military and the public. As a TV meteorologist (at the BBC for five years and now at ITV for nine years) it's been increasingly important to include science in my daily breakfast forecasts to give people a better understanding of the weather and why it's changing. I try to explain everything from pressure charts and the jet stream to sudden stratospheric warming.

In recent years I've been including more and more about climate change. The public appetite for information is increasing and a little understanding goes a long way.

In this book I aim to expand on that process. The climate change crisis and its impact on the Earth can seem incredibly overwhelming. This makes it hard to understand what has got us to this point, what will happen if we don't do anything, and what exactly we, as individuals, can do to help.

In this chapter and throughout the book I want to show you that the science of climate change is **Simple**, the impacts are **Serious** but the problem is **Solvable**. I first heard it described like this in a TED talk by climate scientist Dr James Rae in 2018, and I loved how clear that message is.

As Dr Rae explains, a Simple way to describe climate change is, "CO_2 traps heat, we've added loads of CO_2 to the atmosphere by burning fossil fuels, and as a result the world is getting warmer."

Or, in other words, the world is overheating because it's wrapped in a blanket of pollution.

Now the Serious part. The impacts of climate change are already clear to see. As temperatures rise, we're getting extreme weather events such as heatwaves and floods more often, sea levels are rising, coral is dying and glaciers are melting. All of these are putting human and animal lives in danger all over the world.

Is it Solvable? Yes, because we have the knowledge and tools to avoid the worst effects of climate change. That's what this book is all about – showing you ways that we can all reduce our individual impact on the planet.

I have been asked lots of questions about climate change over the years and hopefully any you do have will be answered in the coming pages.

SIMPLE – WHAT IS CLIMATE CHANGE?

First up, let's remind ourselves what climate change means…

The dictionary definition is as follows:

A change in global or regional climate patterns, in particular a change apparent from the mid to late 20th Century onwards and attributed largely to the increased levels of atmospheric carbon dioxide produced by the use of fossil fuels.

For the perfect world, we need everything to be in balance. As the sun's rays hit the Earth, it warms up. The Earth then radiates that heat back into space, which allows our planet to stay at a stable temperature (in equilibrium). But if more heat is absorbed than is reflected back out, we are tipped out of balance and the temperature of our planet begins to rise.

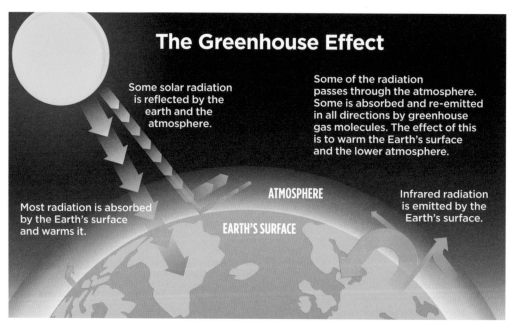

The Greenhouse Effect

Some solar radiation is reflected by the earth and the atmosphere.

Some of the radiation passes through the atmosphere. Some is absorbed and re-emitted in all directions by greenhouse gas molecules. The effect of this is to warm the Earth's surface and the lower atmosphere.

ATMOSPHERE

EARTH'S SURFACE

Most radiation is absorbed by the Earth's surface and warms it.

Infrared radiation is emitted by the Earth's surface.

The atmosphere is like a protective blanket for our planet. The average temperature of the Earth is about 14°C. Without the atmosphere, that temperature would be more like -18°C! During the last 12,000 years, in a period of geological time known as the Holocene Epoch (this started at the end of the Paleolithic Ice Age and continues now) the temperature of the Earth has stayed relatively stable, even though it has risen and fallen many times. But in the last 170 years the Earth's temperature has risen by around 1.2°C above average. And it's this rapid rate of change that is so concerning.

WHY DOES 1.2°C MATTER SO MUCH?

I'm often asked why 1.2°C is a big deal when the temperature changes by about 10°C on any given day. Some people will say, "Look at all that snow... so much for global warming!" But when it comes to the climate, we are not looking at the weather conditions or the temperature at a certain place at a certain time, we are looking at the long-term average overall temperature of the whole planet. The weather in the UK is variable. We will have snow in the winter (but less in future due to climate change) and sun in the summer. Weather is the day-to-day condition of the atmosphere over short timescales, whereas climate is the average of all the weather that happens over longer timescales – typically 30 years.

The reason 1.2°C matters is because our planet is incredibly fragile. Just like us, if the Earth overheats it becomes unwell. If our temperature goes up by 1°C we would have a fever, and we'd rest, see a doctor or take medicine to get better. However, when the Earth's temperature goes up it can't rest because we are constantly using its resources. But scientists can be the Earth's doctors – they can see what the problem is and have prescribed a treatment: we have to stop the things that are polluting our planet and making it overheat!

Climatologist Professor Ed Hawkins from the University of Reading – where I studied Physics and Meteorology – has created the Climate Stripes, pictured on the next page. They're my favourite visualisation of how much and how quickly the Earth has warmed. Every single line represents the temperature of Earth each year compared to the average. The blue is temperature below average and red is temperature above average. You can see that on the left, in 1850, the lines are blue, showing cooler than average temperatures. As we move into the late 1900s, pink lines begin to appear, showing temperatures a little above average, then as we cross into the 2000s, the red lines show temperatures well above average. The very dark red lines in recent years are the most worrying because the rate of warming we are now seeing is alarming.

CLIMATE STRIPES TO SHOW THE WARMING OF THE EARTH OVER THE PAST 170 YEARS

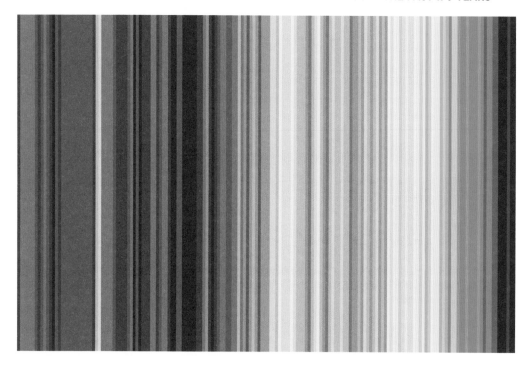

To see Climate Stripes for individual countries and many major cities, visit *showyourstripes.info*

Here are some statistics (I love statistics!) to show you how warm things have become:

- July 2021 was the hottest month ever recorded on Earth.
- 2021 was the 7th warmest year on record.
- 2020 was the joint warmest year on record, tied with 2016. In 2016, the Earth had a helping hand in the form of an El Nino. This is when there is a big upwelling of warm waters in the Pacific Ocean which helps to naturally warm the atmosphere. In 2020 and 2021 we had a La Nina – a cool upwelling of waters, which naturally helps to cool the atmosphere. This makes the record highs for 2020 and 2021 even more remarkable.
- The last eight years have been the warmest on record.
- December 2021 was the 444th consecutive month with temperatures above average.
- Scientists say there is a 99% chance that 2022 will be in the top 10 warmest years ever recorded.

But hasn't the Earth been hotter than this before?

I often hear these two questions: "Hasn't the Earth been hotter than this before?" and "Isn't it just part of the natural cycle of Earth?" Yes and no. The Earth has been warmer than this before but it has never warmed so quickly – and that is the issue. Professor Ed Hawkins also created this bar chart (below) to show the rise and fall of temperatures compared to average over the last 12,000 years of the Holocene, and you can see on the far right how rapidly our planet is warming now.

THE RISE AND FALL OF TEMPERATURES COMPARED TO THE AVERAGE OVER THE LAST 12,000 YEARS

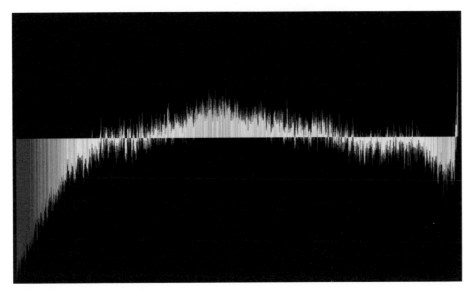

So why is it happening?

This 1.2°C increase in global temperature has been caused by an increase in the concentration of greenhouse gases found in the Earth's atmosphere. Around 99% of the Earth's atmosphere is made up of nitrogen (78%) and oxygen (21%). The remaining 1% is a mixture of water vapour plus greenhouse gases (GHG) known as carbon dioxide, methane, nitrous oxide and fluorinated gases. Greenhouse gases are so called because they act like the glass roof of a greenhouse – they stop heat escaping. It's crazy that such a small percentage can have such a big impact on the temperature of the planet. Before the industrial revolution, which began in around 1760, these three gases remained at relatively stable amounts in the atmosphere. But as mankind began to burn more fossil fuels, use more land for agriculture and cut down forests, the levels of greenhouse gases have risen exponentially. Fast forward to now and carbon dioxide is at its highest level in at least two million years.

GREENHOUSE GASES EXPLAINED

CO_2 – 80% OF GLOBAL GHG EMISSIONS

Carbon dioxide is the gas that is most often talked about when it comes to climate change and that's because it is the most common, even though it makes up only 0.04% of the Earth's atmosphere. Of course, humans release carbon dioxide with every exhale, and carbon is essential for life. But the problems we are seeing with CO_2 are from human activities such as the burning of oil, coal and gas, as well as deforestation. The level of CO_2 in our atmosphere has risen by 50% since 1750. Before the industrial revolution, it was around 278ppm (parts per million). By 1986, that level had gone up by 25% to 348ppm. And in May 2021, it had risen a further 25% to 419ppm – the highest ever recorded. What matters here is how long it took to reach each milestone. It took more than 200 years for the first 25% increase, but only 35 years for the second. And what's more worrying is that any CO_2 we release into the atmosphere sticks around for hundreds, if not thousands, of years.

METHANE – 10% OF GLOBAL GHG EMISSIONS

Methane makes up a smaller percentage of the atmosphere (0.00018%) than CO_2 and it breaks down in 10-15 years, but the big problem with this gas is that it is up to 80 times more warming than CO_2. Scientists say about one-sixth of recent global warming is due to methane emissions, which can be caused by natural sources such as swamps, as well as human activities, including livestock farming (from cow and sheep burps!), paddy fields and the breakdown of waste in landfill. The concentration of methane in the atmosphere has more than doubled since pre-industrial times, reaching 1,900ppb (parts per billion) in 2021, compared to 722ppb in 1750.

NITROUS OXIDE – 7% OF GLOBAL GHG EMISSIONS

This gas is 300 times more warming than carbon dioxide, makes up 0.00003% of the atmosphere and stays around for around 100 years. Nitrous oxide is naturally present in the atmosphere, but about 40% of it comes from human activities such as the use of fertilisers in agriculture and livestock manure, as well as the burning of fossil fuels and other industrial processes. Since 1750, the amount of nitrous oxide in the atmosphere has increased by 23% – 270ppb in 1750 to 334ppb in 2021.

FLUORINATED GASES – 3% OF GLOBAL GHG EMISSIONS

Hydrofluorocarbons, perfluorocarbons, sulfur hexafluoride, and nitrogen trifluoride are synthetic greenhouse gases emitted by a variety of industrial processes as well as coolants in large fridges, freezers and air-conditioning units. They are stronger than natural greenhouse gases and can last for thousands of years. Because of this, their use is heavily regulated.

Scientists work out how much CO_2 there would have been in the atmosphere thousands/millions of years ago by looking at tiny bubbles of ancient air that are trapped in vast ice sheets. They have found that at no point during the last 800,000 years have CO_2 levels been as high as they are now. The last time the level of CO_2 in the atmosphere was above 400ppm (as it is now) was between 2.6 and 5.3 million years ago. During that time, it's estimated that the sea level was about 23.5 metres higher than today and the average temperature was 4°C higher!

How do we know humans are responsible?

There are many factors that can make the Earth warmer and colder but the rapid speed of warming we are seeing at the moment can only be linked to greenhouse gases caused by human activity.

If you look at the graph below, you'll see that the upward curve showing the increase in greenhouse gases caused by human factors almost exactly matches the upward curve showing the rise in the Earth's temperature. You'll also see that the natural causes of temperature change, such as the sun, volcanoes and the Earth's orbit, have only a negligible impact.

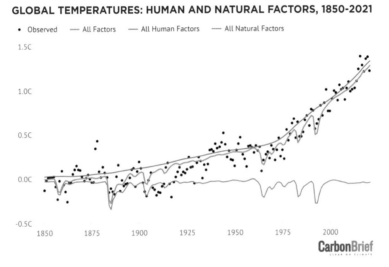

GLOBAL TEMPERATURES: HUMAN AND NATURAL FACTORS, 1850-2021

Natural causes of temperature change on Earth include:

The Earth's orbit
The Earth wobbles on its axis, so its tilt and orbit can change over many thousands of years. This is what has pushed the planet in and out of ice ages. The influence of the orbital changes in the last 125 years have had a negligible impact on the global temperature.

The Sun
The Sun's temperature varies over decades and centuries. These changes have had little or no effect on the Earth's temperature.

Volcanoes
Volcanic activity and eruptions release sulphate chemicals that can actively cool the

Earth for a year or two after an eruption. Human industry emits about 100 times more CO_2 than volcanic activity.

Other human-related causes of temperature change are:

Deforestation

Humans have cut, ploughed and paved more than half of the Earth's surface. While we desperately need trees to absorb CO_2 (which has a cooling effect on the planet, see page 43 for more on 'carbon sinks'), dark forest canopies can actually absorb more heat from the sun than the lighter-coloured ground that is revealed when they are cut down.

Ozone

Ozone is a gas that absorbs harmful ultraviolet light from the sun. It's both a natural and man-made gas found throughout the atmosphere but 90% of ozone gas is found in what we call the ozone layer, about 30km above the Earth's surface. This has a relatively cooling effect on the Earth's temperature. But when ozone is found closer to the Earth's surface, it acts as a greenhouse gas, which traps heat in.

Air pollution

Different types of air pollution have different effects on the atmosphere. Some contribute to global warming; others actually cool the atmosphere but can cause acid rain.

None of the above causes have had anywhere near as much impact as the increase in greenhouse gases, which has led 99.9% of climate scientists to conclude beyond doubt that humans are causing our current climate crisis.

> PROFESSOR ED HAWKINS HAS SAID, "IT IS A STATEMENT OF FACT, WE CANNOT BE ANY MORE CERTAIN; IT IS UNEQUIVOCAL AND INDISPUTABLE THAT HUMANS ARE WARMING THE PLANET."

What is the UK's contribution to greenhouse gases?

The most reliable figures we have are from 2019, with UK emissions estimated at 454.8 million metric tons of carbon dioxide equivalent ($MtCO_2e$). The huge majority of that (80%) was from carbon dioxide itself.

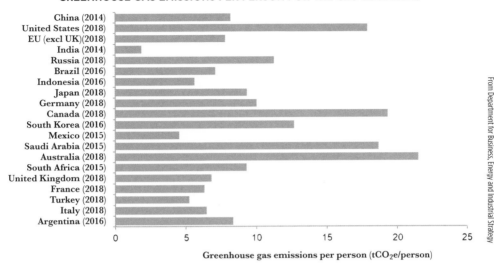

GREENHOUSE GAS EMISSIONS PER PERSON FOR THE G20 COUNTRIES

Greenhouse gas emissions per person (tCO$_2$e/person)

But how does this compare to other countries?

Because the Industrial Revolution began in the UK in around 1760, we were at one point the largest emitters of CO$_2$e in the world. Since then, our levels have stabilised or gone down and other countries have overtaken us. Larger countries, such as America, Australia and Canada emit more but it is important to look at the amount of CO$_2$e emitted per person. If you look at the graph above, you'll see that Australia has the top spot, followed by Canada, Saudi Arabia and America. The UK is 14th, and China 11th. I often hear people ask, "Why should we bother changing our ways when China isn't doing anything?" But, as you can see, their emissions per person are not that much higher than ours. And it's also important to take into account that a lot of their emissions come from the manufacture of items that we use – such as clothes and appliances! In fact, consumption emissions in the UK – emissions that come from items we import – are 37% higher than UK-based emissions. As the first country to start polluting the world, we should be the first to decarbonise.

Our emissions come from lots of different sectors. The area with the highest emissions is transport (27%), followed by energy supply (21%), then business (17%), residential (15%), agriculture (10%), waste management (4%) and 'other' (6%). As you read through the book, you'll find information on how to cut your own emissions in many of these areas of life.

I should point out that our overall greenhouse gas emissions have been going down over the last two decades. In fact, because of the Covid-19 pandemic, the UK's estimated

CO_2e emissions for 2020 are 10.7% less than in 2019. This is largely due to the reduction in road transport because of lockdowns, and reduced business activity. But even without the pandemic, UK emissions are gradually reducing every year. Our total greenhouse gas emissions for 2019 (454.8 $MtCO_2e$) were 43.8% lower than in 1990. This is great news for the UK, but I expect you are now thinking…

If greenhouse gas emissions are falling, what's the emergency?

Remember that greenhouse gases, especially CO_2, have a very long lifetime. Even if we could cut all emissions today, the Earth would continue to heat up for our children and grandchildren. Even though we now emit less, the concentration of greenhouse gases in the atmosphere has never been higher. The Met Office has a really good analogy to explain this.

THE BATHTUB ANALOGY

Take a look at the picture of a bathtub below. The water in the bath shows the amount of carbon dioxide in the atmosphere, and the water coming out of the taps is what we are releasing into the atmosphere every year. During the first year of the pandemic, we turned the taps down a little, but the bath still filled up – just not as much as it would have done without the reduction in travel and industry. We are going to keep getting warmer until we stop (or at least drastically slow down) the amount of greenhouse gases we put into the atmosphere. In an ideal world we would turn the taps off altogether (stop emissions) and pull the plug out so that the level would go down. But if we continue as we are, it won't take long for the bath to overflow – which is the equivalent of the Earth's temperature rising by more than 1.5°C. This is the threshold that was set as part of the Paris Agreement in 2015 and it's the temperature we desperately don't want to exceed (for more on this, turn to page 42).

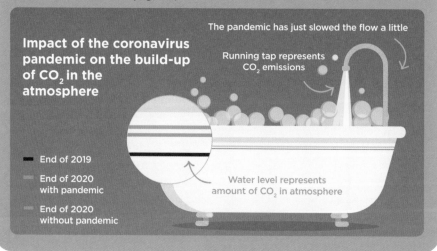

Impact of the coronavirus pandemic on the build-up of CO_2 in the atmosphere

The pandemic has just slowed the flow a little

Running tap represents CO_2 emissions

Water level represents amount of CO_2 in atmosphere

■ End of 2019
■ End of 2020 with pandemic
■ End of 2020 without pandemic

I know that's a lot of information to take in, but I'm hoping it gives you a better understanding of what climate change is, why it is happening and how we know that humans are responsible.

SERIOUS – WHAT ARE THE IMPACTS SO FAR?

Climate change is not something we are fearing in the future, it is something that is already happening now. As Dr William Ripple, Professor of Ecology at Oregon State University, says, "Climate change has arrived and is accelerating faster than many scientists expected."

As temperatures soar, there has been an increase in wildfires across the globe, coral reefs are being destroyed, while the rapid melting of glaciers and ice sheets has resulted in sea levels rising. All these signs are warnings that if we keep going at the rate we are, things will get worse. Let's look at the major impacts of climate change so far…

MELTING GLACIERS AND ICE CAPS

As the temperature of the Earth rises, it's no surprise that glaciers and ice caps are melting – and this is perhaps one of the most visible indicators of climate change. The Arctic is warming two to three times faster than the global average on Earth and since the 1980s glaciers have lost more ice than they have acquired. The fate of glaciers is made in the summer, rather than the winter. During the warmer months, any snow that fell in winter starts to melt away. The hotter it gets and the longer that heat stays, the more snow will melt. In recent years, most of the winter snowfall on many glaciers has melted by mid summer, meaning that snow from previous years is melted during the rest of the summer – this is why the glaciers are retreating.

The poles and high mountainous regions of our planet may feel very far away from us in the UK, but the melting of ice and snow affects all of us either directly or indirectly. Today, 670 million people live in high mountainous regions, and they rely on the ice and snow for their entire existence – from food and water to energy, trade and tourism.

Did you know that 1.5 million Brits travel abroad for ski holidays every year? But it's hard to know how much longer we will be able to do this – a warmer world means a shorter ski season at lower levels. I visited the beautiful town of Tirol, one of the largest glacier ski resorts in Austria. The people there were very worried about the impacts of climate change. Kay Helfricht, an expert on glaciers, told me that the glaciers there had lost 60% of their volume in the last 150 years – and 20% of that loss had taken place over the last 10 years. The glaciers had been losing on average one metre of ice a year, but during one particular hot spell, they lost one metre in a week! When I asked Kay to predict what will happen if we continue to heat the Earth as we are, he told me, "If we keep the climate how it is now, like it has been for the last 30 years, the temperatures will rise by more than 2°C and there won't be any glaciers left in Austria by 2100."

This would be a disaster for Tirol on an economic level. Roland Volderauer of the Stubai Tourist Board said, "A life without tourism would be impossible here – no streets, no cable cars, no jobs. Tourism is our daily bread." In an attempt to stop the ice retreating, glaciers are now being covered in giant fleece blankets to protect them from the summer heat. These are just the impacts in Austria, but the same is happening across the Alps and other mountain ranges around the world.

- The Arctic lost 6,000 gigatonnes of ice between 1993 and 2019, which caused a global average sea level rise of 17mm.
- Glaciers are at their lowest extent in 2000 years.
- Since the 1980s the average glacier has had the equivalent of 27.5 metres of ice sliced off the top.
- Glacier melt has been responsible for 40% of sea level rise since 1901.

Projections for the future:

- If we carry on as we are, there will be a 50% reduction in the volume of ice in glaciers by 2100, and an 80% reduction in small glaciers (such as the one in Tirol) by 2100.
- If all glaciers in the world melted, the average global sea level rise would be 0.3 metres. That might not sound like much but it's enough to put parts of the Humber, Cambridgeshire, Lincolnshire, Kent and the Bristol Channel under water.
- Melting glaciers lead to glacial lake bursts, also known as glacial tsunamis. Glaciers have dips which fill with melt water and create glacial lakes. The more ice that melts, the more they fill up. When they overflow or burst, a huge cascade of water flows downhill, which is disastrous for surrounding villages. In February 2021, there was a devastating flash flood that killed more than 200 people in India's northern state of Uttarakhand. A team of scientists investigating the incident believe a piece of Himalayan glacier ice fell into the water and triggered the flood.

MELTING ARCTIC SEA ICE

Just as the glaciers are starting to retreat, so is the Arctic sea ice. This is formed during the winter and retreats in summer, but it never completely disappears. But as global

THE GREENLAND ICE SHEET

An ice sheet is a mass of glacial land ice that extends more than 50,000km². We have two ice sheets on our planet – one in Greenland and one that covers Antarctica. Between them, they hold 99% of the fresh water we have on our planet. While the Antarctic ice sheet has remained relatively stable despite the rise in temperatures, the Greenland ice sheet has started to decline.

- Between 1979 and 2006, summer ice melt increased by 30%.

- If the ice sheet melted completely, sea levels would rise by 7%.

- In August 2021, rain (instead of snow) fell at the summit of Greenland's ice sheet for the first time in recorded history.

- If all glaciers and ice sheets melted, global sea level would rise by more than 60 metres.

temperatures rise, we are seeing Arctic sea ice decrease dramatically. This has a profound effect on the local habitat, but it also has an impact globally. These icy regions act as refrigerators for the planet. The bright white surfaces reflect heat back into space, which balances out some of the heat absorbed by darker areas around the world. As ice starts to melt to reveal the darker waters (or land) beneath, the Earth absorbs more heat, which leads to more ice melting – a vicious cycle known as positive feedback.

How much sea ice have we lost so far?

- Arctic sea ice is at its lowest in 1,000 years.
- Since 1979 we've lost an area of sea ice that would cover around half of Europe.
- In the last 40 years, we've lost an average of 87,000km² per year – that's a total of 3.4 million km².
- In 2020, late-summer Arctic sea ice was at its second lowest in recorded history.

Future projections:

- If we carry on as we are, the Arctic will be ice-free during summer in 10 to 30 years.

MY VISIT TO SVALBARD IN THE ARCTIC OCEAN

In September 2021, I had the chance to visit Svalbard, a Norwegian archipelago in the Arctic Ocean, halfway between Norway and the North Pole. I went there to look at the impacts of climate change. It's a landscape of jagged mountains, fjords, glaciers and polar bears – but it is changing fast.

If the prediction that the Arctic will be ice-free during summer in the next 30 years comes true, this would have devastating consequences for the people of Svalbard, the animals that live there – including polar bears, reindeer and marine life – and the rest of the world. Before I went I felt like I knew so much about the science of climate change and what it means for everyone on the planet, but nothing could prepare me for the reality.

The Arctic is already warming two to three times faster than the global average, but in Svalbard, it is warming nearly six times faster. Figures from the Norwegian Meteorological Institute show that in the last 50 years the average winter temperature has increased by 7.7 degrees, from -15.9°C to -8.2°C. And the average summer temperature has increased by 2.5 degrees, from around +3.8°C to +6.3°C. To put that into perspective, in the same amount of time, the Earth has warmed by 0.88°C, the UK has warmed by 1.24°C and Svalbard has warmed by 4.9°C. Nowhere else on Earth is heating up this fast.

During my visit I met Kim Holmén from the Norwegian Polar Institute. He took me and the weather team to Breinosa Glacier, to show us how much the glacier has retreated in the last 100 years. I also visited Longyear Glacier with Arne Kristoffersen, who arrived in 1980 as a coal miner. He showed me that the glacier had retreated by around half a kilometre since he'd been there, and had lost up to 40 metres in height in places.

The melting ice is having a huge impact on tourism in Svalbard. Mats McCombe from Hurtigruten Svalbard runs outdoor activities for tourists. He told me that they can no longer offer trips on snowmobiles – which were possible as little as five years ago – because the ice is either too thin or non-existent. Mats took us to the Borebreen Glacier via the Isfjorden. Isfjorden translates to 'ice fjord' but there was no ice – it hasn't frozen in the last 11 winters. At the glacier, I got to see an 'ice carving'. This is when chunks of ice break off and fall into the fjord. It's a natural process, but it is happening more often.

We need to help each other by reducing our impact on the planet. One of the most important messages from Kim that I came home with is that we can live happy and fulfilled lives while adapting to climate change. We shouldn't see it as a sacrifice – what is being sacrificed at the moment is our planet, and that has to change.

Broadcasting from the glaciers in Svalbard

Why does the Arctic matter to us in the UK?

The Arctic is one of the main drivers of our weather in the UK. It affects the atmospheric circulation for the northern hemisphere and the jet stream – the conveyor belt high up in the atmosphere that brings us our weather. The difference in temperatures between the cold Arctic and the warm Equator creates a strong temperature gradient, resulting in a strong jet stream. As the Arctic warms, the temperature gradient decreases, which could weaken the jet stream so that it becomes more meandering – or blocked. This means the weather is more likely to get 'stuck', which could lead to more weather extremes such as wetter wets (think of the floods we saw in Germany in 2021) and hotter hots (like the wildfires Greece experienced in 2021).

DAMAGE TO OCEANS AND CORAL REEF

Our oceans are amazing – they cover 70% of the Earth's surface and they are a major driver of weather and climate. They absorb most of the solar energy reaching the Earth and their currents redistribute that heat around the world. They also absorb 23% of the annual emissions of CO_2e from the atmosphere. But an increase in CO_2e in the atmosphere and the rise in global temperatures is having a big impact.

- The world's oceans recorded the hottest temperatures in history in 2021.
- The heat absorbed by the oceans last year was equivalent to seven Hiroshima atomic bombs detonating each second, 24 hours a day for 365 days a year.
- The warmer the ocean, the higher the sea level because warm water takes up more space (thermal expansion).
- Between 2006 and 2018, the global sea level rose by 4.4cm. It took almost three times the amount of time (35 years) to rise 6.5cm between 1971 and 2006.
- Rising levels of CO_2 in the ocean physically change the chemistry of water. CO_2 lowers the PH in a process known as ocean acidification. Open ocean surface PH has declined globally over the last 40 years and is now the lowest it has been for at least 26,000 years. As the acidity of the ocean increases, its ability to absorb CO_2 from the atmosphere decreases.
- A more acidic ocean affects many organisms and ecosystems. It results in environments that are inhospitable for marine life, while also threatening food security by endangering fisheries and aquaculture.
- We've lost over half of the world's coral reefs since 1950. This is in part because more acidic oceans cause them to die off, and also because of overfishing (for more on this, see page 88). Coral reefs help to protect our coastline by acting as a buffer against waves and storms. They also provide homes for many marine species.
- Many of the world's oceans experienced at least one 'strong' marine heatwave at some point in 2021.

Future projections:

- If we reach 2°C of warming, we'll lose 99% of our coral reefs.
- Warming sea surfaces could intensify tropical storm wind speeds, causing more damage when they reach land.

SEA LEVELS RISING

We've seen global average sea levels rise by 21-24cm since 1880, with about a third of that happening in the last two and a half decades alone. This is a result of land ice melting and adding water to the oceans, and also a rise in temperature of the water, which expands when hot. Around the world we have already seen an increase in coastal erosion, widespread coastal flooding and land becoming permanently submerged. Some of the most alarming stories are:

- The people of the Isle de Jean Charles in Louisiana, USA, became the world's first climate refugees in 2016. The ancestral home of the Biloxi-Chitimacha-Choctaw tribe has shrunk by 98% since 1955 because of rising sea levels and coastal erosion. In 2016 the tribe were awarded funding to help them relocate. Protective marshlands around the coastline of Louisiana are now eroding at a rate of one football field's worth of land an hour.

- The Tuvalu archipelago will be the first nation in the world to disappear due to rising sea levels caused by global warming. With only 11,000 inhabitants, Tuvalu in the Pacific Ocean is the fourth smallest country in the world. Two of the tiny archipelago's nine islands are on the verge of being submerged, and scientists believe that Tuvalu could become uninhabitable in the next 50 years.
- It's predicted that the Marshall Islands, another archipelago in the Pacific Ocean, could be lost to climate change as early as 2080. Most of the Marshall Islands lie less than 2m above sea level, meaning the 55,000 inhabitants are at serious risk.

> **THE CARBON EMISSIONS OF THE RICHEST 1% ARE MORE THAN DOUBLE THE EMISSIONS OF THE POOREST HALF OF HUMANITY. AND OFTEN IT IS THE COUNTRIES WHO ARE CONTRIBUTING THE LEAST IN TERMS OF GREENHOUSE GASES THAT WILL BE THE MOST IMMEDIATELY AND URGENTLY AFFECTED BY CLIMATE CHANGE.**

Future projections:

- By 2050, 300 million people's homes will fall below the current level of coastal flooding.
- Rising sea levels will intensify the impact of hurricanes and typhoons on coastal areas.

IT'S HAPPENING IN THE UK TOO!

It's easy to think that these changes are so far away from us that we won't be affected, but Britain is soon to have its first climate change refugees. The people of Fairbourne, a village in Gwynedd, Wales, have been told that by 2054, their village will be 'decommissioned' because of the threat of sea-level rise and coastal flooding. It has proven too costly to maintain and increase flood defences, so the locals will have to leave their homes before the 450 houses, a pub, post office and several shops are dismantled. The people of Fairbourne may be the first people in the UK going through this, but it's likely that they won't be the last.

I was lucky enough to visit the Isles of Scilly to report on climate change in 2021. It is the most beautiful place, but if the projections of a one-metre sea-level rise happen by 2100, then the main Island of St Mary's would be split into three. They will be the place that is most impacted by climate change in the UK. To see a map of areas of the UK at risk of coastal flooding, visit coastal.climatecentral.org.

FLOODING

Sea-level rise because of climate change is not the only thing to cause flooding around the world. Higher temperatures actually cause more rain because warm air holds more moisture, which increases the risk of extreme rainfall events.

> **FOR EVERY 1°C RISE IN WARMING, THE AIR HOLDS 7% MORE MOISTURE.**

- In July 2021, western Germany experienced devastating flooding when up to two months' worth of rain fell in two days. With more than 200 deaths, it was Germany's deadliest recorded flood in almost 60 years. It's estimated that it cost Germany €4.5 billion (£3.7 billion), and completely changed the landscape.
- China's Henan province experienced a year's worth of rain in just four days in July 2021, which resulted in 302 deaths and more than 92,000 homes being damaged or destroyed. In the city of Zhengzhou, 644.6mm of rainfall was reported in just 24 hours. To put that into perspective, that's the average rainfall for London for an entire year.
- During Storm Ida in September 2021, New York was hit by flash floods, killing at least 43 people. In some areas, 80mm of rain fell in each hour, smashing previous rainfall records, and the first ever flooding state of emergency was called in New York and New Jersey.

HEATWAVES

As temperatures soar, the most obvious side-effect of climate change is that we will experience more frequent heatwaves. In 2021, countries all around the world broke temperature records and experienced the devastating effects of wildfires as a consequence.

- Siracusa, Sicily, reached 48.8°C on 11 August 2021, the highest temperature Europe has ever recorded! Simultaneously, wildfires spread across southern Italy.
- Death Valley in California reached 54.4°C on July 9, equalling a similar 2020 value as the highest recorded in the world since at least the 1930s.
- Cizre, in Turkey, set a national record with a temperature high of 49.1°C.
- Tbilisi in Georgia had its hottest day on record at 40.6°C.
- Extreme heat and dry ground triggered devastating wildfires across many parts of the Mediterranean with Algeria, southern Turkey and Greece especially badly affected.

- Lytton in British Columbia, Canada, reached a sweltering 49.6°C in July 2021 – the highest temperature Canada has ever recorded. It didn't just beat the previous record, set in 1935, by a tiny amount – it beat it by 4.6°C! The next day wildfires destroyed 90% of the town and killed two people.
- Lapland recorded a temperature of 33.6°C in July 2021 – the highest in more than 100 years.
- In January 2022, Australia equalled its hottest day on record with a temperature of 50.7°C in the remote coastal town of Onslow.

LOSS OF LIFE

The impacts of climate change don't just affect humans, they're having a profound effect on the natural habitats of every species on our planet. Here are just a few tragic examples…

- 1 million of the 8 million species on the Earth are threatened with extinction.
- Between 1970 and 2016, there was an average of 68% decrease in population sizes of mammals, birds, amphibians, reptiles and fish.
- Giraffes have seen their population decline by 40% in the last 30 years.
- The global polar bear population is expected to decline by 30% by 2050.
- In 2019, a 42°C heatwave in Australia killed one third (at least 23,000) of the country's spectacled flying fox bats while around about one billion animals perished in wildfires in the same country in 2020.
- It's estimated that 1 billion small sea creatures died during a heat wave in the Salish Sea (off the coast of British Columbia, Canada) in 2021.

The global polar bear population is expected to decline by 30% by 2050

WHAT HAVE WE SEEN IN THE UK?

Images of floods like this in Aberystwyth in Wales in 2021 are becoming more common in the UK

It's easy to think these extreme weather events won't affect us in the UK, but we are already seeing the effects on home turf. We are having hotter, drier summers which will lead to more droughts and warmer, wetter winters, which in turn will cause widespread flooding. The sea level is rising and we already have one community of soon-to-be climate change refugees in the UK.

TEMPERATURES HAVE BEEN CLIMBING...

- A high of 34°C in the UK is becoming more and more common. It has been recorded in seven of the last 10 years, whereas it happened only seven times in the 50 years before that. This means that the baseline is changing – what my daughter Charlotte will think of as 'normal', my mum would consider 'exceptional'.

- April 2021 was the sunniest on record.
- Since 1884, the top 10 warmest years on record have all occurred in the last 20 years.
- It's now 10 times more likely that the UK will record a temperature of 40°C in the coming decades (once in every 100 years instead of once in every 1000). We have NEVER reached 40°C before – our top recorded temperature is 38.7°C.

Higher temperatures have many knock-on effects. During the 2018 heatwave in the UK, a sharp increase in the daily death count coincided with exceptionally high temperatures. Police reported record numbers of emergency calls and an increase in violent crime. On the hottest days, there were transport-related problems such as melting road surfaces and buckling rail tracks. And many water companies had to implement drought plans due to increased demand.

OUR WEATHER IS ALSO GETTING WETTER...

- Since 1862, six of the 10 wettest years in the UK have happened in the last 24 years.
- Winters have been 12% wetter over the last decade compared to the period 1961-1990. This is because warmer air holds more moisture.
- In 2020, Storm Alex brought widespread heavy rainfall to the UK and we had the wettest day the UK had recorded since 1891. It's now believed that this will happen once in every 100 years in our current climate, compared to once in every 300 years in a natural world where humans hadn't caused the planet to warm.

AND SEA LEVELS HAVE BEEN RISING...

- The rate of sea level rise was 1.5mm per year from the start of the 20th Century but between 1993 and 2019, it has increased to more than 3mm per year.
- The sea level has risen by nearly 2cm per decade over the 60 years up to 2018.

It's estimated that 1.5 million properties will be at risk from flooding in England by 2080, and 100,000 homes at risk from coastal erosion.

If you take a look at the graphic below, you will see the future projection for the UK weather based on a 2°C, 3°C and 4°C rise in temperature.

Global warming and future high-impact weather in the UK

	HOT WEATHER	COLD WEATHER	HEAVY RAINFALL	DROUGHTS
	Extremely hot days, where temperatures exceed 25°C, are likely to become much more frequent	Very cold conditions, where temperatures fall below 0°C, are likely to become less and less frequent	Days of intense and prolonged heavy rainfall are likely to increase	Less frequent rainfall will increase occurrences of severe droughts
+4°C	37 days per year	12 days per year	11 days per year	146% more frequent
+3°C	26 days per year	20 days per year	10 days per year	129% more frequent
+2°C	18 days per year	34 days per year	9 days per year	86% more frequent
Present Day	10 days per year	50 days per year	7 days per year	No change in frequency

KEY: = 5 days = 10 days = 1 day = 20%

From The Met Office

The impacts of climate change are clear to see all around our planet. The ice is melting, the sea level is rising, the oceans are dying and our land is burning. Around 30 million people were displaced by extreme weather events such as storms and floods in 2020. And this is what's happening already, with just 1.2°C of temperature rise above average. If we continue the way we are without making any changes, then we are on track for a temperature increase of nearly 3°C by 2100 and almost 167 million homes could be lost to disasters by 2040. We are close to reaching irreversible tipping points!

In February 2021, Sir David Attenborough gave a stark warning to the United Nations Security Council, saying climate change could, within a lifetime, destroy "entire cities and societies". He added, "If we continue on our current path, we will face the collapse of everything that gives us our security, food production, access to fresh water, habitable ambient temperature and ocean food chains… we are today perilously close to tipping points that, once passed, will send global temperatures spiralling catastrophically higher."

WHAT ARE TIPPING POINTS?

The term 'tipping point' is used to describe a threshold that, once crossed, could result in irreversible damage and a system being pushed into an entirely different state. Scientists have identified various elements of the Earth's system at risk of reaching these points of no return, such as the melting of Greenland's ice sheet, coral reef die-off and the thawing of permafrost. When this happens, it's possible there will be dramatic cascading effects, with one tipping point pushing us into another one, like a domino effect. It was thought that we would need warming of 3-5°C to cross most of these thresholds, but the latest evidence suggests we could reach the first tipping points with a 1-2°C temperature increase. Remember, we have already reached 1.2°C!

The Intergovernmental Panel on Climate Change (IPCC) warned that exceeding 2°C of warming could have catastrophic consequences and that we need to keep global warming to 1.5°C. The graphic, right, shows the difference between a 1.5 and 2°C increase in temperature.

Keeping global warming below 1.5°C will:

- Avoid catastrophic sea-level rise.
- Allow some coral reefs to persist.
- Reduce the number of people exposed to flooding, storms, and fires.
- Save money that would need to be spent on disaster recovery and protecting (or moving) cities threatened by sea-level rise.

EFFECTS OF TEMPERATURE RISES OF 1.5°C OR 2°C

1.5°C (2.7°F)	VS	2°C (3.6°F)
21.5cm - 76cm of sea level rise by 2100	Sea Level Rise	Additional 10cm of sea level rise and 10.4 million more people exposed
Loss of **70-90%** of coral reefs	Ecosystems	Loss of **99%** of coral reefs
350 million people in urban areas exposed to severe drought	Extreme Weather	**410 million** people in urban areas exposed to severe drought
At least one sea-ice-free Arctic summer after **100 years**	Arctic Ice	At least one sea-ice-free Arctic summer after **10 years**

SERIOUS

From climatecentral.com

How soon will we reach 1.5°C?

Scientists say we could hit 1.5°C in the next decade as a one-off year, but to officially reach 1.5°C of global warming it would need to be averaged over a longer period. It's difficult to put a date to a certain temperature rise as it will depend on how much we can reduce our emissions. The latest IPCC report suggests that even in the best-case scenario, where we are able to limit climate change to just under 1.5°C by 2100, that we would still reach a peak of 1.5°C in 2040. That's because the global surface temperature will continue to rise until at least the mid century because of emissions already in the atmosphere. Below is a graph showing all the projected warming scenarios, based on very low, low, medium, high and very high emissions.

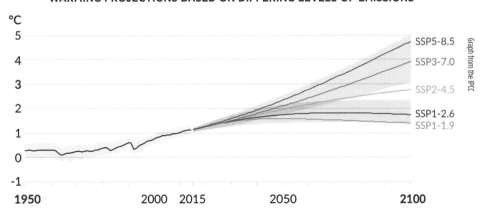

WARMING PROJECTIONS BASED ON DIFFERING LEVELS OF EMISSIONS

Graph from the IPCC

SOLVABLE - SO HOW DO WE FIX THIS?

To stop the planet heating to unthinkably high temperatures, we need strong and sustained reductions in emissions of greenhouse gases. As I explained with the Bathtub Analogy on page 28, even if we reduce the amount of emissions we put into the atmosphere, we will still be adding to what is already there, which will lead to increases in temperatures. This is why reaching what is known as 'net zero' is so important, and has been set out in accordance with the Paris Agreement.

WHAT IS THE PARIS AGREEMENT AND WHY IS IT IMPORTANT?

In 2015, world leaders at the Conference of the Parties (COP) 21 created a legally binding treaty now known as the Paris Agreement. Its goal was to limit global warming to well below 2°C, preferably to 1.5°C, compared to pre-industrial levels. It's so important because, for the first time, it united almost all the world's nations in a single agreement on cutting the greenhouse gas emissions which are causing global warming.

COP21 · CMP11
PARIS 2015
UN CLIMATE CHANGE CONFERENCE

What does net zero actually mean?

Put simply, net zero is a term used when the amount of emissions you release into the atmosphere exactly matches the emissions you remove from the atmosphere. It's also sometimes referred to as carbon neutral. In the UK, we have already started to reduce our greenhouse gas emissions through actions such as investing in renewable forms of energies (see page 73), transitioning to electric cars (page 229) and insulating homes (page 66). We need to reduce them further – and you'll find LOADS of ways you can do this throughout the book.

Any emissions that we are unable to reduce, we need to 'offset'. This means capturing carbon from the atmosphere through natural methods such as planting trees (see right for information on carbon sinks) or by using carbon capture technology. This is where you suck carbon out of the atmosphere and store it, for example in rocks. It's a new technology which countries are investing a lot of money in. But it should be the last option we turn to. First we need to reduce our emissions and then protect our natural carbon sinks.

WHAT ARE CARBON SINKS AND HOW CAN THEY HELP?

A carbon sink is anything that absorbs more CO_2 from the atmosphere than it puts in. Our biggest carbon sinks on Earth are forests, peatland and the ocean. Let's take a look...

FORESTS

Trees are carbon sinks because they take carbon dioxide out of the atmosphere and store it in their trunks. They absorb 2.6 billion metric tons of CO_2 every year, yet an area of forest the size of a football pitch is destroyed every second. This is why cutting trees down (and then sometimes burning them) is so bad because it releases stored carbon back into the atmosphere.

- Trees absorb around 30% of the greenhouse gases we emit into the atmosphere.
- They are literally the lungs of our planet – they take in carbon and release oxygen for us to breathe.
- More than half the world's forests have been destroyed.

I attended COP26, which took place in Glasgow, Scotland, in 2021 (more on this on page 44) and 140 leaders pledged to end deforestation by 2030. We are already cutting down fewer trees and planting more, but some countries are way off the target to increase global forest cover by 3% by the end of the decade – a target set as part of the United Nations Strategic Plan for Forests 2017-2030. For information about the Queen's Green Canopy campaign, see page 243.

PEATLAND

Peatlands cover just 3% of the world's land area but store twice as much carbon as all the trees on the Earth combined. So we are losing stored carbon when peatland is disrupted through drainage to be turned into land for farming, or to be used as compost (see page 119 for more).

It is now widely accepted that peatlands are a natural-based solution to climate change and they featured heavily at COP26. Host nation Scotland is rich in peatland and the Scottish government pledged to restore 250,000 hectares of it by 2030.

OCEANS

Our amazing oceans absorb about a quarter of CO_2 emissions and they're responsible for around 50-80% of oxygen production on Earth. Phytoplankton are the main reason the ocean is one of the biggest carbon sinks. These microscopic marine algae and bacteria absorb about as much carbon as all the plants and trees on land combined. But as we put more and more CO_2 into the atmosphere, our ocean water is becoming more acidic. Acidic water creates an inhospitable environment for some species of phytoplankton, which results in oceans not absorbing as much CO_2.

Another global problem affecting the ocean's effectiveness as a carbon sink – and endangering marine life – is the rising level of plastic pollution. Phytoplankton are eating microplastics, which affects their ability to absorb CO_2. For more on this see page 50.

What are the UK's commitments to tackling climate change?

As the country that started the Industrial Revolution that pumped greenhouse gases into the atmosphere, it seems only right that we show how committed we are to lowering them. During a virtual climate summit with US President Joe Biden in April 2021, when 40 world leaders met to rally the world in tackling the climate crisis, the UK was called 'top of the class' by some. Here's why…

The UK became the first country to declare a Climate Emergency in 2019, we were the first major economy to pass a net zero emissions law – and in June of that year it was announced we would bring all greenhouse gas emissions to net zero by 2050. Also, in 2020, the government announced a 10-point plan for a green industrial revolution to tackle climate change and accelerate our path to net zero. These points are:

- Advancing offshore wind.
- Driving the growth of low carbon hydrogen.
- Delivering new and advanced nuclear power.
- Accelerating the shift to zero-emission vehicles.
- Green public transport, cycling and walking.
- 'Jet zero' and green ships.
- Greener buildings.
- Investing in carbon capture, usage and storage.
- Protecting our natural environment.
- Green finance and innovation.

Then in April 2021, the UK government announced a new target to slash emissions by 78% by 2035 compared to 1990 levels. This included international aviation and shipping in our targets for the first time ever. This was put into law in June 2021.

Each country that signed up to the Paris Agreement submits its plans to reduce carbon emissions and they are measured against a temperature scale to show what that level of warming commitments would result in. As of November 2021, the UK's commitments came out as 'almost sufficient' and would keep warming just below 2°C. So there is more work to be done!

My experience at COP26

In November 2021, I had the honour of attending the 26th annual Conference of the Parties in Glasgow. It was described as the world's best last chance to get runaway climate change under control. As the host, the UK asked every country attending to commit to new targets to reduce emissions to reach net zero by 2050, with the aim of limiting global warming to 1.5°C.

For the first time ever, I have hope that we can reach our goal of limiting warming to 1.5°C. There were a lot of positives, and science and nature were at the centre of the whole conference. All nations committed to real actions, including reducing methane emissions by 30% by 2030, phasing out coal more quickly, speeding up switching to electric vehicles and ending deforestation.

The latest pledges and targets show that with current policies the Earth will warm by 2.9°C by 2100 compared to pre-industrial levels (with a range between 2.1°C to 3.9°C). But an optimistic best-case scenario, implementing all targets, could limit warming to 1.8°C (with a range between 1.5°C to 2.4°C). This is the first time we've reached a value below 2°C, and we want to lower it further. Next year, COP27 will take place in Egypt, where leaders will meet again to increase their commitments in a bid to 'keep 1.5 alive'.

At COP26, it was great to see that while the focus was on leaders and their commitment as nations, there was so much more going on too. Members of the science community were giving talks, there were representatives from each nation showing what was happening on a smaller scale, and indigenous people talked about the reality of climate change for them. Existing and new technologies were being showcased in the science centre and there were real people in the streets passionately singing and talking about the changes they are making in their own lives. It was then that I realised it was a two-pronged approach – where ordinary people and subnations can reach up with innovations, ideas and passion to be met by governments who can implement those changes – that will help us tackle climate change. And that's what this book is all about. When we make changes as individuals, we encourage others to do the same. Then retailers, workplaces, councils and governments will in turn make bigger changes. No one can do everything, but we can all do something.

I hope you can see that climate change really is **Simple**, **Serious**, and **Solvable**. The future of the planet is literally in our hands, so read on to find out how we can all make a difference…

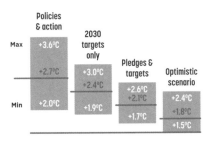

WARMING PROJECTIONS FROM COP26 BASED ON ACTIONS BEING TAKEN

Policies & action
Max +3.6°C
      +2.7°C
Min +2.0°C

2030 targets only
      +3.0°C
      +2.4°C
      +1.9°C

Pledges & targets
      +2.6°C
      +2.1°C
      +1.7°C

Optimistic scenario
      +2.4°C
      +1.8°C
      +1.5°C

It was an honour to attend COP26

THE PROBLEM WITH PLASTIC

I also want to talk about the impact of plastic waste on our planet. From water bottles and clingfilm to telephones and toothbrushes, plastic has become a huge part of our everyday lives in the last 100 years. Look around and you'll see countless plastic items in your home. In the supermarket most things are wrapped in the stuff.

It is, in many ways, a marvellous material. It's inexpensive, flexible, durable and its benefits can be far reaching. In hospitals, for example, single-use plastic is essential for a safe and sterile medical environment. In cars, plastic seatbelts and airbags protect us from harm.

But, like many commodities, plastic has been overused. We've come to rely on unnecessary single-use plastics such as grocery bags, water bottles and take-away coffee cups, which are used for just a few minutes before we discard them. Ninety-nine per cent of all plastics are made from chemicals derived from fossil fuels, so the production of these throwaway items releases billions of metric tons of greenhouse gases into the atmosphere, contributing to the climate change crisis.

On top of that, our planet is literally drowning in it. Of the 8.3 billion metric tons (and counting) of plastic created since the 1950s, 6.3 billion metric tons became waste plastic. With most plastics taking upwards of 400 years to decompose, it is likely that every single piece of plastic that has ever been made still exists in one form or another. Plastic has now been found at the deepest and highest points on Earth. In 2018, a plastic bag was discovered at a depth of 10,975 metres in the Mariana Trench in the Pacific Ocean. And in 2020, microplastics (bits of plastic smaller than 5mm) were discovered in snow near the summit of Earth's highest peak, Mount Everest. It's mind-blowing to think about – and yet, we keep churning plastic out…

Every year, we produce more than 300 million metric tons of plastic waste worldwide, and the UK is responsible for 3.7 million metric tons of that.

DID YOU KNOW?

- Half of all plastic is designed to be used only once and then thrown away.

- The average household in the UK throws out 128 items of plastic every week.

Charlotte and I look out to sea, where so much of our plastic ends up

You might be thinking that most plastic can be recycled, so what's the problem? Well, here's the problem…

In the UK, we actually only recycle around 47% of our plastic waste.

"But we put all of our plastic in the recycling!" I hear you say. You may well do, but there is a lot of confusion in this country about what plastics can and can not be recycled. For example, cheese packaging and the thin plastic bags that spinach comes in are 'not yet recycled' by our local authorities, so even if you put them in recycling, they will end up in landfill. (For more info on recycling and the TerraCycle scheme, which recycles plastics that local authorities can't, see page 244).

And what about those times when you're out of the house and need to throw stuff away? Can you honestly say you always take your plastic rubbish home to recycle it properly? I know I do and, perhaps not surprisingly, it annoys my husband, especially if we buy something while out and we – okay, I – have to carry it until we get home because most towns and cities don't have recycling bins yet. I can't bring myself to put recyclable products into a regular bin because I know they will end up in landfill. Pre Covid, I even used to take things out of the regular waste bin at the train station and put them in the recycling bin they actually provide there.

So, all the plastic that can't be recycled, plus the plastic that can be recycled but we put in the wrong bin (or simply litter!), is either dumped in landfill, ends up in the ocean or is shipped to other countries (more on this later).

In landfill, plastic is starved of sunlight and air (two essential components before it will break down) so it can take hundreds of years to decompose. As it sits there with the rest of the rubbish it releases methane into the atmosphere. Methane, by the way, traps up to 80 times more heat than carbon dioxide, though it only lives in the atmosphere for around 10 years, rather than hundreds of years. Landfill plastic also begins to produce leachate – a toxic liquid formed when waste breaks down. If this begins to leak into the surrounding earth it can pollute the land, ground water, waterways and wildlife.

DID YOU KNOW?

- The UK is the second biggest producer of plastic waste per person in the world, behind America.

- Globally, 91% of waste plastic is not recycled.

What doesn't end up in landfill often makes its way to the ocean. Perhaps, like so many people, you witnessed the devastating effect plastic is having on our coastlines, oceans and sea life in David Attenborough's *Blue Planet II*. One study showed that after watching the series, 88% of people changed their lifestyles to reduce the amount of plastic they used. But we still have a long way to go.

HOW DOES PLASTIC GET INTO THE OCEAN IN THE FIRST PLACE?

Plastic is light, so when we drop litter or it is being transported on bin wagons or sitting in landfill, it gets blown away by the wind or washed by the rain into rivers and down drains. And, if the Pixar film *Finding Nemo* taught you anything, you'll know that all drains lead to the sea! At home, some people flush wet wipes, cotton buds and sanitary products down the toilet, and they either make their way to the sea, or they block our drains (more on this on page 134). Since the pandemic, there has also been an increase of disposable face masks and latex gloves discovered in our seas, adding to the already catastrophic plastic pollution.

DID YOU KNOW?

- A rubbish truck's worth of plastic gets dumped into the ocean every single minute.

- More than 1 million seabirds and 100,000 marine mammals (including whales and dolphins) die from plastic pollution every year.

In the water, plastic can travel thousands of miles. It washes up on beautiful islands which hardly produce any plastic themselves. And it becomes a danger to fish, seabirds and marine mammals that mistake it for food or get trapped in it. Whales have washed up on beaches with huge litterballs of plastic in their stomachs. It's truly heartbreaking.

It also collects in what is known as the Great Pacific Garbage Patch (GPGP) – the largest accumulation zone of ocean plastic on the planet. It covers 1.6 million square kilometres – that's six and a half times the size of the UK! – and it's estimated that there is around 80,000 metric tons of plastic waste in it (the equivalent of 500 jumbo jets).

Plastic pollution is not just a threat to sea life, it's a threat to us. While in the water, plastic begins to break down into smaller pieces, known as microplastics, and these are eaten by small fish

Charlotte sorting through all the "not yet recycled" plastics

– which are eaten by bigger fish, which are eaten by us. So the microplastics make their way up the food chain, onto our plates.

Tiny particles of plastic can also be found in the air we breathe and the water we drink – especially water from plastic bottles. In fact, it's estimated that the average person eats 70,000 pieces of microplastic each year!

Microplastics and fibres have been found in fish, honey, beer, sea salt plus bottled and tap water. We also breathe in tiny plastic particles from our clothes, carpets and other textiles.

It's not yet known what the health implications of consuming microplastic are but, tragically, between 400,000 and one million people die every year from diseases and accidents relating to poorly managed plastic waste in developing countries – and our plastic waste is responsible for some of this!

DID YOU KNOW?

- Sea turtles swimming around the Great Pacific Garbage Patch have up to 74% of their diets composed of plastic.

- If we carry on producing and using plastic in the way we are now, it's estimated there will be more plastic than fish in the sea by 2050.

- We eat a credit-card sized amount of plastic every week.

We, along with other wealthy countries, ship lots of our waste to poorer countries to be recycled. It helps reduce the amount we put into landfill here, it's a cheap way to get rid of it, and it helps us meet our recycling targets. For developing countries, it's a valuable source of income. But plastic that is contaminated (not recyclable or low-quality plastic) ends up sitting in unregulated dump sites where diseases can spread quickly, is washed into the ocean or burned in the open air, polluting the air for local communities.

MICROPLASTICS AND MICROFIBRES

Microplastics are small pieces of plastic that are less than 5mm in length. They're either intentionally created (for example glitter or the microbeads we used to get in face scrubs – thankfully these have been banned now) or they're created when larger bits of plastic break down, such as when plastic bags or bottles are eroded in the sea. Some plastics are so tiny that they can't even be seen by the naked eye. These are known as nanoplastics. Thirty-five per cent of microplastics found in the sea come from the clothes that we wear. Synthetic materials, such as nylon, polyester and acrylic, shed millions of tiny plastic fibres every time they are washed, which get through the water treatment plants and into the sea. There's more on how to shop for clothes sustainably and reduce microfibres in your washing on pages 186 and 193.

DID YOU KNOW?

- It's estimated that plastic pollution kills one person every 30 seconds.

China used to be the world's biggest importer of plastic, but in 2017 it banned the import of most plastic waste from countries like the UK. Since then, many other countries that took the brunt of the extra plastic that would have gone to China – such as Malaysia and Turkey – are following suit in a bid to clean up their own environments. This means we face huge challenges in how we will dispose of our plastic rubbish in future, so it's safe to say we need to change how we consume plastic, and fast…

If this all sounds rather overwhelming, don't lose hope. Things have already started to change for the better. A ban on plastic cutlery, plates, straws, plastic cotton buds, balloon sticks and polystyrene cups in the European Union came into force in July 2021, and the UK Plastic Pact saw companies who are responsible for 80% of plastic packaging pledge to make 100% of packaging recyclable, reusable or compostable by 2025. If we, as consumers, make the choice to cut down on our single-use plastic consumption, it will have an impact on retailers and eventually policy makers to make the changes that are so desperately needed.

There is so much we can do in our own homes. As you go through the book, you'll find loads of simple ways to cut down on single-use plastic. Why not make a note of the ones you can do easily, then start to tick them off on the checklist at the back of the book? Once you start, you'll be on a roll and I guarantee you'll wonder how you ever used so much plastic in the first place. I certainly did! You'll shudder at a single-use plastic bottle and you'll happily carry a Jenga-style stack of food home from the shops to avoid having to buy a plastic bag (my husband does this simply to avoid the 10p charge!). I know we can tackle this ginormous problem together...

All ready to be recycled at the supermarket or by TerraCycle!

HIDDEN PLASTICS

Here are some of the surprising items that contain plastic, and where you will find info on them in the book...

Tea bags - 103
Wine screw caps - 102
Receipts - 102
Wrapping paper - 210
Sanitary towels - 138
Baking paper - 109

WHAT CAN WE DO?

"You cannot get through a single day without having an impact on the world around you. What you do makes a difference and you have to decide what kind of difference you want to make."

Dr Jane Goodall – ethologist

The choices we make every day matter. From the toothpaste we brush our teeth with to the temperature we have our thermostats set at. Every action we take will result in greenhouse gases being emitted into the atmosphere. We can't escape that, but we can choose to reduce the amount we are personally responsible for by making small changes to the way we live.

It's sometimes hard to grasp the scale of the impact we have on the world. But everything we use has been created from the Earth's natural resources. They're harvested, manufactured into goods and then transported to a warehouse or shop. We then travel to the shop to buy the item, use it for a while, then throw it out.

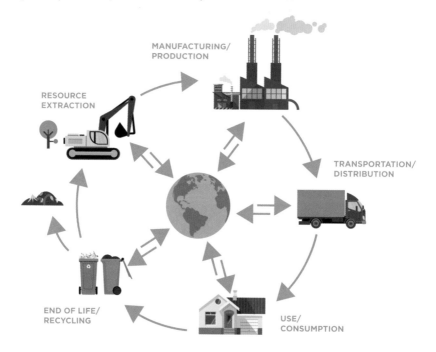

RESOURCE
EXTRACTION

MANUFACTURING/
PRODUCTION

TRANSPORTATION/
DISTRIBUTION

USE/
CONSUMPTION

END OF LIFE/
RECYCLING

Every single part of that process emits greenhouse gas into the atmosphere. And the worst part is that even once we've thrown something 'away', it still pollutes the environment. Because, there is no such place as 'away'.

Think about it. We might throw it in the bin and never have to see it again, but it has to go somewhere. Only 45% of the waste we create in the UK gets recycled, which means the rest is either burned or sent to landfill, where it can sit for HUNDREDS of years before it rots. Charlotte has grasped this concept so well. If she ever sees me putting something in the bin she will say, "No, Mummy, why are you putting it in a hole in the ground?" I have to explain to her that some things really can't be recycled, so there is no other option.

Our goal, then, is to reduce the amount of 'stuff' we bring into our lives in the first place, so there is less to be thrown away. Why? Because the Earth has limited resources and we need to protect them, and because the more stuff we have the higher our carbon footprint will be.

WHAT'S A CARBON FOOTPRINT?

We each have what is known as a carbon footprint. This is a measurement of how much greenhouse gas is emitted into the atmosphere as a result of our choices and activities. These emissions are often measured in CO_2e – carbon dioxide equivalent – for simplicity. It tots up the volume of harmful greenhouse gases, including carbon dioxide, methane and nitrogen, that individuals, products or companies generate.

For the average Brit, this is about 13 metric tons of CO_2e each year – almost double the global average! The bulk (around 75%) of our carbon footprint comes from transport, housing and food and you can find out ways to reduce these in the following chapters.

To take care of the planet which is providing us with so much, we need to live more sustainable lives. The word sustainability gets used a lot these days. But what does it really mean?

SUSTAINABILITY
The quality of not being harmful to the environment or depleting natural resources, and thereby supporting long-term ecological balance.

My aim with this book is to show you that you can live a more sustainable life without disrupting your current life too much. Many of the changes are simple and free, and some are so obvious you'll wonder why you never thought of them before. Others may take a bit more commitment, or perhaps are things you might want to think about doing one day in the future – such as getting an electric car or installing a heat pump at home – but it's all food for thought.

Every single one of the changes in this book will fall under one (or more) of the Eight Rs of Sustainability used in The Waste Hierarchy. **Rethink** how you live, **Refuse** what you do not need, **Reduce** the amount you buy, **Reuse** what you do have, **Rehome** anything you no longer need, **Repair** rather than throw out, **Recycle** everything that can be, **Rot** the rest.

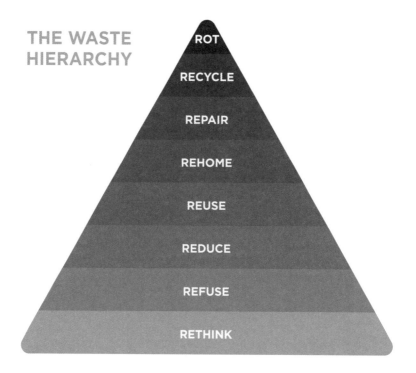

THE WASTE HIERARCHY

ROT
RECYCLE
REPAIR
REHOME
REUSE
REDUCE
REFUSE
RETHINK

You're probably familiar with the recycling motto Reduce, Reuse, Recycle. Well, the Waste Hierarchy expands upon that to give you more options to make the most of the Earth's natural resources before things are either recycled (and therefore put back into the system and made into something else) or left to rot. The idea is that you start at the bottom with Rethink, and work your way up so that Recycling and Rot are the last resorts.

As you go through the chapters of the book, I'll expand on many of the ideas below, but as a general guide…

RETHINK

This is the most important stage – and also my favourite – because it really is the one that makes all the others possible! Step back and think about the type of consumer you want to be and what this means for the environment. You can rethink every choice you make – but that doesn't mean you have to implement all the changes at once. Doing that might mean you get overwhelmed, which could put you off altogether. When I was first researching and writing the book, I definitely tried to do too much at once. I found the easiest way is to work out the things you want to do first and go from there (it always feels good to tick something off a list!).

No matter the area of life – transport, food, clothes or cosmetics etc – ask yourself whether the choice you are making will have a positive or negative impact on the planet. When you break it down, there are so many things you can do differently. Take these examples from just your morning routine. Will you choose to…

- **Have cereal from a cardboard box or from a plastic bag?**
- **Drink loose-leaf tea or a tea bag which contains plastic (who knew?!)?**
- **Have a long shower or a short shower?**
- **Wash your hair with shampoo from a plastic bottle or a shampoo bar?**
- **Brush your teeth with a plastic toothbrush or a bamboo one?**
- **Turn the tap off while you're cleaning your teeth or leave it running?**
- **Use a refillable deodorant or an aerosol?**
- **Make your own packed lunch or buy sandwiches while you're out?**
- **Wrap your packed lunch in clingfilm or Tupperware?**
- **Take water in a reusable bottle or buy a single-use one while you're out?**
- **Have tea or coffee in a reusable cup or buy a takeaway cup?**
- **Download a podcast on your home wifi or stream it over 4G on your journey?**
- **Set the heating timer so it's off while you're out, or leave it running all day?**
- **Walk or drive?**

That's 14 things to decide before you have even left the house! Just imagine how many things you can do differently throughout the day when you take the time to rethink.

REFUSE

Can you say no to things you don't need? Whether that's a new top or the latest smartphone. But the most important one here, for me, is to refuse single-use plastic. You'll have seen on page 47 the devastating effect plastic is having on our natural world. If you're in the supermarket, look out for loose items or those packaged in cardboard, glass or tins instead of plastic (you'll find loads of great tips on page 99). Or you can go one step further and visit a zero-waste store, where you can refill your own containers with store-cupboard staples and cosmetics. More on this on page 107.

If you're out and about and someone offers you a plastic bottle of water or some takeaway lunch in a plastic tub, can you flex your 'no' muscle and politely decline? This is perhaps the most difficult part of Refuse because it can appear rude. But trust me, I've done it and you'll lead by example and get other people thinking.

REDUCE

This one is all about reducing the amount of stuff you have. If you think about what is really important in life, it's not the material possessions you have, but the people around you, the places you go and the experiences you collect. There are lots of ways you can reduce what you have. Firstly, you can go through everything you already have (and lots of the chapters in this book start with a good old clear-out!) and decide what you actually need and what you don't. See Rehome (opposite page) for what you can do with things you want to get rid of.

Then you can choose to buy fewer things. This can be hard in the material world that we live in, but get into the habit of asking yourself if you really need something or if you just want it. Of course, a well thought out purchase of something you actually need that will last a long time is not the problem here. It's the items we buy on a whim or because they are cheap, which get thrown away after a few uses. See page 175 for tips on how to buy less.

> REDUCE CAN ALSO MEAN REDUCING THE AMOUNT YOU USE THINGS, SUCH AS DRIVING LESS, TAKING SHORTER SHOWERS AND NOT SWITCHING ON YOUR HEATING SO MUCH.

REUSE

A big part of a sustainable life is using what you already have, followed by borrowing, hiring and buying second-hand instead of buying new. All of those options mean you are reusing something that is already in circulation. If you have 10 occasion dresses in your wardrobe already, do you really need to buy a new one for the next wedding you go to? If you're having a party, can you hire a party kit instead of buying disposable plates

and cups? What about borrowing a drill from a neighbour? And when you do need to buy, can you see if you can get the item second-hand (and probably half the price!) first? There are so many options before we should ever consider purchasing something new.

And then there is switching from single-use items such as cotton pads, plastic razors and clingfilm to long-lasting reusable ones. You will find SO many sustainable switches in this book, but remember not to buy things for the sake of it. For example, if you want to stop using clingfilm to cover bowls of leftovers, then an upturned plate works just as well as a fancy reusable cover.

Another great way to reuse things is to repurpose them into something else. You can collect jam jars to take to zero-waste stores, use old toothbrushes to clean hard-to-reach areas or save cardboard boxes for children to make into dens. Honestly, you can reuse the most random things. In summer, if Charlotte has a Calippo ice lolly, we'll keep the cardboard tube it comes in so she can drink her orange juice from it!

REHOME

If you no longer want something, can you give it a new life by passing it on to someone else? A big message in this book is 'one person's trash is another person's treasure' and it is so true. There are so many ways to get rid of stuff these days: charity shops, car boot sales, Facebook Marketplace, eBay, Vinted, the list goes on… I have a big pile of stuff in my garage waiting to be taken to a car boot sale. I also choose to buy second-hand when I can.

REPAIR

We live in such a throwaway culture that as soon as something breaks we often toss it aside. But lots of things can be mended when you know how! There is now a law in the UK which means manufacturers have to make spare parts available for items such as washing machines, fridges and TVs. Lots of things can be repaired at home with a bit of know-how. My husband is always fixing things just by watching how-to videos on YouTube (because obviously, he will not want to fork out for something new!). It's important we try to keep goods out of landfill for as long as possible so that all those resources don't go to waste.

RECYCLE

When it is time to finally get rid of something, recycle it if possible. Check out page 244 for tips on what can and cannot be recycled – you might just be surprised! Even though recycling is a fantastic way to reuse our planet's resources (and should ALWAYS be chosen over sending recyclable things to landfill), it is still an energy-intensive process. Which means we shouldn't use the excuse of "well, it can be recycled" as justification for buying something single-use or that we don't need.

Aim to reduce the amount of single-use plastic you bring into your home

ROT

Last and indeed least, we allow things to rot. If something truly has come to the end of its life and can't be reused, repaired, rehomed or recycled, then we have to put it in the regular bin. But we want to keep this to the absolute minimum. While in landfill, rotting goods release harmful greenhouse gases into the atmosphere, and it also means it's the end of the line for the materials used in that item.

When it comes to food waste, allowing it to rot in a compost bin is actually beneficial for the environment because it creates nutrient-rich soil for plants – but we need to reduce the amount of food we throw away too. See page 93 to find out why.

'BUT WILL IT MAKE A DIFFERENCE?'

As I said in my introduction to the book, it's easy to think that one person can't make much of a difference. Especially when a lot of changes need to be implemented from the top down by governments. We can't deny that 100 companies are responsible for 71% of greenhouse gas emissions, and just 20 firms are behind more than half of single-use plastic waste – the stuff that we buy! But big changes can also happen from the bottom up – I don't think we realise the power we actually have.

We, as individuals, have a big role in getting us to net zero. A group called the Climate Change Committee (CCC) looked at all the things that would need to happen in each sector to reduce our emissions and it found that we, as a society, are involved in 59% of them. 43% comes from deciding to use new technologies such as switching to an electric car or heat pump and choosing a green energy provider, but 16% comes from our behavioural changes such as driving less and eating a more plant-based diet. As consumers we have very little control over 41% of our drive to reach net zero because these decisions are related to new technologies and fuel.

The seemingly small, everyday ways we change our lives will not only reduce our individual carbon footprints, they will encourage companies to change their ways too. The more of us who make them, the more change we'll see. Take plastic shampoo bottles, for example. If we all stop buying them and switch to refillables or shampoo bars, cosmetic companies will have no choice but to change the way they package their products. If more people start to take the bus instead of driving, the buses will fill up so local councils will have to provide more services, which will allow more people to get the bus. Change really does start with us!

I remember seeing an Instagram post that said, 'It's just 1 plastic bottle, said 8 billion people,' and it really stuck with me. Imagine what we could do if the 7.7 billion people on this planet really felt like their actions made a difference.

So, it's time for you to be the change you want to see in the world. I'll be with you every step of the way. And together, we can do this.

HOME ENERGY

From heating our houses and hoovering the floor to making a brew and blow-drying our hair, we use energy all day, every day to keep our homes – and ourselves – ticking over nicely. It's estimated that 40% of carbon emissions in the UK come from our homes, so it is one of the most promising areas where small changes really can help us to become more energy-efficient. Reducing the energy you use at home is a win-win situation – it will help the planet and save you money at the same time!

My first forecasting job for the Met Office was at Cardiff Weather Centre. One of my roles was to provide weather forecasts to power companies so they knew how much energy to produce, because it's tricky to store it if it's not used. The colder it gets, the more likely it is that people will put on their heating and leave it on for longer. Plus, on grey, cloudy days, we tend to switch on lights at least an hour earlier than on sunny days. One hour of switched-on lights for millions of households uses up a lot of extra energy!

In other sections of the book I explore how to reduce the environmental impact of using certain appliances and technology at home, such as washing machines (page 196), kettles (page 105), and computers (page 170), but in this section I look at ways to keep our homes warm but energy efficient, and how we can move towards using more sustainable forms of energy, such as switching energy tariffs. Some of these things might be outside of your control – for example if you rent accommodation rather than own your place – but there are others that are easily achievable for everyone. And while some might seem obvious, do you actually do the obvious things?

DID YOU KNOW?

- 40% of carbon emissions in the UK come from households.
- We could achieve 11% of the UK's 2050 carbon emissions target by just taking household energy efficiency measures.

- ***Lower your thermostat by 1°C (then keep going to see how low you can go…)***
  The biggest use of energy in our homes is from heating (and cooling if you live in a warmer climate!). Lowering your thermostat by a degree is a well-known money-saving tip – the less heat you generate, the less energy you use and the less money you spend. This, of course, also means a reduction in the amount of greenhouse gases your home emits.

A study in 2020 showed that almost two-thirds of Brits had their thermostats turned up to more than 20°C. Well, not in my house! Everyone who knows me expects my house to be cold and if they come to visit they bring extra layers. Once, me and my husband came back to our living room to find a friend doing star jumps to keep warm! Technically, according to my husband, we have the heating 'on' all the time, but we have the thermostat set to 16°C, so it doesn't click on unless it dips below that temperature.

'WE ONCE FOUND A FRIEND DOING STAR JUMPS IN OUR HOUSE TO KEEP WARM!'

Sometimes, we even have thermostat wars. My husband can hear the 'click' as the heating switches on from a mile away. If I'm cold I'll click it on, and he will click it off. And it is very rare that we have the heating on before November – it's just not allowed! Things have changed a little since we've had Charlotte, of course. We do turn the thermostat up to 18°C in the cooler months – 19°C would be pushing it and 20°C is as high as it ever goes! I've tried higher, but my husband will say, "It's like a sauna in here – I'm sweating!" and he'll turn it back down.

See how you get on setting yours to 1°C lower, then perhaps try 2°C or even 3°C, especially overnight when you're in bed. Over the course of a year, if you turn down your thermostat by 1°C, you could save up to £40 off your annual energy bill, and cut your carbon footprint by around 300kg CO_2 – the equivalent of driving 754 miles in a car!

- **Set timers on your heating.**
  This is an easy way to cut your heating bills and reduce your energy use. If you set a timer so your heating turns on automatically when you need it most (such as in the morning when everyone is getting up) and turns off when you're not at home (perhaps when you are at work and the kids are at school) then you'll instantly reduce the amount of energy you use throughout the day. We have ours set to low while we are out because heating an empty home is such a waste of energy. It does mean there's often an initial chill when we come back – but that is what jumpers are for!

> **'HEATING AN EMPTY HOME IS SUCH A WASTE OF ENERGY!'**

- **Turn radiators off in rooms you don't use.**
  If you spend most of your time in one or two rooms of your house, do you really need to heat the others? It's a waste of money and energy to heat unused rooms. We turn the radiator to 1 in the spare rooms of our house and keep the doors closed, then turn them up if we have visitors. Draught-proof the doors that lead to any unheated rooms, so that the cold air doesn't seep out into the rest of the warm house. Also, make sure you bleed your radiators a couple of times a year. This removes trapped air, which improves the efficiency of the heating system.

KEEP THE HEAT IN!

In the UK, a lot of our homes are old and poorly insulated, so of all the energy-saving steps you can take, getting your home properly insulated is perhaps the best thing of all. Whenever it is warmer inside than outside, your home will always be losing heat. Approximately 35% of heat is lost through walls, 25% through the roof, 25% through doors and windows and a further 15% through floors. There are some super-simple and free ways to help keep heat in your home, and there are a few ways that will cost you money upfront but will save you in the long run.

- **Close your curtains at night.**

According to research, closing your curtains at dusk can reduce heat loss by 15-17%. This is because the curtains (or blinds) act as a barrier between the warm air in the room and the cold windows – think of it like your duvet keeping the heat in while you sleep and how cold you feel when you take it off. I close all the curtains and doors when it gets to dusk. If I'm out and get back once it's dark, I really notice how much colder the house is with the curtains open.

Did you know?

A window left open overnight in winter will waste enough energy to drive a small car more than 35 miles.

- **Draught-proof doors and windows.**

Unwanted gaps – such as keyholes, letter boxes and around the side of your windows and doors – let in cold air and let out warm air. To reduce heat loss, you can buy draught-proofing accessories fairly cheaply from DIY stores. And if you properly draught-proof your home, you could save £60 on your energy bills every year.

To cover keyholes you can use a piece of tape or buy a keyhole cover (they come in all shapes and sizes to fit different doors). The best way to stop heat escaping through your letterbox is to get one that has brushes on the inside (that's what we have) or attach a letterbox flap. Depending on what type of windows you have, you can attach foam seals around the edges where they open, and you can get the same for the edges of doors. To cover gaps at the bottom of doors, buy brush strips, or maybe one of those cute stuffed draught excluders that come in the shape of sausage dogs! If you have a chimney that is not in use, see if you can fit a draught excluder there too.

Did you know?

If every home in the UK properly draught-proofed their homes, it would save enough energy to heat 400,000 homes, and a total of £190 million a year.

Just a warning note: houses do need to have some form of controlled ventilation to stop them getting damp, such as the vents you find at the top of windows, extractor fans and wall vents. So make sure you don't seal any of these.

- **Get cavity wall insulation.**

Houses built from 1990s onwards usually have wall insulation, but if your house is older it may not have any insulation in the walls at all. Installing wall insulation is not a job you can do yourself – you have to employ an outside company to come and drill holes in your walls and then inject insulation into the cavity. Between September 2020 and March 2021, homeowners were able to apply for a Green Homes Grant voucher to cover the cost of installing cavity and loft insulation. We had someone come out to do ours during the scheme – my husband was pretty excited about getting something for free that would save us money! – but when they got here we discovered we already had it. So no money-saving for us! You can still apply for different grants on the Government website, so do look into what you might be able to get for free. If you do have to pay for it, it's likely to cost you around £725 to insulate the walls of a detached house. This will save you an average of £245 on your yearly energy bills as well as 1080kg of CO_2 – the equivalent energy of charging 137,713 smartphones!

- Insulate your loft.

If your loft is easy to access and has no damp issues, then it should be possible to do this yourself, but you will have to pay for the materials. Loft insulation can be laid between the joists (on the loft floor) or the rafters (that support the roof). The estimated cost for an average home is £395, which will save £215 from energy bills every year – so it will have paid for itself within two years!

Did you know?

Insulating your loft can stop 950kg of CO_2 from entering the atmosphere – the same amount released from driving a car 2,323 miles!

I have a funny story about when we did ours. My husband did most of it, but because he is very tall it was hard for him to reach the edges where the roof goes down to a point. So in I went, all kitted out in salopettes, raincoat, face mask, ski goggles, hat and gloves because I can't stand the fluffy fibres of the insulation. I slid along on a board to the edges, but it was SO hot and cramped that I couldn't do it. I was sweating! And when I turned and tried to get out, I got stung on the bum by a queen wasp who I'd disturbed from her sleep! The lengths we go to to save energy...

- Get under-floor insulation.

Just like cavity wall and loft insulation, making sure your floor is properly insulated will stop lots of heat escaping. This is usually only necessary on the ground floor, but if you have upstairs rooms over unheated spaces such as a garage, they should be insulated too. Some newer homes have solid concrete floors, which can have insulation placed on top of it. But if your home is older, it may have a suspended timber floor. Wool insulation can be laid underneath the floorboards between the joists which hold them up, or a newer technology sprays foam insulation underneath the floorboards with the use of a robot! Insulating your floor can cost from £150 (if you're doing it yourself) and £750 (if you have it done professionally). It can save you up to £65 a year off your energy bills and save about 290kg of CO_2 – the same as recycling 12.7 rubbish bags of waste, instead of sending them to landfill.

LED bulbs use less electricity to produce the same amount of light as halogen bulbs

?

DID YOU KNOW?

- Switching from halogen to more energy-saving bulbs could cut 1.26 million tonnes of carbon emissions a year – the equivalent to removing half a million cars from the UK's roads!

- ***Swap to energy-saving light bulbs.***
  It's estimated that lighting is responsible for 15% of the energy we use in our homes. Lightbulbs have come a long way since traditional incandescent bulbs. These energy-guzzlers use only 10% of the energy they use to produce light, with the rest lost as heat inside the bulb. That's why they are called incandescent – because of the glowing filament inside. Next came halogens, a slightly more energy-efficient filament-style bulb, but since October 2021, they have been phased out across the UK in favour of energy-saving bulbs such as CFLs (compact fluorescent light bulbs) and LEDs (light-emitting diodes). These use less electricity to produce the same amount of light, reducing your energy bills and the carbon footprint of your home.

  CFLs use 75% less energy than a filament bulb and they last 10 times longer, but they contain mercury, which can cause environmental problems when disposing of the bulbs. While you can still buy these in the UK, many people are opting for LEDs instead.

'LEDs use 90% less energy than traditional bulbs'

LEDs use 90% less energy than a traditional bulb, and 90% of the energy they do use goes towards producing light. They also have an exceptionally long life, with many promising 50,000 hours of light (this works out at 17 years if used eight hours a day). This is around 50 times longer than a traditional bulb, 25 times longer than a halogen bulb and eight times longer than a CFL bulb.

> **IF YOU REPLACE ALL THE BULBS IN YOUR HOME WITH LEDS, YOU COULD REDUCE YOUR CARBON EMISSIONS BY 65KG PER YEAR. THAT'S THE EQUIVALENT OF DRIVING YOUR CAR 220 MILES.**

LED bulbs have dropped in price considerably over the years, but they are still a few pounds more than standard bulbs. The price difference is worth it though, when you consider how long they last and what you save on bills and emissions.

- *Turn the lights off when you leave a room...*
  I don't mean to sound like your mother here, but make sure you turn the light off when you leave a room, especially if you still use incandescent or halogen bulbs! While the energy saved won't be massive if you are using LED or CFL bulbs, all those little bits of wasted energy, along with other bad habits we may have, all add up.

  I'm pretty good at turning the lights off when I am downstairs, but if I am upstairs sorting bits and bobs out or just generally faffing, I'll have the lights on in a few rooms as I go between them. If I leave a light on in a bedroom or on the landing, my husband will walk past and shout, "Hello, hello?" to remind me to turn the light off. And now Charlotte has started doing it too!

- *Invest in smart bulbs.*
  If you do leave the house and forget to turn off a light, then having a smart lighting system allows you to turn them off from your phone – super handy if you go out and remember that you left the bathroom light on. It's also a good way to schedule and control turning lights off and on from afar – such as if you are arriving home in the dark and need the outside light to come on, or if you're on holiday but want to make it look like there's someone at home. There are lots of smart bulb and lighting systems to choose from, and they usually require you to download a free phone app to control them.

GET THE GREEN LIGHT!

No, I don't mean give your house a spooky green glow! The National Grid has created a low-energy light bulb that gives off a 'Green Light Signal' when the energy in your area is mainly being supplied from low carbon sources, such as wind or solar. This means you can make smarter choices about when to use your electrical appliances. When the bulb, which can be used in any standard floor or table light, glows green, you know that's the best time to charge your electric car, put on your clothes wash or start the dishwasher cycle. I love this because when we have more knowledge, we can make better choices!

- *Get a smart meter.*

    If you haven't got one already, get your energy company to install a smart meter. I think a lot of us don't even think about how much energy we use or where it comes from (unless you are my husband) – it just arrives in our houses as if by magic! Smart meters allow you to see how much energy you are using almost in real time, which can help you make better choices. If you see the dial going up every time you boil the kettle, for example, you might think twice about repeatedly boiling it! (For how to be more energy efficient with kettles, see page 105).

IT'S ESTIMATED THAT IF EVERYONE INSTALLED SMART METERS – BOTH HOMEOWNERS AND BUSINESSES – IT COULD REDUCE UK CARBON EMISSIONS BY 45 MILLION TONNES – THE EQUIVALENT OF TAKING 26 MILLION CARS OFF THE ROAD FOR A YEAR.

It is fair to say that my husband watches the smart meter more than he watches the telly! We got ours just before Christmas in 2020, two days before I hired a hot tub...

Now, I know a hot tub is not the most environmentally friendly thing to use, but it was the year that Boris cancelled Christmas because of Covid! I was devastated because we couldn't see our relatives and I was worried Charlotte would think she had fewer presents because she'd been naughty. The hot tub was my way of making it special. Being the tight man that he is though, my husband was not so keen on the idea. When I told him I'd managed to get it for an extra day for free, he said, "Great, we've got to heat it and pay for that extra day on our bills!"

'My husband watches the smart meter more than he watches the telly!'

He'd already started watching the smart meter like a hawk when the shower went on, so you can imagine what he was like with the hot tub! The first night he didn't even want to step into it – he just watched me and Charlotte from the conservatory, saying things like, "How much do you think it has cost us so far? £4!!" But he could see how much we were loving it, so he relented and joined us the next day. It did make the whole Christmas period special, even if Greta might not be impressed with my choices...

- **Switch to a green energy company.**
  As the market moves towards embracing more renewable forms of energy – wind, solar and hydro – it's not hard to find an energy company that offers 100% green electricity. There are tariffs available at most of the Big Six – British Gas, EDF Energy, E.ON, Npower, ScottishPower and SSE. But the sticking point comes when you want to find green gas. The only UK company offering 100% green electricity AND gas is Green Energy. Their gas is produced from food, farm and landfill waste (see biogas on page 74). Many other companies, such as Octopus Energy and Ovo Energy, offer 100% green electricity and a smaller percentage of

green gas but 100% carbon neutral gas, meaning they offset any emissions created from their gas sources. We recently switched to Octopus Energy because I wanted us to be with a greener provider.

'We recently switched to Octopus Energy because I wanted us to be with a greener provider'

IN ORDER TO MEET THE PARIS CLIMATE AGREEMENT GOALS, 70% OF ELECTRICITY GENERATION NEEDS TO COME FROM SOLAR AND WIND BY 2050.

Switching providers is easy, but it is important to do as much research as you can. Some energy companies have been known to 'greenwash' their claims. They say they offer 100% green products but in reality they provide green electricity 'where possible', which means the rest still comes from fossil fuels. Most genuine renewable energy companies have a REGO (Renewable Energy Guarantee of Origin) certificate but even these can be bought by companies still using fossil fuels.

WHAT IS RENEWABLE ENERGY?

Renewable energy means energy that comes from sources that won't run out, unlike fossil fuels which are finite sources that also destroy the planet when we mine and use them. The Earth has provided us with all the sun, wind and waves we need to power it. In fact, did you know that in a single hour, the amount of power from the sun that strikes the earth is more than the entire world consumes in a year? I know it's not possible to cover the whole world in solar panels but it gives you an idea of the power freely available.

In order to meet net zero by 2050, the UK needs to take many measures over the next 30 years, including quadrupling offshore wind capacity, in a bid to decarbonise the energy sector. The good news is that renewable energies outperformed fossil fuels for the first time in 2020, providing 43% of UK electricity compared to 37.7% from fossil fuels.

Solar power relies entirely on gathering energy from the sun and turning it into electricity via photovoltaic (PV) cells, so it produces no emissions in the process. There is also an endless supply (for at least a few billion years, anyway!). As of May 2021, around 900,000 UK homes had solar panels installed.

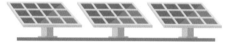

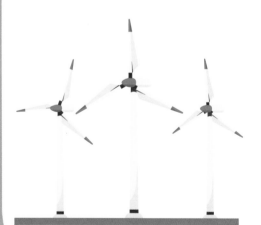

Wind power is created when wind is turned into electricity through wind turbines. Wind is going to be a key player in providing green energy. Turbines are either onshore (installed on land) or offshore (installed in open seawater). During COP26, I visited Whitelee Windfarm, just outside Glasgow, the biggest onshore wind farm in the UK. It's home to 215 wind turbines and has the capacity to produce 539 megawatts of clean, green electricity. That's enough to power around 350,000 homes.

A fun fact: the wind turbines look white but they're actually a light grey and are the average colour of the sky in the UK!

Hydro power harnesses the power of flowing water to produce electricity. This can be from a flowing river, the tide or in man-made installations such as dams. The water spins a turbine, which turns a shaft that is connected to an electric generator.

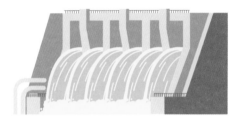

Biogas is a fuel produced by the breakdown of organic matter, such as food scraps or animal waste, in the absence of oxygen. This process is called anaerobic digestion, and it's what happens to our food waste when it is properly recycled (see page 98 for more).

Geothermal energy comes from the heat in the ground and fluids under the Earth's crust. Countries such as New Zealand and Iceland, where there is tectonic activity and they have hot springs, utilise geothermal energy far more than the UK. But it is something that could hold the key to a greener future here too. I visited a geothermal station in Seaham, County Durham, which started using naturally warm water from former coal mines to heat homes. Around 25% of houses in the UK are on top of former mines, which means naturally warm flood water from them is going to waste.

Green hydrogen is a gas that will play a big part in us reaching net zero emissions in sectors that are hard to electrify, such as shipping, aviation and industry. Hydrogen is traditionally made by splitting natural gas into hydrogen and carbon, which releases carbon dioxide into the atmosphere, contributing towards climate change. Green hydrogen, however, is created by using electricity from renewable sources to split water into hydrogen and oxygen, so it releases no harmful gases into the atmosphere in the process.

Supply and demand

If the UK is able to fully electrify through renewable sources rather than using fossil fuels, and demand for electricity continues to rise, there may be supply issues.

For example, if it is not windy and not very sunny, we won't produce as much electricity from wind turbines and solar panels. However, on days when we have excess power (when it is very windy and sunny) and demand is low, that power can be used to create other forms of energy that can be stored and used when other sources are low. Solar and wind energy can be converted into green hydrogen and stored. Pumped-storage hydro power is another option. When there is excess power on the grid it's used to pump water from a low reservoir to a high reservoir. When demand for electricity is high, the water is released back downhill into the lower reservoir, which drives turbines to generate electricity.

Supply and demand could still be an issue, so it's thought that nuclear power, as controversial as it is, will have to play some role in providing the UK with power. As of 2020, nuclear power generated 20% of the UK's electricity.

I visited Whitelee Windfarm near Glasgow

- *Consider getting solar panels installed.*
  This, of course, comes with an upfront cost, but in the long term they will save you money on your bills and in some cases can actually make you money (see below)! And solar panels will drastically cut the emissions your home creates. We don't have solar panels but I would definitely invest in them if I knew we were staying in our house for a long time.

> **GETTING SOLAR PANELS CAN REDUCE YOUR HOME'S CARBON FOOTPRINT BY 80% IN ONE YEAR.**

Below I have answered some of the most commonly asked questions about solar panels…

Does it have to be a sunny day for them to produce electricity?
No, solar panels can produce electricity even on a cloudy day! A bright, sunny day will of course provide you with more energy, but all they need to work is daylight. The panels can't produce electricity at night but energy that is created during the day can be stored in a battery to use overnight.

How much do they cost to install?
This will all depend on the type and size of the system you get, but on average it costs around £4,800 to fit a standard home with solar panels.

What about emissions?
Because solar power relies entirely on gathering energy from the sun and turning it into electricity via photovoltaic (PV) cells, it produces no emissions in the process. There is also an endless supply of sun. The creation of solar panels and their batteries does produce some emissions (like everything we make!), but they last for around 50 years and need little to no maintenance. Conventional heating systems require regular replacement (at around the 10-year mark), which creates a lot of waste and a demand for manufacturing more units.

What can I save from my bills?
The savings you make on your energy bills will depend on the size of your system, how much electricity you use and what time of day you use it – if you can use more energy during the day, when the panels are creating electricity, you will save more. It's estimated that you could save between £90 and £240 a year.

Solar panels could save you up to
£240 a year on your energy bills

How can I make money from them?

In January 2020, the government introduced a scheme called the Smart Export Guarantee for people who install solar panels. This pays you for the solar energy you 'export' to the grid – meaning electricity you generate but don't use yourself. This scheme also works for other renewable forms of energy, such as wind and hydro.

When your current heating system needs replacing, switching to a heat pump will help the planet

DID YOU KNOW?

- Sweden was one of the first countries in the world to introduce a carbon tax, 30 years ago, to encourage a move away from fossil fuels, and today 43% of their homes have a heat pump.

- Heat pumps use 75% less electricity to heat your home than conventional electric heaters.

- ### *Could you switch to a heat pump?*
  This is something to consider when your boiler will next need replacing. We still have a gas boiler – it's 10 years old and is still working, so we won't be ripping it out for a greener option just yet, because that would create unnecessary waste. When the boiler is past the point of repair and it's time to invest in something new, we will look into getting a heat pump. Heat pumps extract warmth from the air or the ground then use a compressor (which runs on electricity) to boost that warmth to a higher temperature which can then be pumped through the heating system in your home. Heat pumps are expensive, and the UK currently has the lowest sales of them in Europe.

Why switch?

They use 75% less electricity to heat your home because they operate at very high efficiencies. For every unit of electricity used, a heat pump creates 4 units of thermal heat. Whereas conventional electric heaters tend to create 1 unit of heat per 1 unit of electricity. Heat pumps can also cool your home in the summer and with current projections for warmer summers in the UK, this is going to be a much-needed addition. Conventional air conditioning units are very energy-intensive.

How much do they cost to install?

At the moment, the technology is very expensive and they can cost between £6,000 and £30,000, so they're a significant investment. In October 2021, the government began offering grants of up to £5,000 to households to replace boilers with heat pumps or other low-carbon technologies. And you can also apply for the Domestic Renewable Heat Incentive (RHI) scheme, which pays you back over the course of seven years if you meet the relevant criteria. For more information, search for Domestic Renewable Heat Incentive on the government website at gov.uk

What about emissions?

Heat pumps use ambient heat from the ground rather than burning fossil fuels to create heat, so are a renewable form of energy. They do run on electricity, though, so the emissions released will depend on where your electricity is coming from. If you are using electricity generated by solar panels (bonus green points for you!), then there will be next to no emissions. If it is running off energy from the national grid, then it's likely that fossil fuels will still be used (another good reason for switching to a greener energy supplier!). But remember, the pumps use 75% less electricity than standard electric heating systems.

How much can I save?

If you are switching from a new gas boiler, then you may not save on running costs, but you will be drastically cutting your carbon emissions. If you are switching from an electric heating system, then you could save up to £920 a year on your energy bills.

Do they work in cold weather?

Yes! The top three countries in Europe to have heat pumps installed in almost half of their homes are Norway, Sweden and Finland, and they are colder countries than the UK.

2.

IN THE
KITCHEN

What's the thing we do most in the kitchen? Cook food. At least, that's what my husband does – I'm pretty lucky because he takes care of most of the meals in our house. Food is such a big part of our lives, which means it's an area where we can really make some positive changes.

People tend to underestimate the greenhouse gas emissions from food. But everything we eat has an impact on the planet. Just like the energy used to heat our homes, the food we fuel our bodies with has a significant carbon footprint. In fact, food production – that's everything from the land, water and resources used to grow our food to the way it is

Food packaging choices have a huge impact on our environment

transported, packaged and disposed of – accounts for a quarter of global greenhouse gases, and takes up half of the world's habitable land.

But let's be honest here, how many of us actually think about where the food on our plates comes from (other than the supermarket)? We are usually so busy that we mindlessly throw food down our throats – and it has often come out of plastic packaging.

But the choices we make about what we eat, the packaging that food comes in and how much we throw away have a huge impact on the environment.

'The choices we make about what we eat, the packaging that food comes in and how much food we throw away have a huge impact on the environment'

It's clear that some degree of diet shift is necessary for us to reduce our carbon emissions, and it is widely known that cutting down on meat is one of the ways we can do this. But that's not the only thing you can do that will make a difference.

In this section I discuss why what we eat matters, how to reduce the amount of food you waste (trust me, as a country we waste a lot!) as well as giving you easy tips on cutting down on the amount of plastic packaging we bring into our kitchens.

WHAT YOU EAT

Where your food comes from, how it is reared/grown and how it is transported all affect the carbon footprint of your meal. The argument about what is the most environmentally-friendly diet is a complicated one. For example, it is widely known that reducing meat consumption will cut down on emissions, but replacing locally reared animal protein with soy-based products flown in from the other side of the world has its own environmental impact. And if you want to eat tomatoes all year round (rather than when they're in season in the UK), then it is actually better, emissions wise, to eat tomatoes grown from the natural heat of the sun in Spain then transported here than tomatoes grown in artificially heated greenhouses in the UK.

But in general, we should try to eat less meat, more fruit and veg, and choose items that are seasonal and grown closer to home. This seems really simple and, yes, you've probably heard it 100 times before, but have you actually made the changes? Here, I'll show you the simple things that will have a big impact on your carbon footprint. Once you know, you might start to think twice about what you eat.

- ***Reduce your meat consumption.***
  The last couple of years have seen a real shift in people's eating habits as we become more conscious of the impact our diets can have on the planet. Around 14% of adults in the UK now follow meat-free diets, and the number of people who gave up meat in 2020 (470,000) was double that of 2019. In 2022, a further 8.8 million Brits say they plan to go meat-free.

  I'll confess straight away that we still eat meat – occasionally! We'd made a conscious effort to reduce our red meat consumption over the last few years and, since writing and researching the book, we've cut down even more. We now have vegetarian and vegan days, and we very rarely eat red meat (unless my husband sneaks beef mince instead of Quorn into the weekly shop). But I love chicken too much to give it up! We eat roast chicken most weeks and use the chicken the next day to make a curry, pasta bake or soup. So I am not about to tell you to go vegan – unless you want to. But how about switching out meat for a plant-based alternative one or two days a week? Why? Well...

  Livestock farming is responsible for 14.5% of all greenhouse gas emissions – that's a huge amount. Not only that, but farming animals also uses and pollutes vast amounts of water, and takes up 83% of agricultural land on earth. So the changes you make to your meat consumption, no matter how small, will make a huge difference to the planet.

'I'll confess straight away that we still eat meat… occasionally!'

Animal-based foods, especially beef and lamb, have a larger carbon footprint than most plant-based foods because of the resources and land needed to rear the animals and their feed, as well as the gases they produce as part of their digestive processes – that's right, their burps! They belch out methane into the atmosphere, which is up to 80 times more potent than CO_2 at trapping heat in the atmosphere. The storage of manure and the use of synthetic fertilisers are also responsible for 65% of all human-related emissions of nitrous oxide, a gas that has 300 times the global warming potential of CO_2.

On top of that, the huge demand for meat has led to more and more land around the world being taken over for beef production and animal feed. This is now one of the leading causes of deforestation – and we should all know by now that we need trees! The more land we use to rear livestock, the more wildlife we are pushing to near-extinction, reducing the world's biodiversity. Globally, a frightening one acre of land is cleared for animal farming every second.

The less meat we eat, the less demand there is and the less land is needed to rear the animals and their feed – which in turn means we will save water and reduce greenhouse gas emissions.

One of the common things I hear people ask about cutting down on meat is, 'Where will you get your protein from?' And the truth is: in loads of foods! Eggs and fish are high in protein, and as vegan diets become more popular there are so many plant-based protein alternatives to burgers, sausages and mince (although try to steer clear of overly processed products). Other good sources of protein include tofu, chickpeas, quinoa, rice, lentils, beans, oats, nuts and seeds. Most adults need around 0.75g of protein per kilo of body weight per day (which works out at about 45g for the average woman or 55g for the average man), which can be easily reached by eating a varied diet. See the chart, right…

PROTEIN-RICH FOODS

Food	Portion	Protein
Chicken breast	100g	27g
Pork loin	100g	27g
Beef mince	100g	26g
Lamb chop	100g	24g
Salmon fillet	100g	23g
Beyond burger (plant-based)	100g	17g
Eggs	120g (2 medium eggs)	14g
Quorn mince	100g	13g
Lentils	120g (3 tbsp)	9g
Quinoa	185g (5 tbsp when cooked)	9g
Chickpeas	105g (3 tbsp)	8g
Tofu	100g	8g
Peanuts	30g	8g
Pumpkin seeds	30g	7g
Wholegrain rice	75g uncooked	7g
Baked beans	120g (3 tbsp)	6g
Oats	40g	4g

Top tip: Aubergine gives meals that 'meaty' texture if you think you will miss it.

Having meat-free meals like this could aid your health and help the environment at the same time

If you make one meat-free meal a week, in one month you'll have four new recipes under your belt. And you never know, you might decide to cut down even further.

Making a shift towards a more plant-based diet comes with benefits for your health too. Cutting down on meat, especially red meat, can reduce your risk of heart disease, some cancers and diabetes. In fact, adding in more fruits, grains, lentils, wholegrains and nuts into your diet will also support a healthy heart.

You'll be pleased to hear (and so will my husband) that cutting down on meat can save you money and time too. On average, plant-based meals cost 40% less than those containing meat and fish and take a third of the amount of time to prepare.

- **_Buy local, sustainably produced meat._**
  If you do still eat meat, (and let's face it – the majority of us do!), then we need to find better ways to do it. Buying meat that's reared in Britain using sustainable and ethical farming practices (see the box, right) is the best way. If you can, get it from a local butcher or farm shop so you can trace where it comes from. It is more difficult to find this information when shopping in a supermarket, but look out for Soil Association,

Organic or RSPCA-assured logos so you know the meat you are eating is from animals that were well cared for.

What we want to avoid is buying meat that has been raised intensively. Intensive farms are there to produce meat (and eggs and dairy) as quickly as possible to keep up with high demand. Often, the animals are kept indoors and bred to grow abnormally and quickly. If we want to do our bit for the planet, buying local, grass-fed meat will cut demand for such farms, give animals a better quality of life, reclaim land and reduce emissions.

BEST OF BRITISH

It's not possible to lump all farms around the world into one group – every country has different farming techniques so emissions will be vastly different. While we do have some intensive farming here, we have a lot of farms which use grass-fed, grazing systems to produce some of the most sustainable meat in the world. In fact, according to the latest 2020 report from the Government's Committee on Climate Change, greenhouse gas emissions from UK beef are about half the global average. Many British farms are taking measures to reduce their emissions, such as keeping stock levels down, changing cow feed (which can reduce the amount of methane burps!) and installing solar panels. Grazing systems can also have a positive impact on the planet. Large areas of grass help to capture carbon (see page 112 for more) and manure from the livestock helps to boost organic matter in the soil.

- ***Reduce dairy.***
  For the same reasons that we want to reduce our meat intake – land use, methane from cow burps etc – we also want to cut down on dairy. One of the easiest ways to do this is to replace dairy milk with plant-based versions. It can take a bit of getting used to, but I've tried quite a few of them now and have found two I like. I wasn't a fan of oat milk in my tea. It tastes like oats (obviously) and, I know it sounds silly, but I felt like I had porridge in my cuppa! So I have almond milk in tea (which I barely drink anyway), and oat milk on my cereal.

All plant-based milks are better for the environment than cow's milk because they use less land, less water and generate fewer greenhouse gases. But they do come with their own impact on the environment.

Here's a chart showing the emissions, land and water needed to make one glass (200ml) of dairy, almond, oat, rice and soy milk.

	Emissions (kg)	Land (sq m)	Water use (litre)
Dairy	0.62	1.79	125.6
Almond	0.14	0.1	74.3
Oat	0.18	0.15	9.6
Rice	0.24	0.07	54
Soya	0.2	0.13	5.6

Almond milk creates the smallest amount of greenhouse gases because the trees capture a lot of CO_2 as they grow. Soy milk uses the least water, and rice milk needs the least land. Oat milk strikes a good balance between all three and is often cited as the most environmentally friendly for that reason.

> **DID YOU KNOW? PRODUCING A GLASS OF DAIRY MILK RESULTS IN ALMOST THREE TIMES THE GREENHOUSE GAS EMISSIONS OF ANY NON-DAIRY MILKS.**

Unfortunately, switching to a plant-based milk is one of the things that isn't going to save you money. A litre of oat milk is around £1.70-£2, depending on the brand, whereas you can get just over a litre of cow's milk for 89p. But think of the positives!

> **DAIRY-FREE MILKS USUALLY COME IN TETRA PAK CARTONS, WHICH CAN'T ALWAYS BE RECYCLED AT HOME. SEE PAGE 248 FOR HOW TO RECYCLE THESE PROPERLY.**

- ***Cut down on the amount of fish you eat.***
  I thought I was doing really well in my mission to save the planet by eating a little bit of chicken and choosing fish over meat. I'm a terrible cook, but the one thing I do make is a prawn stir-fry because you can't go wrong. My go-to meal when I eat out is fish and chips and Charlotte loves a fish-finger sandwich. But then I

watched *Seaspiracy* on Netflix (another important show to watch if you haven't seen it) and now I feel bad for eating fish too!

'I thought I was doing well in my mission to save the planet by eating fish over meat...but now I feel bad!'

The problem is that many fishing practices are not sustainable. Because the demand for fish is high, too many fish are being caught at once, so their populations are depleted and they are unable to bounce back. The popular fishing method of bottom trawling, where heavy nets are dragged across the seabed to catch fish, is well known for wreaking havoc on ecosystems. This method allows companies to catch a lot of fish in one go, but it also means that anything that gets in the nets' way is caught too. Some species are being fished to the brink of extinction simply as by-products of this method, and other marine life such as turtles, seabirds and even whales have been caught up in the nets too. This is heartbreaking.

This kind of overfishing is also affecting the ocean's ability to act as a carbon sink – a natural reservoir that captures carbon (see page 43 for more on carbon sinks). As the nets are repeatedly dragged across the seabed, they disrupt marine sediments which have captured carbon, releasing the carbon back into the atmosphere. The nets also wipe out deep-sea corals – biodiverse ecosystems which take hundreds of years to form. In the same way that bull-dozing a forest has a knock-on effect on all the smaller plants in the forest, as well as the animals living there, destroying coral has the same effect, and we are losing vital ecosystems at an alarming rate.

Fishing gear adds to the huge amount of plastic left in the sea (see page 46 for more on the problem with plastic) which also affects how much carbon is captured. Phytoplankton living on the surface of the ocean capture carbon and sink to the bottom of the ocean where the carbon is stored. When the phytoplankton eat microplastic, they become more buoyant, so they aren't able to sink as quickly, and the carbon is released.

?

DID YOU KNOW?

- **46% of the plastic in The Great Pacific Garbage Patch is made up of fishing gear.**

- **Fishing boats that trawl the bottom of the ocean release as much carbon per year as the aviation industry.**

- **Every year, there is 25 million acres of deforestation but ocean floors are destroyed by trawlers at a rate of 3.9 billion acres a year!**

- **Longline fishing lays enough lines a day to wrap around the world 500 times!**

So, how does that fish-finger sandwich sound to you now? Of course, it's beyond our power as individual consumers to ensure that sustainable fishing methods are put into place, but we CAN cut the demand for fish by reducing the amount we eat. Fish and seafood is an excellent source of Omega 3, which is important for a healthy body and mind, so I'm not saying cut it out completely. Just be more mindful about how much you eat and how it is farmed. Look out for sustainability labels on the fish, and don't be afraid to ask where the fish comes from at a fish counter or your local chip shop. Farmed shellfish, such as mussels, clams and oysters are some of the most eco-friendly sea food, and you can find out more by searching for 'Good Fish Guide' online, where fish is rated with a traffic-light system for sustainability.

- ***Eat what's in season.***
  All crops have a natural growth period, which is largely determined by climate and soil quality. But these days, we can get every kind of food at every time of the year. This is known as globally seasonal – the food is grown while it is in season in one country, then transported to another country to be eaten. (You can probably guess that one issue with this is transport emissions!)

It's convenient for us and it's what we're used to now. It means we get fresh produce and a wide variety of nutrients all year round, but it puts a strain on the land where the food is grown. High demand means intensive farming, which uses pesticides and synthetic fertilisers to grow as many crops as possible. Over time this is destroying soil quality, which means the crops contain fewer nutrients.

'When crops are in season they're cheaper to buy and taste so much better'

We've lost touch with what grows in each season in the UK, so it will take a shift in mindset to start eating more seasonally.

Start by making the most of the crops that are in abundance. For example, strawberries are the superstars of summer, pumpkins and squash are celebrated in autumn and cauliflowers and leeks are the wonders of winter. Different times of the year call for different types of food. In summer, fresh green salads are delicious – and the ground provides us with just the right ingredients – but in autumn and winter it is time to hunker down and get cosy with root vegetables (abundant at that time of year) in soups and stews.

When crops are in season, they're cheaper to buy and they taste so much better too. If you pick up something out of season in the supermarket, it's likely to have been flown in from another country or grown here using artificial heat – which both ramp up its carbon footprint.

Eating food that is grown close to home can reconnect us with the land and reduce carbon emissions from transport. Food that comes a long way also comes in more packaging to protect it!

SEASONAL FRUIT AND VEG IN THE UK

JANUARY
VEG: Beetroot, Brussels Sprouts, Cabbage, Carrots, Celeriac, Celery, Chicory, Jerusalem Artichokes, Kale, Leeks, Mushrooms, Onions, Parsnips, Spring Greens, Spring Onions, Squash, Swedes, Turnips

FRUIT: Apples, Pears

FEBRUARY
VEG: Beetroot, Brussels Sprouts, Cabbage, Carrots, Celeriac, Chicory, Jerusalem Artichokes, Kale, Leeks, Mushrooms, Onions, Parsnips, Purple Sprouting Broccoli, Spring Greens, Spring Onions, Squash, Swedes

FRUIT: Apples, Pears

MARCH
VEG: Artichoke, Beetroot, Cabbage, Carrots, Chicory, Cucumber, Leeks, Parsnip, Purple Sprouting Broccoli, Radishes, Sorrel, Spring Greens, Spring Onions, Watercress

FRUIT: Rhubarb

APRIL
VEG: Artichoke, Beetroot, Cabbage, Carrots, Chicory, New Potatoes, Kale, Morel Mushrooms, Parsnips, Radishes, Rocket, Sorrel, Spinach, Spring Greens, Spring Onions, Watercress

FRUIT: Rhubarb

MAY
VEG: Artichoke, Asparagus, Aubergine, Beetroot, Chicory, Chillies, Elderflowers, Lettuce, Marrow, New Potatoes, Peas, Peppers, Radishes, Rocket, Samphire, Sorrel, Spinach, Spring Greens, Spring Onions, Watercress

FRUIT: Rhubarb, Strawberries

JUNE
VEG: Asparagus, Aubergine, Beetroot, Broad Beans, Broccoli, Cauliflower, Chicory, Chillies, Courgettes, Cucumber, Elderflowers, Lettuce, Marrow, New Potatoes, Peas, Peppers, Radishes, Rocket, Runner Beans, Samphire, Sorrel, Spring Greens, Spring Onions, Summer Squash, Swiss Chard, Turnips, Watercress

FRUIT: Blackcurrants, Cherries, Gooseberries, Raspberries, Redcurrants, Rhubarb, Strawberries, Tayberries

JULY
VEG: Aubergine, Beetroot, Broad Beans, Broccoli, Carrots, Cauliflower, Chicory, Chillies, Courgettes, Cucumber, Fennel, French Beans, Garlic, Kohlrabi, New Potatoes, Onions, Peas, Potatoes, Radishes, Rocket, Runner Beans, Samphire, Sorrel, Spring Greens, Spring Onions, Summer Squash, Swish Chard, Tomatoes, Turnips, Watercress

FRUIT: Blackberries, Blackcurrants, Blueberries, Cherries, Gooseberries, Greengages, Loganberries, Raspberries, Redcurrants, Rhubarb, Strawberries

AUGUST
VEG: Aubergine, Beetroot, Broad Beans, Broccoli, Carrots, Cauliflower, Chicory, Chillies, Courgettes, Cucumber, Fennel, French Beans, Garlic, Kohlrabi, Leeks, Lettuce, Mangetout, Marrow, Mushrooms, Parsnips, Peas, Peppers, Potatoes, Pumpkin, Radishes, Rocket, Runner Beans, Samphire, Sorrel, Spring Greens, Spring Onions, Summer Squash, Sweetcorn, Swiss Chard, Tomatoes, Watercress

FRUIT: Blackberries, Blackcurrants, Cherries, Damsons, Greengages, Loganberries, Plums, Raspberries, Redcurrants, Rhubarb, Strawberries

SEPTEMBER
VEG: Aubergine, Beetroot, Broccoli, Brussels Sprouts, Butternut Squash, Carrots, Cauliflower, Celery, Courgettes, Chicory, Chillies, Cucumber, Garlic, Kale, Kohlrabi, Leeks, Lettuce, Mangetout, Marrow, Onions, Parsnips, Peas, Peppers, Potatoes, Pumpkin, Radishes, Rocket, Runner Beans, Samphire, Sorrel, Spinach, Spring Greens, Spring Onions, Summer Squash, Sweetcorn, Swiss Chard, Tomatoes, Turnips, Watercress, Wild Mushrooms

FRUIT: Blackberries, Damsons, Pears, Plums, Raspberries, Rhubarb, Strawberries

OCTOBER
VEG: Aubergine, Beetroot, Broccoli, Brussels Sprouts, Butternut Squash, Carrots, Cauliflower, Celeriac, Celery, Chestnuts, Chicory, Chillies, Courgette, Cucumber, Kale, Leeks, Lettuce, Marrow, Onions, Parsnips, Peas, Potatoes, Pumpkin, Radishes, Rocket, Runner Beans, Spinach, Spring Greens, Spring Onions, Summer Squash, Swede, Sweetcorn, Swiss Chard, Tomatoes, Turnips, Watercress, Wild Mushrooms, Winter Squash

FRUIT: Apples, Blackberries, Elderberries, Pears

NOVEMBER
VEG: Beetroot, Brussels Sprouts, Butternut Squash, Cabbage, Carrots, Cauliflower, Celeriac, Celery, Chestnuts, Chicory, Jerusalem Artichokes, Kale, Leeks, Onions, Parsnips, Potatoes, Pumpkin, Swede, Swiss Chard, Turnips, Watercress, Wild Mushrooms, Winter Squash

FRUIT: Apples, Cranberries, Elderberries, Pears

DECEMBER
VEG: Beetroot, Brussels Sprouts, Carrots, Celeriac, Celery, Chestnuts, Chicory, Jerusalem Artichokes, Kale, Leeks, Mushrooms, Onions, Parsnips, Potatoes, Pumpkin, Red Cabbage, Swede, Swiss Chard, Turnips, Watercress, Winter Squash

FRUIT: Apples, Cranberries, Pears

- *Go organic where you can.*
  Organic fruit and veg is more expensive because it is governed by regulations which severely restrict the use of pesticides and artificial fertilisers – two things that have a detrimental effect on the health of our soil – and us. Organic farming is considered more sustainable because the lack of pesticides and fertilisers, and the use of a wider variety of plants, means a better quality of soil. Better quality of soil leads to better quality crops, and healthier humans!

FARMERS' MARKETS AND VEG BOXES

Visiting a farmers' market or farm shop for your fruit and veg is a good way to get locally grown produce that is in season. It is also usually without plastic packaging and can be cheaper than the supermarket. This is not an option for everyone though, so alternatively you could sign up for fruit and veg box deliveries, such as Abel & Cole or Riverford Organic Farmers, who will deliver a box of seasonal organic fruit and/or veg to your door each week. If you have a hunt on local Facebook community pages, it's likely there will be local farm shops that offer box deliveries too. Prices are usually around £10 for a small box, which is enough for two people for a week. If you're shopping in the supermarket, look out for accreditation labels such as Organic, LEAF (Linking Environment and Farming) or Assured Food Standard (the Red Tractor logo).

I've recently started getting fruit and veg from oddbox.co.uk, a company determined to cut down on food waste. The fruit and veg comes directly from the farmer and includes all the items that would normally be turned away because they look 'odd', but are still perfectly good to eat. You can choose small, medium or large and have it delivered weekly or every two weeks. I'm super impressed and Charlotte loved unboxing it.

- ***Grow your own!***
  The best way to reconnect to the earth, reduce transport emissions and packaging, plus to help out our soil, is to grow your own food. Nothing beats the taste of fresh fruit, veg and herbs you have grown yourself. And it's the ultimate way to shorten your food chain! We have an allotment and it has been hard work – but so rewarding. And you don't need an allotment or even a big garden to make a start. To find out more, see page 120.

FOOD WASTE

How much food do you think you throw away every week? Just a few scraps here and there? Alarmingly, UK households throw away an average of six meals a week! Yes, some of it is peelings and scraps, but a lot is made up of food that's gone past its best, food we don't like, and leftovers that we decide we don't want.

Food waste alone produces 8-10% of all global greenhouse gas emissions (which is four times more than flying!). This is because when food ends up in landfill, it releases harmful methane gas into the environment, something not many of us think about when we're scraping food off our plates. But it's not just the greenhouse gas emissions from rotting food we need to think about here – throwing all that food away is a waste of all the resources needed to grow, transport, package and cook it.

Think about the whole process. Our food is planted or born, then fed and watered as it grows before being harvested or slaughtered, usually using machines. It is then transported for storage before it is packaged and transported again to food shops. In shops it might need to be refrigerated, then we travel to buy the food, take it home and keep it in our fridges. If the food goes off before we even get to use it, ALL of the energy (greenhouse gases) and resources have been for nothing. It's really sad when you think about it. And if we cook it (using more energy) and then throw it away because we made too much or don't like it, we can add even more emissions to the pile.

'It's really sad when you think about all the resources and energy that is wasted when we throw food away'

While some food is wasted before it even gets to the supermarkets, and supermarkets also throw out too much at the end of the day, the biggest culprits for food waste are the consumers – us, in other words. In fact, 70% of food waste comes from our homes, and it's something we can so easily reduce by planning our meals, freezing leftovers and composting food scraps.

Charlotte loves making smoothies from leftovers

DID YOU KNOW?

- Food waste alone produces 8-10% of all global greenhouse gas emissions.

- 9.5 million tonnes of edible food is thrown away by households every year in the UK!

- Over a year, the average family throws away around £700 of food shopping.

- If we all stopped wasting the food which could have been eaten, it would have the same CO_2 impact as taking one in four cars off UK roads.

THE 5 MOST COMMONLY WASTED FOODS IN BRITISH HOMES:

Potatoes – **5.8 million whole potatoes are thrown out every day.**

Bread – **24 million slices go to waste every day.**

Milk – **5.8 million glasses of milk are poured away every day.**

Bananas – **1.4 million bananas are binned every day.**

Salad – **178 million bags of salad a year are chucked out every year.**

- *First things first, let's do a stocktake.*

  Go through your cupboards and see what you've got. This is a bit of a mantra for many areas of your life, such as in the bathroom (see page 126). When cooking, it's easier to grab the first tin or packet you see in the cupboard than rifling through to the back, so it's likely you have tins of beans, soup and jars of sauce you didn't know about – and many might be past their use-by dates! Once you know what you've got, organise your cupboards so that the things with the shortest use-by dates are at the front, and see if you can plan meals that incorporate them. Then make it your mission to do a mini stocktake once a month to avoid things going past their use-by dates and ending up in the bin.

  > *'You probably have tins of beans, soups and jars of sauce that you don't know about at the back of your cupboards'*

  A word on 'best before' and 'use-by' dates – take them with a pinch of salt. Obviously if it is milk or meat or fish, then don't risk it. But when it comes to tinned food or dried store-cupboard staples, a few days or even weeks probably won't do you any harm. At least, that's my rule!

- *Plan your meals, then make a list and stick to it.*

  An obvious but important one. If you know what meals you are going to make, you only need to buy the ingredients you need for them, and nothing else. This will massively reduce the chances of you having food left over that will go to waste – not to mention any 'treats' or little extras that you normally add to your trolley at the supermarket. It's simple: don't buy what you don't need.

  It's nice knowing what you are eating each day. I like to have variety throughout the week, rather than ending up with pasta three days in a row because of lack of planning. We used to do our food shop without planning and we'd end up with vegetables that didn't go with the meals we made and would end up being thrown away. We now plan five meals and move them around depending on our plans for the week. It makes life so much easier.

?

DID YOU KNOW?

- 41% of food is thrown away because we don't use it on time, 28% is wasted because we don't like it, 25% ends up in the bin because we cooked, prepared or were served too much and the last 6% for other reasons.

- The average UK household throws away 20% of all food purchased.

- Globally, 931 million tonnes of food is wasted. That's the weight of 23 million loaded 40-tonne trucks. Put bumper to bumper – that's enough to circle the world seven times.

- ***Don't shop hungry!***
  You know the score – if you go shopping when you are hungry it's far more likely you'll buy unhealthy snacks and treats (in lots of packaging!) instead of the foods you actually need to make proper meals. And once you've had your sugar fix, those extra items might go to waste. Or you'll eat them all. Either way, not great for you or the planet, so make sure you eat before you shop.

- ***Freeze leftovers and any food that will go out of date before you use it.***
  If we cook a chilli, spaghetti bolognese or curry, we always make a huge batch then portion it out and freeze what we don't eat that day. For Charlotte, I blitz some of the mixture up in the blender and then put it in small pots in the freezer. In the same way you do a stocktake of your cupboards, keep an eye on the leftovers you freeze. I've often found things a year or two later that I've forgotten about… and it's probably not safe to defrost and eat at that point!

Some of these things might seem obvious, but you can easily freeze loaves of bread, bottles of milk and cheese. If you have fresh herbs that you won't finish, chop them up and put them in ice-cube trays with some olive oil to freeze. You can do the same with chopped garlic too, and you can even chop up avocado and freeze it. There really should be no excuse for throwing things away if you keep an eye on when things are 'going off'.

FOOD BANKS
If you know you won't eat something before it's past its best, then donate it to a local food bank – there will be someone who will happily take it off your hands!

- *Make soups or smoothies...*

  Fruit and veg that is past its best can be made into smoothies or soups to save the food going to waste. Charlotte has great fun making fruit smoothies with me, and it's a great way to know she is getting her five a day. I even add in half-eaten bananas that she starts and doesn't finish. She especially loves drinking them with her new bamboo straw!

  Soup is a big favourite for lunch in our house. If we have lots of veg left in the fridge it's a fab way of using it up before it goes off, and it packs loads of nutrients into one meal.

- *Look out for wonky fruit and veg!*

  This will save food from going to waste in the supermarket. Most people tend to pick the most perfectly formed and shiny fruit and veg without even realising, so could you give a home to the oddly shaped but just as good?

> **DID YOU KNOW?**
> **MORE THAN 4.5 MILLION METRIC TONS OF FRUIT AND VEG IS THROWN OUT EVERY YEAR IN THE UK.**

One easy thing you can do is pick the lonely single bananas that have fallen off the bunch – I always do. They are much more likely to be overlooked by shoppers and end up becoming one of the 1.4 million bananas we throw away every day in the UK! If the pandemic taught us anything, it is that we all love banana bread – so even completely overripe bananas have a use. Plus, you can freeze bananas and use them as the base for 'nice cream' by whizzing them up in a blender with other fruits.

'Pick the lonely single bananas that have fallen off the bunch to stop them being thrown away'

GOOD NEWS: Marks & Spencer have started selling paper bags of overripe bananas for 25p to save on food waste. And for just £1.50, Lidl sell 5kg boxes of fruit and veg that are slightly discoloured, damaged or deteriorated but still good enough to eat.

- *Shop in the reduced section at supermarkets.*

  While these items are usually wrapped in plastic, if no one buys them, both the food AND the packaging will be thrown out. So you can at least save the food from landfill.

- ***Dispose responsibly of any food waste you do have.***
  The best thing we can do with our food is to eat all of it, but some food scraps are inevitable, like teabags, peelings and bones. The most important thing to remember is that food waste should NOT end up in landfill, where it will rot and release methane (just like the cow's burps!). This is a greenhouse gas even more harmful for the environment than carbon dioxide.

FOOD WASTE CADDIES

Most councils now pick up food waste separately from your general rubbish. They provide a food waste caddy that you line with a compostable bag and fill with food scraps. After the council has picked up the scraps, food waste is usually recycled in one of two ways: in-vessel composting or anaerobic digestion. Both of these give the waste another life…

- ***In-vessel composting*** – food waste is mixed with garden waste, shredded and then composted in an enclosed system at high temperatures for 2-4 weeks. The compost is then left outside to mature for 1-3 months before being used as soil conditioner.

- ***Anaerobic digestion*** – microorganisms break down food waste, manure, slurries and energy crops (crops grown specifically to be combusted for energy) without oxygen inside an enclosed system. As it breaks down, the mass gives off methane, which is collected and turned into biogas, which can be used as electricity, heat and fuel. In the end it breaks down to a nutrient-rich substance called digestate that can be used as fertiliser.

If you don't have a food waste caddy then contact your local council and they will send you one for free. If your council doesn't offer food waste pick-ups, could you write to your MP to ask him or her to push for one? We have a food waste bin and a compost bin at home, plus a compost bin at the allotment.

'My husband calls our food waste bin the 'Greta' bin, because it's one of the ways I'm trying to save the planet!'

When we first got our food waste bin, my husband called it my 'Greta' bin (after Greta Thunberg) because it was my latest way of trying to save the planet. I kept a bowl in the kitchen for him to put food scraps in, but I kept finding tea bags or peelings in the main bin and had to fish them out and tell him off! If I didn't put the food waste from the bowl in the bin outside, he'd say, "If you don't put this in the Greta bin tonight, I'm throwing it away!"

GARDEN COMPOSTING

You can compost your own food scraps at home and then use the compost on your garden. See page 119 for how to set up your own.

SAVVY SUPERMARKET SHOPPING

In an ideal world we'd all visit our local farmer's market, butchers and refill stores (see page 107 for more) but the reality of food shopping these days (especially as a busy mum) is a mad dash around the supermarket, or a home delivery. We've done our food shopping online since Charlotte was born. Because she was premature, she had a weakened immune system, so we were advised not to go to the supermarkets because (pre-Covid) lots of people liked to lean into prams to look at babies!

'Charlotte won Star Of The Week for being a good role model to her peers and I cried in the school playground because I was so proud'

Charlotte was two before we took her to the supermarket for the first time. She loved it, but I felt quite anxious because she wanted to touch EVERYTHING. Now, she gets so excited when the Tesco man comes and loves helping to pack away our food. She even comments if something is wrapped in plastic, the little eco-warrior that she is! At school, they have a supermarket in their roleplay area and she won Star Of The Week once for 'being a brilliant role model to her peers and teaching them how to play appropriately in Tesco'. I won't lie, I cried in the playground because I was so proud.

So, let's all follow Charlotte's lead, and make our weekly shops more sustainable…

> ALWAYS TAKE REUSABLE BAGS WITH YOU! AS I SAID IN THE PLASTIC SECTION, IF I FORGET MY BAG, I'D RATHER TRY AND CARRY ALL THE ITEMS IN A BIG PILE BACK TO MY CAR THAN HAVE TO BUY A NEW ONE!

- **Buy in bulk.** The larger the packet, the less packaging you use in the long run. Think toilet rolls, bags of rice, and sharing bags of crisps. Did you know you can freeze opened packets of crisps? So there's no excuse for you to finish the whole bag now…

As you know, my husband is a fan of saving money, so he always buys in bulk and when things are on offer (once he has made sure it is actually a better deal). We get huge bags of rice (which use far less plastic than lots of smaller ones) and they work out much cheaper. As an example, a 10kg bag of Laila basmati rice is £13.50 at Tesco, which works out 25p cheaper per kg than Tesco's own basmati rice in 1kg bags. But it's a whopping 3.5 times cheaper than buying 1kg bags of Tilda basmati rice.

'The larger the packet, the less packaging you use in the long run'

We also tend to buy large tubs of yoghurt and then portion out the yoghurt in little tubs for Charlotte. It can get a bit messy if the lid falls off, so it's worth investing in a reusable pouch, such as The DoddleBag (£12.99 for eight), which you can wash and reuse over and over. These bags are also great for filling with homemade baby purees.

- *Look out for products wrapped in paper, cardboard or glass*, which are much more widely recycled than plastic. We tend to be set in our ways with the products we buy, but you can find sugar and flour in paper, pasta and rice in cardboard and ketchups and sauces in jars. For extra zero-waste points, hang onto the jars to reuse in other ways (see below). If you're a fan of fizzy drinks or juice, see if you can find a version you like in glass bottles rather than plastic. The only plastic bottle of drink that I buy these days is squash, because I am rubbish at drinking water. But I get the biggest size possible to reduce the amount of plastic. If I could find one in a glass bottle, I'd buy it! If you drink a lot of fizzy drinks, then buying a SodaStream would benefit the planet and save you money in the long run.

GIVE YOUR GLASS JARS A NEW LIFE AS...

- **Food storage.** Use them at refill stores to stock up on things such as pasta, oats, raisins, nuts.

- **Small flower vases.** They can look amazing when decorated with lace, ribbons or hessian for weddings and celebrations.

- **Utensil holders.** Keep things tidy in the kitchen.

- **Tupperware.** Leftovers can just as easily be stored in glass jars as plastic tubs.

- **Candle holders.** You could go one step further and make your own candles in the jars, too. We had lots hanging from trees at our wedding.

- **Quirky drinking glasses.** You can never have too many glasses!

- **Craft projects.** You can use them to organise your craft accessories or in crafty projects. In summer, me and Charlotte made perfume from flower petals in used jars. It's a great activity for parties and barbecues too.

Glass jars are great for taking to refill stores

Glass jars can be used as small vases

PUT DOWN PALM OIL!

Palm oil is one of the biggest causes of deforestation, which has a significant impact on climate change, biodiversity and is a threat to many already endangered species. It's currently found in more than half of all supermarket products, from bread and chocolate to toothpaste and shampoo. Only 5% of the world's supply is certified as 'sustainable', so check labels before you buy and see if you can find alternative products. Retailers such as Iceland have already started to phase out products containing palm oil from their own brand items.

- **Choose loose fruit and veg.**

  A lot of fruit and veg comes bagged up or wrapped in a thin plastic film to protect it from damage and to keep it fresh while being transported. It is exactly this type of plastic that can't currently be recycled by our local councils. If you can, choose loose items such as single onions, courgettes and apples rather than pre-packaged. You can either take them home loose as they are, or bring your own paper bags (even plastic if you have them – better than throwing them away!) to fill up. It's often cheaper too (and you know we like to save money!). A single red onion costs around 21p, whereas a pack of three costs 85p – 28p each.

  Top tip: For home deliveries, choose the loose fruit/veg options and select 'deliver with no bags'. During the pandemic, our delivery started arriving with everything in plastic bags again, so I now have a mountain of them in my garage (The Great Garage Garbage Patch, as my husband calls it!) which are waiting to be taken to the supermarket to be recycled.

- **Say no to receipts.**

  They may look like ordinary paper but the majority are made from a type of thermal paper that contains plastic, so can't be recycled. Unless you need a receipt for proof of purchase, always say no before it has been printed out!

  'Receipts might look like paper, but the majority are made from a type of thermal paper that contains plastic'

- **Buy fresh bread from the supermarket bakery rather than bread in plastic bags.**

  If you have fussy kids who only like the packaged stuff, then collect the bread bags and recycle them at larger supermarkets. If you often end up throwing half a loaf of bread away because it has gone mouldy before you have a chance to eat it, freeze what you know you won't use as soon as you get home. I know some people buy the smaller 'half' loaves to avoid this but you end up bringing more plastic home per slice of bread that way! We often buy two loaves at once, put one straight in the freezer, then defrost it the night before we'll need it.

- **Wine – put a cork in it!**

  Don't worry, you can still enjoy a tipple, but when choosing which wine to buy there's more than just the grape variety and price to think about... there's also the type of seal it has, too! Opt for bottles with real cork stoppers rather than plastic ones or screw caps. Why? It's obvious why we don't want plastic stoppers (they're cunningly made to look just like corks, so keep your eyes peeled) but not as obvious when it comes to screw caps. It's another case of hidden plastics, I'm afraid. While the cap itself is made from aluminium, the cap liner is made from plastic, which means they can't easily be recycled by local authorities. When recycling glass wine bottles, the advice is to remove the caps, and I suspect most of the caps end up in general waste. Cork, on the other hand, can be composted or broken up and sprinkled into your flowerbeds. And while it is a limited resource, the harvesting of cork is sustainable because the tree is not cut down in the process.

There are some really fab eco-friendly wine brands these days. Sea Change wines are great. They use real corks, there's no unnecessary foil wrap around the top of the bottle, and every bottle you buy helps fund ocean conservation. I've seen adverts for wine in paper bottles too (crazy, right!) and if you want to be completely zero waste, you can get wine (plus beer and spirits) refills in some zero-waste stores.

- *Take your own containers.*
  We all know to bring our own bags to the supermarket these days, but what about our own Tupperware? Instead of buying meat, cheese, fish and antipasti items prepackaged, take your own containers to the supermarket and get them to fill them up at the deli counters.

- *Go big on crisps.*
  Crisp packets are one of those annoying items that can't be recycled by your local authority, but they can usually be recycled at large supermarkets or with the TerraCycle scheme (more on page 251). One thing you can do to reduce the amount of packaging you need to recycle is to buy bigger sharing packs and then portion the crisps into smaller containers for kids (and big kids!).

> **BRITS GET THROUGH AN AVERAGE OF 209 CRISP PACKETS PER PERSON IN A YEAR.**

- *Choose your tea wisely.*
  As Brits, tea is a big part of our lives. When I worked as a forecaster for the RAF in my twenties, I used to get through 12 cups on a 12-hour night shift! I actually stopped drinking tea when I moved into broadcasting to protect my vocal cords, but my husband loves a cuppa, and Charlotte has some fruit teas that have biodegradable tea bags.

> - 96% of people who drink tea in the UK use tea bags rather than loose-leaf.
> - Brits drink around 100 million cups of tea a day.

Tea bags contain hidden plastics!

So what's the problem with tea, you ask? I'll give you one guess… hidden plastics in the tea bags! And I don't just mean the fancy triangle, silky-feeling posh ones you can get either. I mean the bog-standard paper-looking tea bags. They're mostly made from natural plant-fibres, but to avoid them falling apart when we pour boiling water over them, they are held together by a small amount of polypropylene plastic sealant.

This won't biodegrade, so if you've ever put one in your compost bin, it's likely you found a tiny tea bag skeleton in there after a while! The other problem with the plastic in tea bags, is that billions of particles of microplastic are released into each cup, which we then drink. This is not currently deemed to be unsafe, but I don't know about you, I'd rather not be drinking plastic!

'Tea bags release billions of particles of microplastic into each cup'

Top tip: If you have a cupboard full of standard tea bags at home, use what you already have first before buying anything new. When it comes to disposing of them, let them cool down then split open the tea bags so you can tip the tea into your food-waste bin or compost, then throw the tea bag in with the normal rubbish. At least that way the used tea won't end up in landfill!

Clipper Tea was the first brand in the UK to release 'plastic-free' tea bags. They are sealed with a biodegradable form of plastic made from plant cellulose, which will degrade in time and can be put in your compost bin. You can also find bags that are stitched together with cotton, or you can make the switch to loose-leaf tea.

My husband is very particular about his tea so he was a bit wary when I suggested we switch to loose-leaf. Even though it can be a bit more of a faff – I told him I would clean out the teapot but I never have, oops! – he's actually admitted it does make a much nicer cup of tea. Win!

Of course, if you can refill your loose-leaf tea at a refill store rather than buying it in packaging then you get extra zero-waste points.

BREW BETTER...

Did you know that your kettle eats up around 6% of the electricity used in your home? Brits love tea, so much so that energy companies even keep an eye on when people are most likely to be popping on the kettle (such as in the interval of football matches or after big cliffhanger episodes of soaps) because there will be a surge on the grid. Here's how you can reduce the energy (and water) your kettle eats up...

- **Watch your kettle!** They say a watched pot never boils. But guess what? It does. What's more, it's likely that if you walk away while the kettle is boiling you'll forget, then come back and boil it again. And maybe even again!

- **Only boil what you need.** Filling your kettle with more water than you need not only takes longer to boil, it uses more energy, and you probably end up wasting the remaining water. I measured out water in two cups, poured it into the kettle then added a tiny bit more and marked on the kettle where the water came up to so I'd know how much to boil to make tea for me and my husband.

- **Use a thermos flask.** One of my friends' parents told me that they boil the kettle in the morning then fill up a thermos flask with the hot water. They use that throughout the day to make their cups of tea. I think this is genius.

- **Descale regularly.** If your kettle is full of limescale, it will take more energy to boil.

MAKE FOOD FROM SCRATCH

One way of reducing the amount of packaging you bring into your home is to make food from scratch, such as sauces, bread or pasta. When we have spaghetti bolognese (with Quorn mince!) we make our own sauce with passata, onion and herbs. It's also a really nice activity to share with Charlotte. We often have 'fajita Fridays' and Charlotte helps my husband make the flatbreads. We started one week when we'd forgotten to buy some, and the homemade ones were so tasty that we carried on. They also cost around 10% of the supermarket price to make.

Charlotte is now a pro at rolling out the dough

PLANET-FRIENDLY PETS...

Did you know the average dog has a carbon footprint of around 1 metric ton of CO_2 every year – that's the equivalent of one flight from Paris to New York. And cats weigh in at around 310kg, which works out the same as driving for 900 miles. So is there anything we can do to reduce this? Yes! The environmental impact of pets largely comes from their diets, vet care and accessories...

- Just like humans, a diet rich in beef or lamb will generate more emissions than one of chicken or fish. But check that the fish is from sustainable sources!

- If your pets eat wet food, opt for tins over the pouches, which can't yet be recycled.

- Look out for dry-food bags that can be recycled.

- Choose cat litter that is made from wood or grains that are biodegradable or compostable.

- Make sure your poop bags are biodegradable so that they break down with the waste. This could save 700 plastic bags per dog going to landfill every year.

- When choosing toys, avoid flimsy plastic ones that can fall apart more easily.

REFILL REVOLUTION

You can get extra 'green' points by visiting zero-waste shops. These are places that let you take your own empty containers to stock up on store-cupboard essentials such as pasta, oats and nuts (plus liquid essentials such as shampoo, conditioner and washing detergent – see the bathroom section on page 124). They are starting to pop up all over the country either as permanent shops, mobile shops or at market stalls. I visit one locally to top up my toiletries and dried food every few months. Charlotte loves filling up our tubs and jars at the refill stations. Some supermarkets are also starting to provide their own refill stations. Waitrose began offering 'unpacked' items in larger stores in 2019, and Sainsbury's and M&S have followed suit.

'Charlotte loves filling up our tubs and jars at refill stores'

I've also mentioned this in the bathroom section, but Tesco have teamed up with Loop to offer refillable products that you can buy in store. It's being trialled in some UK stores at the moment. You can buy your favourite items off the shelf, such as ketchup or coffee, but in refillable containers. The items are the same price as the 'normal' products but you pay a small deposit for the container, which you get back when you return it. Loop professionally cleans all the containers and then they're used again in store, so it's zero-waste. Imagine if we could do this for our entire supermarket shop one day! Visit Exploreloop.com/tesco for more information.

SUSTAINABLE SWITCHES

Here are some ideas to get rid of the amount of plastic and single-use items in your kitchen.

- ***Clingfilm.***
  If you have food leftovers in a bowl, you can use a plate to cover the bowl, or invest in some reusable silicone lids. They are plastic, but they will last forever! They come in all different sizes (you can even get them to cover half an onion or a lemon) and create a great seal on top of bowls. I have lots of products from GreenIslandCo.com, including reusable silicone lids and food toppers, plus compostable sponges.

> **DID YOU KNOW?**
> **745,000 MILES OF CLING FILM IS USED BY HOUSEHOLDS ACROSS BRITAIN EVERY YEAR – ENOUGH TO GO AROUND THE CIRCUMFERENCE OF THE WORLD 30 TIMES OVER.**

Another eco alternative is to use beeswax wraps. The heat from your hands allows you to mould these around items that you need to keep fresh. We use them for wrapping sandwiches when we have picnics in the summer.

Some of the amazing reusable products I now use in the kitchen

---

WHAT ABOUT FOIL?

Aluminium foil is better than clingfilm because it can be recycled, but it's still a single-use product that's better to avoid, so consider using any of the suggestions mentioned above instead. To properly recycle foil, it must be free from any food residue and it also has to be big enough for recycling sorting centres to recognise. Save up any foil you use and once you have enough to roll into a sphere the size of a tennis ball, put it in your recycling. For more tips on recycling, see page 244.

- **Baking paper.**

  Whether you call it parchment paper, baking paper or greaseproof paper, it is, unfortunately, not just paper, so it can't be recycled. Because its job is to repel fat, it has a thin silicone lining (a little like coffee cups) that is hard to separate from the plastic, rendering the whole thing unrecyclable. I bet you're now thinking about all those times you mistakenly put it in the recycling. Yep, me too!

  ### 'Baking paper is not actually paper, so it can't be recycled'

  You can buy biodegradable and compostable baking paper, which would be a better option, or look into reusable silicone baking sheets. Yes, they are plastic, but if you can use them again and again, then you are avoiding more things ending up in landfill.

- **Kitchen roll.**

  Kitchen roll might seem pretty harmless because it is made of paper, but it's another single-use item that often can't be recycled. A dry, clean piece of kitchen roll might be accepted for recycling by some local councils, but we usually use paper towel for clearing up messes! If it's contaminated with food or cleaning products, that paper should never be thrown in the recycling because it can ruin whole batches of otherwise usable recycling. Kitchen roll that has a bit of food on it can go in the food-waste bin, but anything with soap or cleaning agents on has to go in the normal bin.

> **DID YOU KNOW?**
> **EVERY DAY, 51,000 TREES ARE FELLED TO MEET THE DAILY DEMAND FOR SINGLE-USE PAPER TOWELS.**

I buy kitchen roll every now and again because I can't deny how convenient it is, but I've also invested in some reusable cloths. As soon as I had this idea, my husband was annoyed (as he is about all my 'great' ideas), but they are really useful. Cloths or flannels can be wrapped around an old kitchen roll holder or kept in the drawer. They are really good for spills and wiping toddlers' faces. In fact, they're better than kitchen roll, which can fall apart quite easily.

You can buy 20 sheets of reusable bamboo kitchen roll online for around £7.50. This might sound a lot, but each sheet can be used 80 times, so they should last you as long as 34 rolls of standard kitchen towel.

If you really can't live without it, look for an eco version in the supermarket – many now sell rolls made from recycled paper and in paper packaging.

3.

IN THE GARDEN

The garden might not be part of the home you naturally think of when it comes to reducing your carbon footprint, but through reconnecting with nature and creating a space where wildlife and plants can flourish, we can have a positive impact on the planet – and our wellbeing. We have so much to thank nature for – it's time we started to give something back.

During lockdown, we all found ourselves spending more time outdoors. In fact, 92% of people said their gardens were important to them in terms of health and wellbeing during 2020, and gardening is well known as a way to ease stress. It's also a great form of exercise.

Most people who live to 100 or more all do some kind of gardening. And during the pandemic, we saw more younger people taking up the hobby – including me (yes, I am classing myself as young!). We have an allotment now, and it has been so lovely to see Charlotte getting stuck in and helping to plant and harvest our food.

There's so much we can do that will reduce our gardens' emissions, boost biodiversity and create healthy green spaces that will actually benefit the planet. From the type of lawn you choose to buying an environmentally friendly mower or composting food scraps and garden waste, everything helps. Here's what you can do.

?

DID YOU KNOW?

- You can burn up to 300 calories an hour doing light gardening.

- Gardens in Britain cover an area larger than all of the country's nature reserves combined.

- Alarming figures show that 7,000 people are dying every year from living in areas with a lack of green space because of toxic pollutants.

- ***Choose real grass over fake.***
  Having a perfect lawn is something we Brits seem to be obsessed with. We all want to keep up with the Joneses and this has led to more and more people choosing an artificial lawn over real grass. Sales soared during lockdown when we all spent more time outdoors! I see the appeal – doesn't need to be mowed, watered or otherwise maintained, always looks neat – but a fake lawn contributes absolutely nothing to the environment and can actually cause problems. If I visit friends who have artificial grass I instantly frown and they know what I'm thinking!

  By smothering more of our natural areas with plastic, we are disrupting the natural ecosystem. Fake grass stops earthworms and burrowing insects like solitary bees from getting through to the soil. Manufacturing the plastic it's made from releases carbon dioxide into the atmosphere – and when it needs replacing, that's more plastic going into landfill and taking hundreds of years to break down!

  Real grass, although not so easy to maintain, offers so many benefits to the planet. Like all living plants, grass sucks up carbon dioxide and releases oxygen into the atmosphere. Green spaces also have a cooling effect on our planet, whereas artificial grass heats it up. On a hot day, the average temperature of real grass in the sun is 38.1°C, whereas fake grass soars to a scorching 62.3°C.

KEEP YOUR COOL

As well as capturing carbon, plants have the ability to cool the atmosphere – when they get hot, they release a vapour which cools them and the air around them. This is particularly important in towns and cities, where pavements and roads absorb more heat than green areas, which can lead to dangerous rises in temperatures. Around 80% of the UK population live in urban areas. If you're one of them, you might be thinking, "Well, I haven't got a big garden, so what can I do?" But even the smallest gardens and balconies make a difference. It might not seem like it, but gardens take up 29.5% of land in most cities – so that's a lot of green space to work with!

Summer bedding plants grow well in pots and will brighten up balconies and windowsills. Vegetables such as tomatoes, lettuce, carrots and potatoes, as well as all types of herbs, will thrive in pots too. If you can, attach vertical planters to walls so you can get as many plants in your 'garden' as possible. If this proves impractical, could you grow climbing plants such as sweet peas and guide them up the wall with a trellis?

Another benefit of a real lawn is that it can absorb significant amounts of water, which can help reduce the impact of heavy rainfall and reduce flooding. Because plastic grass can't absorb water, the water runs off and this increases the likelihood of flooding.

Real lawns are home to millions of creatures, some so small we can't even see them. All those caterpillars, slugs, worms and snails are food for birds, too. You might be thinking you don't want these creatures on your lawn – but sometimes I think we forget that we're not the only living creatures on this earth!

Did you know that grass is a very good indicator of the effects of climate change. It's the first thing that starts growing and the last thing to stop growing. For every 1°C the mean temperature rises by the end of winter, grass will start growing six days earlier in spring. Between 2012 and 2019 there were 15% more growing days compared to 1961-1990, which just goes to show how much warmer the UK is getting.

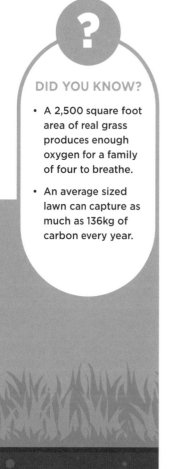

DID YOU KNOW?

- A 2,500 square foot area of real grass produces enough oxygen for a family of four to breathe.

- An average sized lawn can capture as much as 136kg of carbon every year.

- ***Use an electric or cordless lawn mower instead of a petrol one.***
  If you are concerned about the carbon footprint of driving a petrol or diesel car, then it's worth thinking about what is in your shed too! Petrol lawnmowers produce 11 times more polluting emissions than a car – that's crazy! I'm not saying just throw out your functioning petrol mower right now – that would create waste – but when the time comes to buy a new one, could you pick a 'greener' option?

The most environmentally friendly grass-cutting machines are manual reel mowers. These are powered by your own strength and have a blade that turns with the wheels, so they create no emissions except those released in making them. If this just won't cut it for you (pun intended), then a cordless or electric mower is a much better choice than a petrol one.

Cordless mowers have a battery that you charge and they use less electricity than models that have to be plugged in while mowing. The level of emissions released by charging or mowing depends on where your electricity is coming

Don't water your lawn! This may come as a surprise, but the Royal Horticultural Society says lawns are very resilient and don't need to be watered. For more information, see page 158.

from. For more information on renewable sources of energy see page 73.

If you have an average-sized lawn with no steep inclines, then a manual or push lawn mower – all the movement comes from your own effort – is the best option. They are easy to use and give you a bit of a workout while you mow the grass! If you have a large lawn and have to push the mower up a hill, then an electric self-propelled model will make the job easier but will produce more emissions thanks to the power needed to keep it moving.

At home we still have an old petrol mower which does work but takes many, many pulls of the cord to get going. When it needs replacing we will get a cordless one. Last year I worked with Honda on their lawn and garden products and was really impressed by their electric range. A good model is an investment, too. You want something that is going to last – it's a case of 'buy nice or buy twice'.

?

DID YOU KNOW?

- The average petrol lawnmower emits as much CO_2 in one hour as driving a car just under 100 miles!

- ***Leave some of your lawn 'wild'.***
Sometimes the best thing we can do for nature is to do nothing. Just look at what happened during the lockdowns – wildlife returned to our gardens and even our cities! Could you leave a patch of your lawn unmowed? Allowing the grass to grow and wildflowers to bloom does wonders for wildlife – it's like a jungle for insects to hide out in, and the flowers will attract pollinating insects such as bees, butterflies and hoverflies. Studies have shown that more than 200 species of wildflower – such as clover, daisies and buttercups – would grow on lawns if we would only let them.

Helping out the bee population is really, really important and this is one way you can do it. Pollinating bees are vital for stable and healthy food supplies. They help the growth of so many of the foods we rely on, such as pears, blueberries, courgettes and almonds. But the reduction of natural spaces, along with pesticide use and rising temperatures, means we have seen a global decline in bee populations. In fact, some species are under the threat of extinction! In the UK, we have 275 species of bee, but only 10% of these are social bees, such as the honeybee and bumblebee – the vast majority are solitary bees. These bees live alone rather than in colonies, and they are our top pollinators, so we need to give them a helping hand.

Try leaving a patch of grass – no matter how small – to grow and see what flowers you already have there. If you want to throw our pollinators an extra lifeline, you could sprinkle a packet of wildflower seeds on the patch in autumn and see what grows in spring. The pollen and nectar from the plants will attract flower pollinators such as bees, butterflies and beetles, and the long grass also provides a safe space for frogs and hedgehogs.

BEE OUR GUEST!

Bees need a safe place to nest, so making a bee hotel is a great way to help them – and it's also a lovely activity to do with kids. We have two bug hotels in our garden and Charlotte loves spotting them when we're outside.

You will need:
1 plant pot
Hollow canes such as bamboo
Twigs
Stones

Tip: Choose canes that have openings between 2-10mm in diameter. Some bees, such as the small scissor bee, like very small spaces, while red mason bees prefer a bit more room.

1. Cut your hollow canes to 1cm shorter than the height on your plant pot (children will need assistance here!) and use sandpaper to smooth over the cut ends (any rough edges or splinters could damage bee wings).

2. Fill up the plant pot with the canes, hollow openings facing outwards, until it is tightly packed. Then fill any spaces around the canes with twigs.

3. When your bee hotel is ready to use, put it on its side and use large stones to secure it so it doesn't roll around. Place it in an area that gets sunlight and angle it slightly downwards to let rainwater escape.

4. You'll know when you have a hotel guest if you see some of the bamboo openings have been plugged with mud, leaves or resin.

HELP THE HEDGEHOGS

Hedgehogs wander up to one mile every night in search of food, but they're struggling to find pathways in and out of gardens when we opt for fences over hedges. These cute little creatures play a key role in our ecosystem by helping to keep the insect population under control and, just like the bees, their numbers are starting to decline. One of the best things you can do to help them is to make sure they can get in and out of your garden by creating access holes.

- ***Plant trees and shrubs strategically to save money!***
  You can use trees, hedges and shrubs as natural insulation for your home in winter by planting them in positions where they will block prevailing winds. This can save you money on your heating bills and reduce the amount of energy you use (for more energy-saving tips, see page 62). In summer, having trees that cast shade on the house will help to keep your home cooler and reduce the need for electric fans or air conditioning.

- ***Use peat-free compost.***
  Peat compost has been a popular choice for gardeners because it's cheap and so rich in organic matter. But making it and using it causes big problems for the natural world. Peat bogs are one of nature's biggest carbon sinks (for more info, see page 43), along with oceans and forests. The peat is formed when bog plants decompose. Decomposing plants would usually release carbon dioxide into the atmosphere, but because they break down in a watery, oxygen-free environment, it's turned into carbon and locked away – until it gets disturbed, that is. To mine peat bogs for garden compost, the bogs are drained. This immediately begins to release carbon dioxide into the atmosphere. And when we spread peat compost over flower beds or fields, that carbon quickly turns into carbon dioxide and is released into the atmosphere. When we get rid of our peat bogs, we are also getting rid of the unique wildlife that lives in them.

  When choosing compost, look for peat-free alternatives that contain wood chips, or consider making your own (see right). For the first year after taking over our allotment we bought big bags of manure from the garden centre and turned over the soil. Now we have a compost bin which we will use in the coming years.

Digging up potatoes in our allotment!

- ***Make your own compost***

  This is a fantastic (and cheap!) way to transform your food waste and garden waste into nutrient-rich food for your garden. Around 50% of the food we throw away can be composted, so it saves food going to landfill, where it will release harmful greenhouse gases into the atmosphere (see page 93 for more). We've had a compost bin in our garden for years, and we use it to pot up new plants every year.

  A lot of local authorities have teamed up with Getcomposting.com to provide cheap compost bins and accessories. If you visit the website and enter your postcode, you can get a bin for as little as £10. If your postcode is not recognised, then search on your local council's website instead. Once you have a bin, here's how you can start off your compost…

- ***Find the right place to put your bin.***

  Ideally, position your bin on bare soil and in an area of your garden that gets the sun. That way it's easy for beneficial microbes and insects to get at the rotting matter from underneath, and the heat from the sun will help it to decompose. If you have to place your bin on concrete or decking, consider creating a raised bed with soil for the bin to sit on, or add soil or organic compost to the bottom of the bin to help it out. For more tips, visit Recylenow.com and search 'compost'.

DID YOU KNOW?

- Peat bogs store twice as much carbon as all the world's forests.

- Composting for just one year can save the same amount of greenhouse gases as your kettle produces annually, or your washing machine produces in three months.

- Every 20,000 people who compost can divert more than 10,000 metric tons of organic waste from landfill while growing 400-plus metric tons of fresh food every year (by using that compost on fruit/veg gardens).

- *Add the right 'ingredients'.*
  It's important to feed your compost pile well so that the microorganisms that break down the waste don't get overwhelmed and can multiply well. You should aim for a balance of 50% 'greens' – quick to rot and provide nitrogen, protein and heat – and 50% 'browns' – carbon and carbohydrate-rich materials that are slower to rot.

Greens	Browns	Other compostable items	Don't compost
Grass cuttings, fruit and veg peelings, house plants, coffee grounds, tea leaves, animal manure (but not from dogs or cats), plant trimmings (perennials and annuals)	Cardboard (cereal packets, egg boxes, toilet roll tubes), paper, autumn leaves, straw and hay, twigs, old bedding plants	Wood ash (in moderation), hair, nail clippings, egg shells, natural fibres such as cotton and wool	Meat, fish and dairy (these can attract vermin), cooked food scraps, cat litter

- *Wait a while.*
  It takes around nine to 12 months before compost is ready to use. So keep filling it with green and brown materials and let nature do its job. You'll know it's ready when it's crumbly, dark, resembles moist soil and gives off an earthy smell.

- *Use it in your garden.*
  You take the compost from the bottom of the bin, either through a hatch or by lifting the bin slightly. You can then spread it around border plants, use it to fill plant pots or to enrich your veg patch.

- *Grow your own fruit, veg and herbs.*
  What better way to use your own compost than to grow your own veg? A complete closed-loop system – no emissions from transport, packaging or food waste!

Now, if you're completely new to growing your own food, it can be hard to know where to begin – but my advice is to start small. You can grow herbs such as basil and mint in pots in the house (you don't even need a garden!), then perhaps experiment with a tomato plant and see if you catch the grow-your-own bug! I

Having an allotment has helped Charlotte know where food comes from

think you will – there is something really special about planting a seed and watching it grow, then being able to eat what you've grown. Somehow it just tastes better.

We are lucky because we have a good-sized garden. We've always grown tomatoes and strawberries, and we have apple, pear, cherry and plum trees, too. Then, in 2021, we decided to step things up a little bit and get our allotment. I'd been inspired by the Potty Plotters – two gardeners from Derbyshire who teach allotment amateurs the basics – when I met them while filming a TV show about being more sustainable. There was such a community feel to their world. And seeing children's faces when they had grown something, picked it and tasted it was priceless – they were so proud!

Both me and my husband would love to be completely sustainable and live off the land – but for different reasons. I want to do our bit for the planet and he is just really grumpy and doesn't like people! But getting an allotment was something for us to do as a family, a way of getting outdoors and a great way to teach Charlotte where food comes from.

?

DID YOU KNOW?

- One full allotment (250 square metres) should feed a family of four for one year.

A super proud Charlotte with her home-grown potatoes

But let me tell you, an allotment is hard work! Our first year was all about learning. Before you even begin you have to get the patch ready – so lots of digging, weeding and turning soil, which took ages. There were times I'd hear my husband ranting, "Why are we doing this? I could get a bag of carrots for 50p. 50p!!"

Even when things started to grow, we ended up with more weeds than plant shoots! I realised we should have put a plastic sheet down to stop the weeds coming through (I know, I know… plastic!). When I went to buy one with Charlotte, she said, "No, Mummy, plastic is bad for our planet, why are you getting it?" I could see people looking at me and thinking, 'Get out of that one…' I was proud and mortified in equal parts!

After a while, we finally got the hang of allotmenteering, and Charlotte absolutely loved sowing the seeds in pots – which we kept in the greenhouse to begin with. She watered them every day and it was lovely to see her face when the first shoots appeared. She would shout and make us come and look. I've even found her talking to the plants! When it was time to plant them in the allotment, she had her own wheelbarrow and digging set – like any four-year-old, she loves to be 'helpful'!

Top tip: A fellow allotmenteer told me that the best thing to grow is something you like to eat. That seems pretty obvious, but it's all too tempting to pick something that is easy or quick to grow, that you will get a big yield from. Take artichokes for example, they're easy to grow and you get loads – but if you don't like them, what is the point? It just creates more food waste!

Our plan was to grow potatoes, onions, carrots, tomatoes, runner beans, beetroot, courgettes, broccoli, cauliflowers, corn on the cob, strawberries and sunflowers. We had success with just over half of these, especially the potatoes, carrots and tomatoes. The rest were eaten by deer, birds and something else – possibly squirrels – but that didn't matter, we had grown our own vegetables!

And when we ate them, they were so much tastier. We loved each and every one of our home-grown plants, even down to the tiniest onion (and they were really tiny – some didn't get much bigger than when we planted them!), Nothing went to waste because we had lovingly grown them. People just don't have that direct connection with supermarket fruit and veg. But we should, because it has also been grown for us to eat.

It's especially rewarding that we are teaching Charlotte to have that connection too – she won't let any food be thrown away now. We know what we will be growing for this year and we can't wait!

4.

IN THE
BATHROOM

Walk in your bathroom and what do you see? Aside from the obvious toilet, sink and a bath and/or shower, it's likely your shelves, drawers and cupboards will be filled with – you guessed it – plastic!

The bathroom is one of the areas in my life that I've been able to make the most changes to live more sustainably. I'm slowly switching to natural products that are plastic-free, and I'm condensing them down as I go. It's so easy to do and I genuinely feel better for it.

LAURA'S EVERYDAY BATHROOM LIST:

- Face wash
- Make-up remover
- Toner
- Moisturiser
- Eye cream
- Shower gel
- My husband's bar of soap to shave with
- Razor
- Shampoo
- Conditioner
- Cotton pads
- Cotton buds
- Toothbrush
- Toothpaste
- Floss
- Mouthwash
- Deodorant

Of course, then there are the items I use less frequently:

- Face scrub
- Oil and serum
- My 'for best' shower gel
- Body scrub
- Hair mask
- Face masks
- Sanitary products

That's a LOT of products, plus a lot of packaging – but I have since cut down on lots. I did (and still do) use products sparingly. I only wash my hair 2-3 times a week so I could make two or three shampoo and conditioner bottles last me the year.

First things first, I recommend you make a list of the items you use in the bathroom everyday (this can be plastic and non plastic).

When you take the time to write things down, it can be quite shocking how many things we (think we) need to get ready in the morning or before we go to bed. Or, you might be like my husband and only use one bar of soap in the shower for everything – how is that even possible? When I did my list before I started to make some switches (left), I realised I used so many items!

Now you've got your list, could you condense it? As my husband's shower routine proves, there is often little difference between the soap we use to wash our hair and the soap we use to wash our bodies. We may not all be as angelic as him, but cutting down does come with many benefits. As well as reducing the amount of plastic in your bathroom, it will also save you money – and decluttering is great for our minds too.

Keep in mind that making changes to your skincare products is a really personal journey and sometimes it can take a while to find the ones that work for you. For example, some people love shampoo bars (including me!) and others don't. So take your time and make the swaps that feel right for you. Remember, every small change makes a big difference when we all chip in!

Below is a guide to what I, and some of my planet-loving friends, have found useful.

- ***Use what you already have.***
  If you're anything like me, you'll have 10s if not 100s of toiletries in drawers and cupboards. I did a stock take and was amazed at how much stuff I had. There were full bottles of things I thought I'd run out of, fancy bottles of body lotion (you know the ones that come in gift sets but never get used) and so many travel-size bottles (see tip, right).

  The most eco thing to do here is use everything you have, rather than going out to buy more sustainable things. But if you know you won't use something, don't leave it in the cupboard to go off or throw it away – see if any of your friends would like it. One person's trash is another person's treasure! When we ran out of Charlotte's shampoo we started to use up the travel-size bottles I found.

Sorting through my toiletries so I could use up everything I had first

THE AVERAGE PERSON SPENDS £400 ON BEAUTY PRODUCTS EACH YEAR IN THE UK.

'The most eco thing you can do is use what you have, rather than going out to buy new sustainable things'

Whenever you finish a product, make sure your empty bottles are washed out and recycled properly (see page 245) or kept for using at refill stores (see page 131). If it's the travel-size ones, these are handy to keep for when you go on holiday or for putting sun cream in for when you're out and about. Remember: rethink, reuse, repurpose!

Top tip: Say no to free stuff if you don't need it. I'm a sucker for free things, especially those fancy little bottles of travel-size shampoo and body wash you get in hotels. If it's a nice brand, I'll always grab them. Why? Because they are free and it is human nature to be excited about free things. I like to put them in the spare room for infrequent overnight guests to make it look like a hotel. But they are never used and just gather dust. Well, I've now got so many travel-size products I could open my own hotel! So, after years of hoarding, I'm finally using them up!

?

DID YOU KNOW?

- The average household in the UK uses 216 plastic hair care bottles a year.

- Globally, 80 billion plastic shampoo and conditioner bottles get thrown out every year.

- Recyclable bathroom waste accounts for up to 40% of total landfill waste in the UK.

- A typical household in the UK also goes through 24 bottles of shower gel, 24 tubes of toothpaste, 12 bottles of moisturiser and 108 loo rolls each year.

GREENWASHING

Greenwashing is a term used for when companies spend more time and money on marketing themselves as environmentally friendly than on minimising their environmental impact. It is quite common in the cosmetic and beauty industry. So it's worth delving a little deeper before purchasing by checking out their ingredients as well as the packaging they come in.

• ***Consider switching to eco products.***
When you've used up what you do have and it's time to invest in something new, look into brands that are kind to the environment, your skin and animals. Some commercial products contain chemicals and cleaning agents that can cause irritation to our skin and be harmful to aquatic life, and some still test on animals. See the box, right, for what to look out for when buying natural products. Usually, if you are buying from an eco brand, their products come in no packaging (naked!), or they're in glass, metal or cardboard. If companies do use plastic, it is usually fully recycled or recyclable.

There are so many out there, and I'll list my favourites as I go through. I heard about lots of the products I use through word of mouth, so talk to friends or ask on social media. Lots of eco companies are small businesses, so if you like their products, it's really lovely to spread the word to others. I now get loads of adverts popping up on my social media accounts, which can be helpful – but watch out for companies pretending to be more eco than they are, known as greenwashing.

DON'T GET IN A LATHER!

Here are some things to look out for when choosing natural skincare products

SLS free

Sodium lauryl sulphate and its cousin sodium lauryl ether sulphate (SLES) are cleansing agents known as surfactants, and are responsible for the lather in liquid soaps. While SLS and SLES have been deemed safe to use on skin, they can be drying and cause skin irritations, especially for people with sensitive skin or eczema.

Cruelty free

Many companies still test on animals. Although their policies may say they don't, if they sell their products in China, they are legally required to test on animals.

Organic

Products that are labelled organic mean the ingredients that go into them were farmed under stricter standards, and won't have been grown using pesticides, chemical fertilisers or antibiotics.

0% aluminium in deodorants

Aluminium salts are used in antiperspirants to block sweat ducts, stopping sweat from reaching the surface of the skin. The first issue here is that our bodies are actually designed to sweat, but in recent years there have been safety concerns about whether the aluminium is absorbed into our bodies, causing adverse effects.

Unscented, fragrance-free or scented with essential oils

Synthetic fragrances, often listed as just 'fragrance' or 'parfum' on an ingredients list, are made from any number of chemicals that come from petroleum. They can cause skin irritation, allergies and asthma and are sometimes referred to as the new second-hand smoke!

Reef safe

This is a big one for sun cream. The term reef safe is not always regulated, so check the ingredients list to look for physical UVA and UVB filters, such as zinc oxide and titanium dioxide, rather than chemical filters which are connected to coral reef deterioration.

Free from phthalates, paraben, bisphenol A and triclosan

These four chemicals are widely used in cosmetics, but there is concern over our exposure to them because they are suspected endocrine disruptors, which mimic or interact with our bodies' hormone levels. To be on the safe side, look for products that don't contain them.

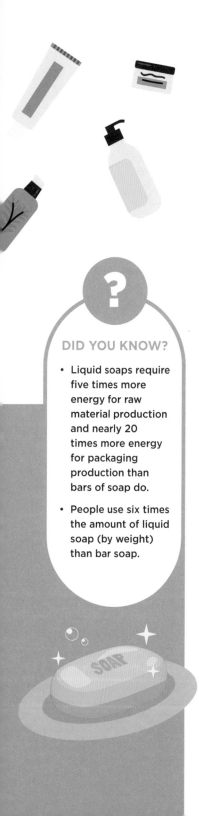

- **When you've run out of your liquid products (shampoo, conditioner, facewash, shower gel etc) see if you can cut back on plastic by:**

  – *Buying in bulk.* Bulk buying is always cheaper, and you'll be consuming significantly less plastic if you purchase 1-5 litre tubs of shampoo or conditioner instead of multiple smaller bottles. Keep any smaller bottles you already have to decant the product into, to make it easier to use in the bath or shower. Brands such as Faith In Nature, Minimal and Alter/native all offer products in 5-litre bottles. To compare prices, Faith In Nature's 400ml bottle retails for £5.79 but their 5-litre tubs are £50 – that's a whopping £22.37 saved and one large plastic bottle used instead of 12.5 smaller ones.

  – *Switch to products in glass or metal.* While glass and metal are heavier materials than plastic so emit more carbon emissions through transportation, the benefit is that they are much more widely recycled than plastic. And they can be endlessly recycled back to their original form without impairing the quality. Whereas plastic can only be recycled back to its original form (so a plastic bottle becomes a plastic bottle again) one or two times before it will be 'downcycled' into something else, such as fleece clothing or carpet. Those items are then not usually recyclable.

  I use a moisturiser in a glass jar from UpCircle Beauty which is actually part of a refill scheme too. I rinse it out, send the container back via free post and they refill it and send it back to me – zero waste.

  – *Try shampoo, conditioner and soap bars.* They have come a long way since your grandma's bar of Imperial Leather (but this is still my husband's favourite – what a surprise!) And it's easy to see why they are a fantastic switch from plastic. Many come completely naked (no packaging) so have absolutely no waste, but if they are packaged it's usually a very thin bit of FSC certified cardboard that can be recycled. They're lighter to transport, so create fewer emissions and they last MUCH longer than liquid soaps do.

I use a shampoo bar and conditioner bar from a lovely brand called Earth Kind, and they come in little metal tins (that can be reused) to keep them dry and clean in between washes. You are meant to rub the bar up and down your hair, but some people rub it in their hands to make bubbles and then wash as normal. There aren't as many bubbles as I'm used to so sometimes I rub too much and get too much product on my hair, so it goes a bit slippery and shiny! If you find bars too tricky, you can dissolve them in warm water in a pot and pour the liquid into an old shampoo or conditioner bottle to use. When you've been using liquid soap your whole life, it takes a while to get used to bars, but I won't go back now – and my hairdresser says my hair is great. I suffer from psoriasis around my hairline so I always opted for gentle shampoos and conditioners before, but I've not had any adverse effects using the bar.

> **'I USE A SHAMPOO BAR NOW AND MY HAIRDRESSER SAYS MY HAIR IS GREAT!'**

I've now also swapped my face wash and body wash for a combined soap bar, so that is saving money, plastic and space on my bathroom shelves!

– Go to a refill store or sign up to a refill service. Zero-waste stores are popping up all over the place these days. You can take your own containers along and refill shampoo, body wash, conditioner and handwash from their 5 or 20-litre tubs. There's no waste, because you are reusing bottles you already have, and the stores return their large containers to the brands who reuse them. The shops also tend to sell the bars of soap mentioned above, plus lots of lovely eco items. I loved visiting my refill shop – I came away with loads of ideas of what I'd like to buy in future (because, remember, I don't want to buy new when I still have things to use up at home).

If there are no stores near you, check out local markets. One of my friends refills her products at a mobile van that parks up in local villages. Facebook community groups are great for finding out if any of these exist in your local area.

There's also the option to sign up to online refill schemes, such as Fiils.co. You order reusable bottles from them and they send out refill pouches when you run out, which you clean and send back for them to recycle.

HIGH-STREET HEROES

Some high-street brands have started to offer refill services in a bid to cut back on single-use plastic and unnecessary packaging. At The Body Shop larger stores you can purchase aluminium bottles to refill your shampoo, conditioner, body wash and moisturiser while also saving 20% on the price. And Tesco has partnered with Loop to help reduce the amount of packaging waste on lots of items, including skincare and beauty products. At larger stores, you can buy your favourite products in reusable containers, which you pay a small deposit for. When you return the empty containers, Loop hygienically cleans and refills them before they are used again in store. A closed loop system.

So, now we've covered our liquid soaps in single-use plastic, what else can we cut back on in the bathroom to reduce our carbon emissions and help the environment? The answer is, loads…

- ***Cotton wool and cotton pads.*** Okay, so they aren't plastic but they usually come in plastic packaging, they're single-use and use up a lot of resources to produce. Cotton is a thirsty plant and can drink up to 29,000 litres of water for every 1kg of cotton. Non-organic cotton also uses more pesticides and insecticides to grow than any other single major crop in the world! They don't make things easy for us, do they? In some cases, cotton wool might be necessary for hygiene reasons, but if you mainly use them for removing make-up or applying toner, it's more environmentally friendly to purchase reusable cotton pads that can be thrown in your washing machine with your clothes and used again. They still use up resources to make, but their impact is lower and some companies make them out of offcuts from other products, further reducing waste.

> ***'I chose reusable cotton pads in black – so they don't show any stains!'***

You can get round ones and square ones (fewer offcuts so less waste!) in various colours. I opted for black ones, so they show fewer stains from removing my mascara. A pack of 10 costs between £5 and £10, but they save you money in the long run.

If you can't live without cotton buds, make sure they are biodegradable or reusable

ON AVERAGE, ONE REUSABLE COTTON PAD CAN BE USED UP TO 300 TIMES. IF YOU HAVE A PACK OF 10, THAT MEANS THEY WILL LAST YOU OVER EIGHT YEARS.

Top tip: *Reusable cotton pads can be used for removing nail varnish too, I just make sure I keep one aside for this (so I never accidentally use it near my eyes) which I wash and reuse.*

- **Cotton buds.** These are one of the most common things found washed up on beaches or in the stomach of sea life. If you watched *Blue Planet II*, you might recall seeing the image of the tiny seahorse with its tail wrapped around a cotton bud. Luckily, cotton buds with plastic sticks were banned in the UK at the end of 2020, and they're now available with cardboard or bamboo sticks, but often still come in plastic tubs. Regardless of what they are made of, you should never, ever flush these down the loo.

> **22 COTTON BUDS WERE FOUND FOR EVERY 100 METRES OF BEACH IN THE UK DURING A BEACH CLEAN SURVEY IN 2018.**

They're usually referred to as ear buds because people use them to clean out their ears. But did you know that you should never actually put these in your ears? The official medical advice is to not put anything smaller than your elbow in your ear (I'm not entirely sure why or how you'd go about doing that!). 1.5 million cotton buds are produced every day, only to be thrown in the bin. So the best thing you can do is give these up completely. If you use them for make-up touch ups or for cleaning hard-to-reach areas, then consider switching from single-use cotton buds to a reusable plastic one. Yes, it's plastic, but it will last you for years.

> **1 REUSABLE COTTON BUD REPLACES 1,000 SINGLE-USE ONES.**

- **Wet wipes.** There seems to be a wet wipe for everything these days, and there is no denying they are super convenient, but their cost to the environment is huge. People flushing wet wipes down the toilet causes 93% of sewer blocks in the UK – and it costs around £100 million a year to unblock them. Yikes. Who pays for that? Ultimately, us.

> **IN THE UK ALONE, WE USE 11 BILLION WET WIPES A YEAR.**

You may be familiar with the term fatbergs – a gross modern phenomenon where fats congeal with personal hygiene products, such as wet wipes and sanitary products, to form huge masses that block sewers. These blockages can cause raw sewage to overflow into rivers and streams.

> THE BIGGEST EVER FATBERG WAS FOUND IN AN UNDERGROUND SEWER IN LIVERPOOL IN 2019. AT 84 METRES LONG, IT WAS LONGER THAN A PASSENGER PLANE AND WEIGHED 90 METRIC TONS – AROUND THE SAME AS 13 AFRICAN ELEPHANTS. WET WIPES, COTTON WOOL, NAPPIES, COTTON BUDS AND DENTAL FLOSS ARE JUST SOME OF THE ITEMS THAT WERE FOUND IN THE MASS.

Many people don't realise that wet wipes contain plastic. They're designed to stay wet so they don't break down in water like toilet paper would, so they should never be put down the toilet, even when they claim to be flushable. What doesn't get stuck in our drains ends up in the ocean – posing the same threat to sea life that plastic bags do – or they sit in landfill for years.

If you do need to use wet wipes, look for biodegradable ones and put them in the bin, not the toilet. You can even find compostable ones too. But the real solution here is to stop using them altogether. I use muslin cloths to take off my make-up rather than wet wipes. I have two make-up removers – one from The Body Shop that comes in a tin that is fully recyclable and returnable to store, and another that is more luxurious from a brand called Ishga. It's made in Scotland from organic seaweed and it's lovely for taking off a full-face of make-up that has been on all day. I put on my product then I use a hot cloth to remove it.

- **_Deodorant._** Which camp do you fall into – spray or roll-on? I was 100% a roll-on antiperspirant girl. The difference between a deodorant and an antiperspirant is that deodorants neutralise odour-producing bacteria while antiperspirants actually stop us sweating, usually by adding a form of aluminium to the ingredients which blocks our pores (see Don't Get In A Lather on page 129).

79% of people in the UK buy deodorant as part of their weekly shop – which equates to around 50 million people. When you think that most deodorants come in plastic or aerosol cans designed to be thrown away, that is a lot of waste! Not to mention the fact that spray products add to our indoor air pollution, and most commercial deodorants don't contain natural ingredients.

I love visiting my local refill store
– such amazing products

ABOUT 600 MILLION AEROSOL CANS ARE USED IN THE UK EVERY YEAR – AND THE PRODUCTS USUALLY HOUSED IN THEM ARE DEODORANTS, ANTIPERSPIRANTS AND BODY SPRAYS.

When I went to a local eco store to check out their natural deodorants, I was totally confused by all the options. There were deodorant pastes in glass jars or stick deodorants in metal containers, both of which are designed to be refilled. But I ended up coming home with a potassium crystal stick that comes in cork packaging (cork is sustainable because to harvest it, you don't have to cut down the tree). Why did I choose that one? Because the guy in the shop told me that it lasted forever – and, as you know, we like to save money in our house! I now realise he may have been kidding me, but it was £12 and I've had it for a year so far, which is pretty good going. I just wet the crystal and rub it under my arms, and I've not noticed any extra sweating or smelly BO!

'THE MAN IN THE SHOP TOLD ME MY CRYSTAL DEODORANT WOULD LAST FOREVER – I THINK HE MIGHT HAVE BEEN KIDDING!'

I should warn you though that some people do experience a 'detox effect' when they switch from antiperspirant to natural deodorant. Natural deodorants don't stop you sweating, and as your body gets rid of built-up toxins, BO can increase. It usually passes within two-four weeks though, so stick with it if you can!

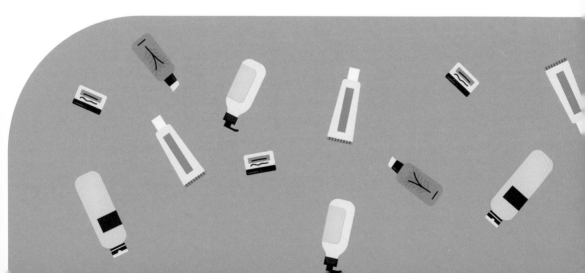

DID YOU KNOW?

- One pack of sanitary towels can contain up to 4 plastic bags worth of plastic.

- The average person uses 22 sanitary towels or tampons per period – 11,000 in a lifetime – which all end up in landfill, blocked in drains or, even worse, in the sea.

- Tampons, pads and pant liners generate more than 200,000 metric tons of waste every year.

- ***Sanitary products.***
Conventional sanitary towels and tampons cause big problems for the environment. Although sanitary towels look like they're made of cotton, they're actually 90% plastic and the rest is wood pulp. Tampons are made from cotton (which uses vast amounts of water plus pesticides and insecticides to grow) and plastic. And, of course, once they have human blood on them, they can't be recycled so they all get sent to landfill.

What's bonkers is that tampons and pads are designed to be used for a maximum of eight hours, but they'll probably take longer to decompose in landfill than an average person's life. They also manage to make their way into our drains, which causes fatbergs (see page 135) and into our oceans. During a beach clean in 2013, the Marine Conservation Society found 428 tampons and applicators per 4.4kms, and 1,291 sanitary towels per 13.3km.

Sanitary products also contain chemicals and fragrance neutralisers that can be irritating to our skin, so it was a no-brainer for me to switch to non-disposable sanitary products. I never thought I'd say this, but making the switch was something I got pretty excited about. There are loads of options available, so hopefully you'll find one that works for you.

> *'I never thought I'd say this, but I got pretty excited about sanitary products'*

– **Reusable sanitary pads** are cloth pads with an absorbent core. They are used just as you would a disposable pad, but instead of throwing them away you rinse them in cold water after use, then store them in a waterproof bag until you can throw them in with your normal laundry on a cool wash. They come in all sizes, from pant liners to maxi, and while they are more expensive to buy than a pack of disposables (they start at around £4 per pad), they can be used for around five years. This can save you around £2,000 over a lifetime.

– **Period pants** have an absorbent gusset but look just like regular pants. If you find the reusable pads a little bulky

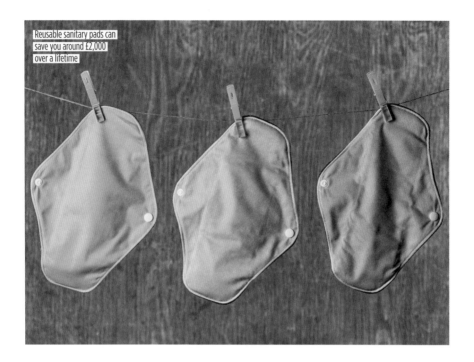

Reusable sanitary pads can save you around £2,000 over a lifetime

(some people do, some people don't) these could be a great option because the absorbent gusset is relatively thin. The washing instructions for these are pretty much the same as the reusable pads but they do come in as the most expensive option. Prices start at around £15 per pair.

– **Menstrual cups** are a great alternative if you prefer using tampons to pads. They're made of soft, flexible material such as rubber or silicone and you wear them inside the vagina as you would a tampon. Once in, they form a suction cup to stop any leaks and they collect your period rather than absorbing it. Once you get over the oddness of removing the cup, emptying your period away and then washing and reusing, you'll wonder how you ever lived without one of these – or so I am told! As with other reusable products, they're more money up front – on average around £20 – but they save you loads in the long run because they can be used for around 10 years if looked after well.

If you do prefer to use disposables – I get it, switching to reusables can be a big change and disposables are convenient – try and choose organic and biodegradable ones. That way you are reducing the harm to yourself and the environment from the pesticides and plastic waste. Also choose tampons with no applicator (because they are usually plastic) or invest in a reusable applicator that you can use again and again.

> **MOST OF US WILL USE AROUND 300 TOOTHBRUSHES IN A LIFETIME – AND THEY ALL END UP IN LANDFILL.**

- *Toothbrush.*

  Toothbrushes are one of those items that are difficult to recycle because they contain different types of plastic (plastic for the handle, rubber for the grip) – and the nylon bristles are not recyclable at all. So while we only use each brush for a few months, they're designed to stick around for a lifetime. Electric toothbrushes can be used for much longer, but you still have to replace the heads, and when you do need to replace the whole unit, they have to be recycled with electrical waste – so I reckon most end up in the normal bin. To reduce waste, keep hold of your plastic toothbrush when you've finished with them to use for cleaning around taps, between tiles and other hard-to-reach areas in the kitchen and bathroom.

  The eco alternative here is to switch to a bamboo toothbrush. I'm a big fan, and I even managed to convert Charlotte. She'd had her eye on one of the least eco toothbrushes you can possibly get – you know the all-singing, all-dancing kids' electric ones where you can't even get to the battery compartment to change the batteries? When it was time to get her a new brush, she saw one on the shelf and was so excited, but I showed her a bamboo one and explained to her that this one would be so much better for the environment. And I was SO surprised when she changed her mind and picked the bamboo one. She said, "Mummy, I want this one, it's kind to our planet." Proud mum moment. She now loves brushing her teeth more than ever and we love doing it with our matching toothbrushes!

  'Charlotte chose a bamboo toothbrush over an all-singing, all-dancing electric kids' one – a proud mum moment!'

  Bamboo handles can be thrown into home composting or gardening waste to break down (although they do take around six months to decompose). Just make sure you check what material the bristles are made of first – if they are nylon, remove them with a pair of pliers first and throw them in the ordinary bin. Or, you can give the toothbrush a second life by using the handles as plant sticks and canes, or in arts and crafts with kids. Now that is something to smile about!

- *Dental floss.*

  Most floss is made from waxed nylon and, just like plastic, is derived from oil. Conventional floss can't be recycled and it takes years to decompose. It also comes

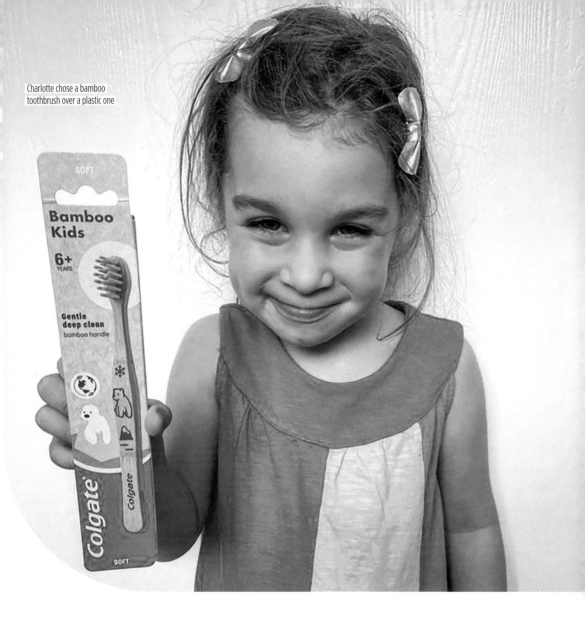

in a plastic container with a metal blade, which means that can't easily be recycled either. An environmentally friendly alternative is silk or bamboo floss that come in small glass jars with metal cutters on top. I have a little roll and it works just as well as my 'old' dental floss – it's minty and does the job. To keep packaging down, I bought a refill and just use a small pair of scissors to cut it to the right length.

- **_Toothpaste._**
  Because toothpaste tubes are a mix of plastic and aluminium, they're another item that can't be recycled in your usual recycling bin. You can, however, recycle them using the TerraCycle scheme (for more details, visit page 252). Conventional toothpastes can also

include potentially harmful ingredients such as triclosan, parabens and phthalates (see Don't Get In A Lather on page 129). The best eco paste I've been able to find from a 'well-known' brand is Colgate's Smile For Good toothpaste – the tube is made from the same plastic as a plastic milk bottle, but in a squeezable form, so it can be recycled at home, but you must cut the top off and clean it out first. They also list their ingredients on the front with an explanation of why each one is included in the paste.

'I popped one in my mouth with some water and hoped for the best'

If you want to go completely plastic free with all-natural ingredients, you can opt for toothpaste tablets that come in glass jars. I have some and, not going to lie, they're quite strange. I wasn't actually sure what to do with them so popped one in my mouth with a bit of water and hoped for the best. As I started to chew, it felt grainy and like it wasn't foaming up, but when I looked in the mirror it had. My teeth don't feel as clean when I use them, but other people rave about them. Like I said, it is a personal journey and you do what you can! I'm going to persevere for now (or until someone says I have bad breath!).

- **Razors.**
  You're probably bored by me saying this now, but disposable and plastic razors, like toothbrushes and toothpaste tubes, are made of different types of plastic, plus the metal blades, so they can't be recycled in household recycling (they can, however, be recycled

Bars of soap, toothpaste tablets and bamboo toothbrushes... easy plastic-free bathroom switches

through TerraCycle, see page 252). They're yet another item we use for such a small amount of time but will sit around in landfill for centuries. Using the plastic razors that you change the heads on is better than disposable razors, but the heads can't be recycled and they often come in mountains of plastic packaging.

> **AN ESTIMATED 5.5 MILLION PEOPLE USE DISPOSABLE PLASTIC RAZORS IN THE UK**

For hygiene reasons – in beauty salons, tattoo parlours and hospitals, for example – disposables might be the only way. But at home, we have the choice to buy a good old-fashioned metal safety razor – which will last you for life. With these, you change the blades only, not the whole head, and you can get them in attractive bamboo designs too. Remember to never put razor blades in the general bin – they're very dangerous, even when blunt. You can collect them in a tin and take them to your local recycling centre when the tin is full. Metal safety razors are actually not much more money (around £15-£20) than a longer-lasting plastic one, and the blades are a couple of pounds to replace.

- *Toilet paper.*
  Okay, so I'm not going to tell you to ditch the loo roll or use reusable paper – imagine! – but there are ways we can make things more environmentally friendly.

  – **Choose toilet paper that has been made from recycled paper,** and opt for rolls that come in paper packaging instead of plastic. Most supermarkets now offer an eco version or you can order them online at places like WhoGivesACrap.com. In some zero-waste stores you can get completely naked loo rolls in cardboard boxes of 12 or 24.

  – **Buy in bulk.** In the same way that buying shampoo in bulk is more environmentally friendly than buying smaller bottles, buying larger packs of loo roll is too. For example, think of a four-pack of rolls versus a 24-pack. That's six trips to the shop instead of one (so six x the transport emissions) plus almost six times the amount of plastic. Buying bulk will save you money too. Four-packs are around £2.20, making each roll 55p per roll, whereas 24-packs are around £9.25, which makes each roll 38p – a saving of over 25%!

DID YOU KNOW?

- We use roughly 8-9 sheets of toilet paper per trip to the loo and an average of 57 sheets a day!

- You will use 384 trees worth of toilet roll in your life!

- In the UK we cut down 7 million trees a year for toilet roll.

5.

SAVE WATER

Water is the most precious resource on our planet. Without it, we simply couldn't survive. Not only is drinking water essential for our health, it's also important for hygiene, cleaning and in the production of many of the things that we consume every day – from the food we eat to the clothes we wear.

When you think about water, you may be thinking about the British weather. It always seems to be raining (at least, that's what the rest of the world thinks!) so the idea that we might run low sounds kinda crazy, right? Well, it's not. Think back to all those hot summers when we've had hosepipe bans because of drought. Now, as climate change makes our summers even more hot and dry, and with the UK population set to rise by an estimated 10 million people over the next 30 years, there's every chance we will suffer from water shortages if we don't act now to save what we can.

62% OF PEOPLE IN THE UK ADMIT THEY DON'T DRINK THE RECOMMENDED 2 LITRES OF WATER A DAY (THAT'S AROUND 8 GLASSES).

?

DID YOU KNOW?

- It is estimated that England will face water shortages by 2050 unless we save water fast.

- Our water usage is increasing at twice the rate of population growth.

- 1 in 3 people in the world don't have access to safe, clean drinking water.

- We use approximately 143 litres of water each a day in the UK.

We are lucky enough to have clean, healthy water on tap in our country, but the Earth does not have an endless supply of fresh water. While 71% of the Earth's surface is covered in water, only around 3% of it is fresh – the rest is in the ocean and too salty to use. Most of the fresh water we do have is locked in ice caps and glaciers, which means we rely on a very small amount – around 1% – to live off. To put that into perspective, if all the water on Earth was scaled down to fit in a one gallon (4.5 litre) container, only one tablespoon would be usable.

When you add up the water we use each day to drink, clean (ourselves and clothes, dishes etc) plus watering the garden, it's estimated that we get through around 143 litres each per day.

But that's not taking into account the amount of water that is needed in the production of EVERYTHING we use each day – from our clothes and cars to food and furniture. If you watched David Attenborough's Netflix show *Breaking Boundaries* (if you haven't, it's well worth a watch), you might recall the staggering fact that…

WE NEED 3,000 LITRES OF FRESH WATER PER PERSON, PER DAY TO SURVIVE.

WOW. This includes water for drinking, hygiene, cleaning and industry, but more than 2,000 litres of this comes from the production of our food. It waters and nurtures the plants that feed people and animals, and the animals that we eat need to drink too (another reason to eat all the food we grow and not throw it away!).

Elsewhere in the book you'll find tips on how you can cut your global water usage through the clothes you wear (page 193) and the food you eat (page 80). But here, let's focus on the water we use in our homes and gardens.

Always turn off the tap while brushing your teeth

The Environment Agency is urging us to drop our daily water usage by 33 litres – from 143 litres to 110 litres – to avoid a shortage in the UK in the next 25 years. If we manage to do that, it would also save us around £20 a year per person on our energy bills.

If you follow the tips below, it is really easy to save that much and more! So, what are you waiting for?

IN THE BATHROOM

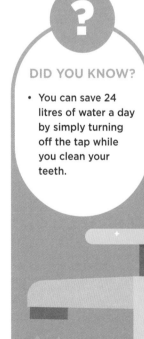

- ***Turn off the tap when you're brushing your teeth.***
  It's so simple but do you do it? If you leave the tap running, it uses up six litres every minute. That means that if you clean your teeth for the recommended two minutes, twice a day, you're literally pouring 24 litres of water down the drain that could have been saved.

  My husband has always turned the tap off as a way to save money – so this is an eco hack that will leave you better off too! And I've already taught Charlotte to do this as well. If

Could you reduce your shower time?

I do leave the tap running now, she will tell me off. So, if a four-year-old can do it…

'Charlotte tells me off if I leave the tap running!'

Top tip: The same goes for when you are washing your hands or your face. It's estimated that you could save 22 litres a day by turning off the tap while you lather up your hands with soap (for the recommended 20-30 seconds) while washing them.

Pause for thought: In some developing countries, people (mainly women and children) walk an average of six kilometres a day just to get clean water – yet here we are wasting litres of it.

- ### Choose a shower over a bath.
  Most people love a nice relaxing bath every now and again, but I am not one of those people. In fact, it's been years since I had one, and I didn't find it relaxing – I just got bored!

HOW MUCH WATER DOES YOUR SHOWER USE?

One way to figure this out is to take a one-litre container into the shower with you and time how long it takes to fill it up with the shower head. Then, if you multiply that amount by how many minutes you are in the shower, you can work out how much water you use. My shower pumps out one litre every nine seconds – that's 6.66 litres a minute. Mmmh, should I read anything into the fact that 666 is the devil's number? Probably not.

So this one has been easy for me. If you have a shower at home, it's 'usually' more water efficient to have a shower than a bath for your daily wash. I say 'usually' because not all showers pump out water at the same speed and we don't all shower for the same amount of time. An average electric shower, for example, sprays out around five litres per minute, which means you'd have to be in there for 15-20 minutes to use the same amount of water as you would in a bath. But some power showers can use up to 15 litres per minute, meaning you need to be in and out in under six minutes to use less water than you would in a bath.

WOULD YOU SHARE YOUR BATH WATER?

We do in our house. Our shower is over the bath, so I put the plug in while I'm showering and Charlotte will sit in the bath and have a splash around. Then sometimes, my husband will get in afterwards. I know some people think this is gross, but how dirty do you have to be to leave the water unusable for the next person? Apparently, every now and then property pro and TV presenter Sarah Beeny also gets in the same bath water as her husband and four sons to conserve water, and singer Robbie Williams and his wife Ayda share a bath to cut down on bills. So maybe not so gross, after all...

DID YOU KNOW?

- The average length of time people spend in the shower in the UK is eight minutes.

- *Time how long it takes you in the shower.*
  How long do you think you spend in the shower? On a day when I don't wash my hair, I can be in and out in three minutes (that's around 20 litres of water). Woop. But when I timed my 'full' shower – wash and condition hair, shave legs, body scrub etc – it took me nine minutes (a whopping 60

litres!). I honestly thought I was much quicker than that. It's more than the average shower time, which is eight minutes (people aged 55-65 take around five minutes, whereas 18 to 24-year-olds take almost 12 minutes). To conserve water, water companies recommend we shower for no longer than four minutes, so I was determined to cut down on my time.

Why not time your next shower and see how long you really spend in there?

- ***Reduce your shower time by… singing your favourite song!***

Who doesn't love singing in the shower? I sing at the top of my lungs. I love music, and your voice always sounds so much better in the shower. Well guess what? It turns out singing to your favourite tune might be one of the best ways of cutting down your shower time.

DID YOU KNOW?

- Reducing your shower time by one minute can save your household up to £120 a year.

When I started looking into this, I discovered a remarkable story about how Cape Town in South Africa managed to reverse an impending water shortage in 2018 with a two-minute shower song campaign. Sanlam, one of the country's leading insurance companies, asked South Africa's biggest pop stars to record new, shorter versions of their popular songs, with the idea that people could put the song on as they jumped in the shower, sing along and be finished by the time it ended. And do you know what? It worked. After six months, the city had reduced its water usage by half, and they averted 'Day Zero' – the day they had predicted they would run out of water. It shows just what is achievable by working together.

'So far I've got my 'full' shower – wash and condition hair, shave legs and body scrub – down to six minutes (just under 40 litres of water)'

Anyone who knows me, knows I don't need an excuse to whack on some Bon Jovi, so I decided to give this shower song a go. I chose *Living On A Prayer* because it is just over four minutes long (the recommended shower time), and so far I've got my full shower down to six minutes (which is the length of Queen's *Bohemian Rhapsody* – doable for most people). Even by shaving off one minute I'm saving 6.66 litres each time, which will save us money on our water bill – so you can imagine how happy my husband is about that! The money that is, not me singing Bon Jovi!

Which song will you pick?

- **Have a 'Navy shower'.**
When I talked to my husband about this section of the book, he said he already knows how to save water… and doesn't need a lecture on it! He often has what is referred to as a 'Navy shower' because it's a method used to conserve fresh water on ships. You run the water to initially wet your body and rinse, but turn it off while you shampoo your hair and lather your body with soap. I'll be honest, I really struggle to do this because I get really cold, but if you are tougher than me, give it a go.

- **Fix a water-saving device to your shower head.**
It all depends on what kind of shower you have – dual, electric, power, rainfall – but these showerheads can regulate the flow of the water and cut usage by up to 50%. They are not recommended for electric showers because they are already water efficient, and they can possibly damage the shower – so make sure you do your research first.

Did you know you can get free water-saving devices from your water provider? These include things like a regulated shower head, a four-minute shower timer, a special hosepipe nozzle, save-a-flush bags and a kitchen tap aerator. My water supplier, South East Water, has all these things and more – when I told my husband it was like Christmas Day! Check with your supplier to see what freebies you can get. While a big part of this book is about not buying things we don't need, and also not taking free stuff just for the sake of it, if you will actually use these free things then they'll help you save water… and money!

- ***Think before you flush!***
  Did you know that the largest use of household water is flushing the toilet? Followed shortly by having a bath or shower.

  We never flush the toilet if we get up for a wee in the middle of the night (something we learned to do when Charlotte was a baby so the flush didn't wake her up!). And if we are going out we try to remember to just flush once after all three of us have been to the loo – which saves 26 litres!

  If you have a dual-flush toilet (one with two buttons – full flush and short flush), always use the short flush button for liquid waste. It's estimated that this can save 67% of water compared to a toilet that has a single-handle flush.

  My motto is, "If it's yellow let it mellow – if it's brown, flush it down!"

IN THE KITCHEN

- ***Use a dishwasher instead of washing by hand.***
  Surprised? I know I was. I assumed it would be far 'greener' to wash dishes by hand. But it turns out that not only are dishwashers between four to 10 times more water efficient than washing by hand per place setting, they produce fewer greenhouse gas emissions in the heating of that water, too.

  The majority of modern dishwashers use around 11-13 litres of water per cycle, whereas the average sink holds around 20 litres of water. Add to that the fact that the sink water usually needs changing at least once during a wash and that some people also run the tap to rinse soap suds off, and it's not looking good for hand-washers.

  In terms of energy, one study showed that, on average, hand-washing 32 sets of dishes per week over a 10-year period produced 5,620kg of greenhouse gases to heat the water (using a gas boiler, which most UK houses have).

DID YOU KNOW?

- It takes up to 13 litres of water per toilet flush – which means you could be flushing 91 litres of water down the loo every day.

Using a dishwasher saves more water than washing dishes by hand

Doing the same thing in a dishwasher produced 2,090kg greenhouse gases (using electricity). For more on reducing your home energy emissions, go to page 62.

We use a dishwasher in our house, but there are a few things that can't go in it, such as some of Charlotte's plates and wine glasses. We save up anything that can't go in and wash them in one bowl of water at the end of the day. We also use that dirty water to clean any jars or tubs heading for the recycling bin – they don't need to be squeaky clean and they certainly don't need their own jacuzzi!

> *'We use dirty dishwater to clean any jars or tubs that are heading for the recycling bin'*

- **Don't rinse your plates before you put them in the dishwasher.**
  If you're someone who puts your dishwasher on every day (more on this in the next point) then it's unlikely that any food residue will be stuck fast in that time. If you are still worried about this, you can give them a quick soak in the sink at the end of washing up (with used, dirty water) or

?

DID YOU KNOW?

- Pre-rinsing dishes can use up to 24 litres of water!

If you haven't got a dishwasher, there are still ways you can use less water while washing by hand...

- Scrape off any leftovers or sauces (never into the bin, always into a food waste bin or compost – check out page 93 on reducing food waste!) with a silicone spatula straight away to avoid any difficult-to-remove stains.

- If there are stains, soak the plates in a couple of centimetres of water in a bowl before washing.

- Never wash the dishes under running water! Remember – we run off around six litres a minute! Use a washing-up bowl instead.

- Wash the glasses and cleanest things first – save the dirtiest pans until the end of the wash.

- Have the water as hot as you can to make sure your dishes come up as clean as possible (see eco washing-up gloves on page 156).

give them a wipe over with a wet sponge. That way, no extra water is being used.

- ***Always fully load the dishwasher before putting it on.***
  A dishwasher uses the same amount of water and energy to clean the contents whether it's a half or full load, so it is a no-brainer to wait until you have enough dishes to fill it before turning it on.

Luckily, I'm not allowed to load the dishwasher in our house because apparently I do it 'wrong'. I load it 'my way', which is nicely stacked, getting as much in as possible – but that often means there will be some stuff left on the side that won't fit in. I'm sure the way I do it is right, but if my husband sees the dishwasher before it goes on he will somehow manage to fit everything in! It comes out clean but, let's be clear… he is doing it wrong. But if he thinks he is best at doing it I'll leave it to him and, yippee, another household chore I don't have to do!

'I'm not allowed to load the dishwasher in our house because I do it wrong'

Top tip: Use the eco setting. This takes longer than a standard wash but it uses around 20% less water and energy.

Waiting until you have a full load of washing before doing a clothes wash will save you water and energy

IN THE UTILITY

- ***Wash only full loads in the washing machine.***
  The amount of water a washing machine uses per wash varies greatly depending on what type you have. Older machines used to use a whopping 150 litres (more than the amount of water we each use every day!) per cycle, but these days, the average amount is about 50 litres – the more water-efficient models use around 33 litres, and the less efficient types use 77 litres.

  If you have only a small amount of items to wash, then use the half-load button if your machine has one so it uses less water. But the best option is to wait until you have a full load to save on water and energy. Which in turn saves you money!

Top tip: Avoid using the extra rinse cycle too. For more on clothes washing, see page 196.

DID YOU KNOW?

- Most modern washing machines still use up to 50 litres of water per cycle.

CLEVER CLEANING

As in the bathroom, there are some great ways you can cut down on plastic for a more environmentally-friendly dish- and clothes-washing experience.

Sponges

The washing-up sponges we are used to are made from synthetic plastic fibres, so will take years to break down, and while you're using them, they release microfibres into our waterways (see page 52 for more on this). Here are some alternatives you can try out...

- **A wooden brush with natural bristles.** These are much better for the environment than a plastic brush with plastic bristles, although I tried one and didn't get on with it – it was hard to reach the bottom of things. I'll admit I reverted to my old plastic sponges before finding compostable ones.

Loofahs and compostable sponges will reduce plastic while washing up

- **Loofahs.** Made from the loofah plant, these sponges swell up and become soft when submerged, and last for months. I found that they are not quite as good at getting into tight corners (like the bottom rim of cups) as a traditional sponge but they still work well. When you need to replace them you can compost them at home or they will break down in the normal waste far quicker than a plastic sponge.

- **Compostable sponges.** If you have a home compost (see page 119 for more) then these are a great option. Available online or at eco stores, they are 100% plastic-free and are as flexible as traditional plastic sponges, so can get into all those hard-to-reach areas. I get mine from Green Island, who plant a tree for every order. A pack of three costs £6.95 and they last for ages.

Washing-up gloves

I actually don't wear gloves to wash up – mainly because I hardly wash up (sorry husband!) but my mum does and I know loads of people prefer to wear them to protect their hands and get a better grip on things. Standard rubber gloves are not recyclable at home, and the rubber often comes from plantations, one of the biggest causes of deforestation in the Amazon. Marigolds can be recycled with TerraCycle (see more on page 252) but

I tried Smol cleaning capsules

most people throw these in the normal bin, and they end up in landfill. The best option would be to take a leaf out of my book – completely avoid doing any washing up at all! But if you can't wash up without them, then check out...

- **Natural rubber gloves.** These are made from natural rubber from responsibly managed plantations (which don't endanger rainforests), are 100% plastic-free and can be composted at home. When you are finished, cut them up into tiny pieces to put them in the compost.

Washing-up liquid and laundry detergent

Traditional washing-up liquid and detergents come in plastic bottles and can be harmful for aquatic life (poor fish, again!), but there are loads of alternative eco cleaning products. Just as with your bathroom products, you can...

- **Use an eco brand.** There are loads of well-known ones now, such as Ecover and Method, who use plant-based or recycled plastic for their bottles. Their products contain far fewer nasties than standard brands, too.

- **Buy in bulk.** Five-litre bottles reduce the amount of plastic you use and will save you money! We are still using up our huge bottle of Fairy but we will switch to a more eco brand when it has run out.

- **Think inside the box.** Powder detergent in a box is a great option if you want to

cut out plastic completely. In fact, it's what we use at home. Be aware, though, that many standard brands still contain chemicals that can be harmful to the environment and irritating to skin. So choose powders from eco brands.

- **Start refilling.** Keep hold of an empty plastic bottle and visit a refill store. They will supply an eco-friendly detergent, fabric softener or washing-up liquid, and you won't end up with any plastic waste. You can also sign up for refills online. I tried a free trial with Smol (see picture) for dishwasher and clothes wash and they were great. They cost much the same as supermarket brands so I'll definitely be making the swap when we've used up the products we already have. Also check out Ecover and Splosh.

- **Try laundry strips.** Sometimes called sheets, these are dehydrated strips of hypo-allergenic and environmentally-friendly laundry detergent that you pop inside your machine. They dissolve in the machine's water, and the packaging is usually cardboard. TruEarth is a popular brand.

Charlotte loves using the hosepipe so we let her use it sparingly with trigger nozzle fitted

IN THE GARDEN

DID YOU KNOW?

- In one hour, a hosepipe can use the same amount of water as a whole family would use in two days.

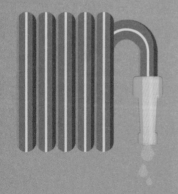

- ***Avoid using a hosepipe…***
There's a reason we sometimes have hosepipe bans during hot summers – they use so much water! The average pipe uses 170 litres of water in 10 minutes. I can't deny that the alternatives take a little more effort, but it's worth it for the amount of water (and money) you can save. Why not try…

– ***Use a watering can to water plants.*** Prioritise plants in hanging baskets and pots over bedding plants, as well as seedlings and young plants. Avoid watering under the midday sun, as the water evaporates before it can get to the roots and can scorch the plants. Aim to water first thing in the morning or in the evening.

– ***Leave your lawn alone***. If you're using a sprinkler system to water your grass, think again… sprinklers can use up to 1,000 litres an hour! The advice from The Environment Agency is actually not to water grass at all – unless it is new grass that needs some encouragement to grow. No matter what the weather, lawns will always bounce back. Last spring, our lawn was looking pretty patchy after the cold and dry months, but following a few weeks of rain it was like a jungle! If you really have to water your lawn, use a watering can and, in the same way as watering plants, do it in the morning or evening to avoid the midday sun.

IF YOU HAVE TO USE A HOSEPIPE, FIT IT WITH A TRIGGER NOZZLE SO YOU ARE IN CONTROL OF THE WATER FLOW.

Top tip: *If you leave grass cuttings on the lawn after you've cut it, it helps to add moisture and nutrients to the soil and stops it getting parched.*

– ***Wash your car using a bucket of water and a sponge.*** Start at the top of the car and work your way down, rinsing off the soap suds with a watering can.

– ***Get a water butt to collect rainwater.*** While climate change will make our summers hotter and drier, it is also making our winters warmer and wetter. So the advice is to save up water in the winter to use in summer. On average, the annual rainfall in the UK is around 1.2 metres. That's nearly enough to fill up a water butt, or anything else that can hold water. At a flower show I visited there was a green garden that had been built to cope with the changing climate. It had a small pond to collect the extra water in winter to avoid flooding, and to store it for use in summer.

For more on being a 'green' gardener, see page 110.

GET INTO THE HABIT OF REUSING WATER
You're paying for the water, so you might as well make the most of it!

- Wash items that will go into the recycling bin in dirty washing-up water instead of running the tap!

- Save the water you cook pasta and rice in to water your plants.

- The water you use to boil vegetables can be used to make gravy.

- Use a tub to collect water when you are waiting for it to run hot (in the shower or bath, for example) or cold (to drink) and use this to water your plants, refill the kettle or flush the toilet.

- Washing-up water and bath water can be reused to water non-edible plants.

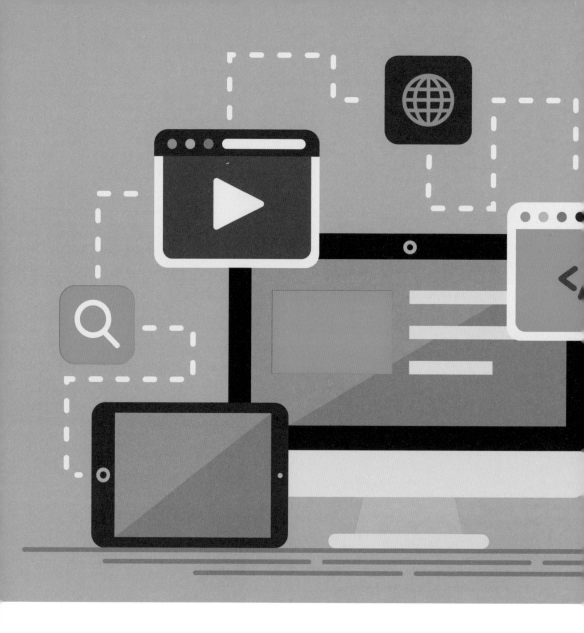

6.

DIGITAL

Depending on what time of day you are reading this, it is likely that you've already messaged a few friends, scrolled through Instagram, done a Google search and sent out a couple of emails. You may have listened to a podcast or streamed a TV show.

It's hard to imagine living without the internet today. I couldn't have written this book without being able to research online. And since the pandemic, it's also become a vital way of keeping in touch with people. Internet use sky-rocketed during lockdowns

- It's estimated that the carbon footprint of our gadgets, the internet and all the systems supporting them account for 3.7% of global greenhouse gas emissions.

- The cumulative emissions from internet usage amount to around 1.7 billion metric tons a year – 45% more than the aviation industry.

- When Cristiano Ronaldo posts an image on Instagram, 36 megawatt hours of power are needed to show it to his 240million followers. That's enough electricity to power 10 UK homes for a year.

because many in-person activities, such as meet-ups with friends, toddler groups, exercise classes and work meetings all moved online. I did the weather forecast from my home for three months in 2020, and I had weekly Zoom calls with friends and family – we called them 'pub nights' and had quizzes, drinks and giggles.

In some ways, this has been a great way to reduce our impact on the environment. Video calls have helped cut transport emissions and sending information by email has saved reams of paperwork printed out in offices. But as with everything we do in life, using gadgets and surfing the internet takes its own toll on the planet.

Video meetings have helped cut transport emissions

Making tech gadgets – such as phones, tablets and computers – is a carbon-intensive process, which uses precious metals, materials and energy. Once they are made, they continue to use energy with every email we send, every photo we upload or TV show we stream. I'd never really thought about how the internet 'works' before, but all of the world's online traffic goes through data centres – huge buildings that house servers which store, process and distribute everything we do online. And these data centres need electricity to run them.

It's estimated that data centres are responsible for 1-2% of global electricity usage, but carbon emissions are often disputed because some centres use renewable energy sources while others use fossil fuels.

40% OF THE ENERGY USED IN DATA CENTRES IS TO KEEP THE TECH EQUIPMENT COOL. ONE WAY TECH COMPANIES ARE STARTING TO CUT THEIR EMISSIONS IS BY MOVING THEIR DATA CENTRES TO COLDER COUNTRIES. SOME UNDERWATER CENTRES HAVE EVEN BEEN TRIALLED.

While the energy needed for a single internet search (around 1 KJ – enough to power a 60W light bulb for 17 seconds) or to send one email is relatively small – there are now 4.1 billion people using the internet (53.6% of the world's population) so all those little bits of energy add up – along with the greenhouse gases they produce.

DID YOU KNOW?

- The number of data centres around the world has grown from 500,000 in 2012 to more than 7 million today.

- The amount of energy used by data centres continues to double every four years, meaning they have the fastest-growing carbon footprint of any area in the IT sector.

The emissions from our internet searches all add up

And we are now spending more time than ever on our devices. It's estimated that the average person in the UK spends 6.4 hours a day online. Unless you are going to live completely off-grid, we all rely on the internet for work, keeping in touch with friends and for entertainment.

Making changes here is about becoming more mindful about what you do and how you do it, as well as looking after the gadgets you already own. As with all sections in this book, the smallest changes can make a big difference to our carbon footprint if we all play our part.

Here's what you can do….

DID YOU KNOW?

- Globally, the world's email usage generates as much CO_2 as having an extra seven million cars on the roads.

- The average person (in the developed world) adds 136kg of CO_2 to their carbon footprint from the emails they send and receive – the equivalent of driving 230 miles.

- ***Clear out your email inbox.***
  You should know by now that a lot of these sections start with a good old clear out! Every email you have in your inbox requires energy to be stored on servers. So go through and delete emails you no longer need. After that, make a habit of deleting unwanted emails at the end of the day or week. I'm guilty of having loads of unread emails. I save them for 'later' if I can't answer them straight away – but they build up! Now I have a weekly clear out and it is very therapeutic.

> **TOP TIP:**
> Unsubscribe from marketing emails or newsletters you're no longer interested in. You can also block ads that you are sent. This can reduce your carbon footprint as well as saving you money – if you don't get discount emails from brands, you will be less likely to buy!

- ***Send fewer emails.***
  Every email we send uses electricity to transport it, for servers to pass it on and then for it to be displayed on our screens. The average email (with no picture attachment) uses about 4g of CO_2. A small amount, but we send a whopping 300 billion emails EVERY DAY across the globe.

Apparently, Brits send 64 million unnecessary emails every day, with 'thank you' and 'thanks' coming in at the top. I make a point of never replying to emails with two word answers and have done for over a year. Although, I think I need to update my email signature or spread the word more to explain that because I often get emails from people asking me if I received their email… I did, but I am trying to save the planet over here! It also makes a pretty good excuse if I just forget to reply, too…

'I make a point of never replying to emails with two-word answers'

• **Use a green web browser.**
We have become so used to Google as our main internet search engine that 'to google' has become a transitive verb! Since 2007 Google has been carbon-neutral, which means they offset their CO_2 emissions by investing in green projects. The company also uses 100% renewable energy.

But there is a way you can make your random internet searches do good. The search engine Ecosia plants a tree for every 45 searches you perform, which helps to remove carbon from the atmosphere. Here's what they say on their website: 'Every search with Ecosia actually removes about 1 kg of CO_2 from the atmosphere. This means that, if Ecosia were as big as Google, it could absorb 15% of all global CO_2 emissions.'

I've been using Ecosia on my laptop and phones for two years. And my searches have planted around 3,000 trees.

Another one to look out for is Gexia, where the sponsored ads that you see generate income to fund social projects around the world.

?

DID YOU KNOW?

• If every adult in the UK sent one less 'thank you' email, it could save 16,433 metric tons of carbon a year – the equivalent of cancelling 81,152 flights from the UK to Madrid.

• Sending 65 emails is roughly equivalent to driving 1km in a car.

• 300 billion emails are sent every day.

ECOSIA PLANTS A TREE FOR EVERY 45 SEARCHES YOU PERFORM.

> **TOP TIP:**
>
> If you know what website you want to go to, put the web address directly into the top bar on the browser, rather than searching for it and clicking on a link.

- *Cut down your screen time.*
  We already know that reducing our screen time is beneficial for our wellbeing. Constant scrolling and comparing our lives to other people's seemingly perfect Instagram realities can leave us feeling pretty rubbish about ourselves. So cutting back can help to improve sleep, boost motivation and self-esteem, and reduce feelings of anxiety.

'Reducing screen time helps to improve sleep, boost motivation and self-esteem, and reduce feelings of anxiety'

It can also help reduce our digital carbon footprint too. The more time we spend on devices the more emissions we create.

THE AVERAGE PERSON IN THE UK SPENDS 6.4 HOURS A DAY ON THE INTERNET – LISTENING TO MUSIC, SCROLLING ON SOCIAL MEDIA, WATCHING TV AND MORE.

Using your phone for an hour a day (and, let's be honest, it is often way more than that!) produces the equivalent of 63kg of CO_2 a year – about the same as driving 158 miles in an average car. If you use your phone for five hours a day, that's 790 miles in a car. Almost as far as driving from John O'Groats to Land's End.

Here's how you can try to cut down…

– Get familiar with how much time you DO spend on your phone. iPhones have a Screen Time Function you can turn on which tells you your average every week. And Androids have a similar function within their Digital Wellbeing app. The figures can be pretty alarming if you have never kept track before…

My average during the week is around 4-5 hours while I am working, especially if I am on the road because I use my phone to get my weather information and update social media. At the weekend I spend around 2 hours a day on my phone.

– Set a usage limit. If knowing your screen time isn't enough to deter you, then you can set usage limits on individual apps in the same place you find the Screen Time function on your phone. The apps will send you an alert telling you when you have used up your limit. You can override it – but it at least allows you to keep track of how much time you are spending on your phone.

– Disable notifications on apps that don't need your attention immediately. Seeing a message pop up on your phone every few minutes is distracting and means you'll keep picking up your phone. An hour later you're still lost in a social media spiral (or is that just me?). I keep notifications for messaging apps such as WhatsApp, but I have all notifications turned off for social media accounts.

– Avoid using your phone first thing in the morning or last thing at night. This is a case of doing what I say and not what I do, because I can't help looking at emails, Twitter and the Daily Mail 'sidebar of shame' before I go to bed. It's a ritual for me and I always fall straight to sleep. Don't judge me!

> *'I can't help looking at the Daily Mail 'sidebar of shame'*
> *before I go to bed'*

A good way to stop scrolling while you're in bed is to charge your phone outside of the bedroom. That way you actually have to get out of bed to pick up your phone.

– Have screen-free times/zones. This could be deciding not to look at your phone until after you've had your breakfast, or keeping phones out of the bedroom at all times – anything that carves out a little space where there is no online activity. I make a conscious effort not to use my phone when I'm with Charlotte and when I do need to, I leave the room. We also never have phones at dinner time.

CHARLOTTE'S SCREEN TIME

Charlotte was premature so her brain was already overstimulated by being out in the big wide world when she should still have been in my tummy. Because of that, we had no screen time for her until she was two years old, and since then it has been very limited. She will watch a few episodes of *Paw Patrol* or *Peppa Pig* in the morning and around dinner time, but that is it. We bought her a tablet last Christmas because we know they are a big part of life for her generation, and she has some fun games on there that she likes to play.

- ***Put your phone on low-power mode.***
  This saves the battery on your phone by stopping automatic uploads and downloads – such as app updates, podcast downloads and photo syncing to the cloud – that happen in the background. This reduces the energy your phone or tablet consumes and means you won't have to charge your phone as often.

Top tip: Avoid charging your phone at night. Most smartphones take around 3-4 hours to fully charge. If your phone is plugged in for longer than that, it will keep using energy every time your battery drops to 99%.

- ***Get savvy about streaming.***
  Whether you're watching YouTube videos, TikTok dance-offs or the latest Netflix series, streaming videos account for 60% of internet traffic.

There are a few things you can do to reduce the energy you use while streaming videos. The first, of course, would be to watch fewer of them, but why not try to…

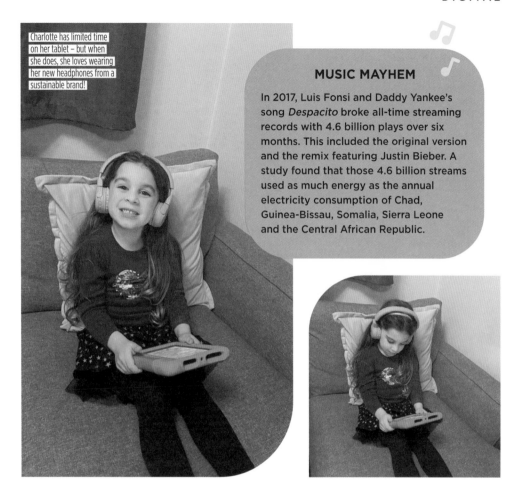

Charlotte has limited time on her tablet – but when she does, she loves wearing her new headphones from a sustainable brand!

MUSIC MAYHEM

In 2017, Luis Fonsi and Daddy Yankee's song *Despacito* broke all-time streaming records with 4.6 billion plays over six months. This included the original version and the remix featuring Justin Bieber. A study found that those 4.6 billion streams used as much energy as the annual electricity consumption of Chad, Guinea-Bissau, Somalia, Sierra Leone and the Central African Republic.

– Use WiFi rather than 4G.

If you're at home or somewhere you have access to WiFi, always use this over your mobile data. 4G mobile networks consume four times the amount of electricity as WiFi and it can eat into your data too, which could cost you more money.

– Watch on a smaller screen.

The smaller the device, the less energy needed to watch something. A 50-inch LED TV used 100 times the energy of a smart phone to watch the same show.

– Watch in lower definition.

Most streaming sites – such as ITV Hub or Amazon Prime – give you the option of watching in Standard Definition (SD) rather than Higher Definition (HD). If you're watching a movie on a big TV, then sure, HD will make the experience better. But if you're watching something on your small phone screen, do you really need to watch it in HD?

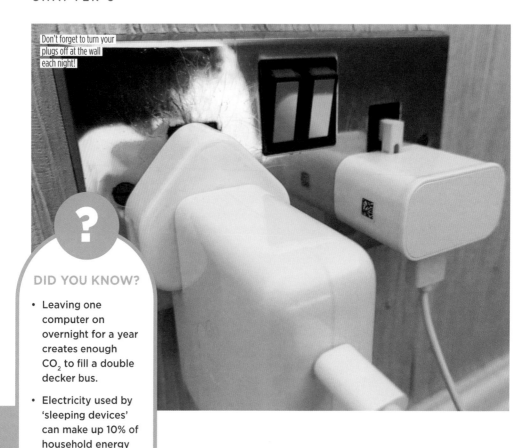

Don't forget to turn your plugs off at the wall each night!

- ***Turn off your gadgets and unplug them from the wall.***

  Do you turn off your TV, computer, games console and Alexa at night or leave them on standby? Take a TV for example – you may have turned it off with the remote but if you leave it plugged in at the wall, it is still using low levels of energy to be able to spring back into life at the touch of a button.

  The same applies for toasters, kettles and blenders – items you'd assume don't use any electricity unless you're actually using them. 'Phantom energy' is a term used for the energy used by an appliance or gadget when it is turned off but still plugged into the mains. Apparently, the average house has 40 products that are constantly drawing power, even when they are not in active use. Even though the energy going to these sleeping devices is small, it all adds up.

'We turn everything off at the plug every night apart from our phone chargers'

We turn everything off at the plug every night apart from our phone chargers – which I should actually get into the habit of doing during the day so I don't over charge my phone!

- ***Keep hold of your phones.***
  Most people replace their mobile phones every two years, usually coinciding with when a new model comes out and our mobile plans allow us to 'upgrade'. But there is often nothing wrong with the phone we are getting rid of – in fact, if looked after well, smartphones should last between five and 10 years. And as 80% of the carbon emissions associated with a mobile phone are generated during manufacturing, rather than how we use it afterwards, it makes sense to hold on to them for as long as possible. So next time you get the call to say you can upgrade, ask yourself if you really need a 'new' device?

'I'm not sucked in by the latest model of phone – mine has to be dying before I will get a new one'

I'm not sucked in by the latest model of phone – mine literally has to be dying for me to buy a new one. If a new one comes out when I do need a new phone, I'll get the model before because it is cheaper, and I'll also make sure it is a refurbished one. That way the phone is getting a longer life. You would honestly not know that it wasn't new.

TOP TIP:

Most places that repair phone screens also offer a battery replacement service. So if your battery power is poor, it doesn't necessarily mean you need to get a new phone.

- *Trade in or recycle electrical equipment.*
  If you are getting rid of a smartphone, or any electrical gadget such as a toaster, kettle or pair of straighteners, make sure you dispose of them responsibly.

> IN THE UK, AROUND 1 MILLION TONNES OF ELECTRICAL WASTE – SUCH AS KEYBOARDS, PHONES, MONITORS AND CIRCUIT BOARDS – IS DISPOSED OF EACH YEAR. GLOBALLY, THIS FIGURE REACHES 53 MILLION TONNES.

If electrical waste ends up in landfills, it can leak harmful chemicals into the soil and water. If it ends up being burnt, the fumes release chemicals into the air. But if the items are still in working order you can avoid this in several ways…

– *Trade in your old mobile when upgrading.* Doing so also allows you to get money off the new phone, and the old one will be reconditioned and resold. If you have old mobile phones hidden away in drawers, get in touch with your mobile network provider to see if they will take them. I always do this!

– *Donate your old phones or tablets* to charities that supply them to people in need, either in the UK or overseas.

– *Sell your items on eBay or Facebook Marketplace.* Remember, your trash might be someone else's treasure!

– *Give them to charity shops.* Only do this if the electrical items are fully usable. If you wouldn't buy it, then it is likely no one else will – and the charity shop will have to get rid of it.

If your electrical goods have truly seen better days and are unusable, you can recycle them at your local recycling centre. Check out recyclenow.com for more details.

> IT'S ESTIMATED THAT BRITS THROW AWAY MORE THAN 600 MILLION BATTERIES EVERY YEAR, WHICH RESULTS IN MORE THAN 20,000 METRIC TONS OF BATTERY WASTE STRAIGHT TO THE LANDFILL. SWITCH TO RECHARGEABLE BATTERIES INSTEAD OR RECYCLE THEM PROPERLY (SEE PAGE 252).

Donate your old phones to charities that need them

7.

BUY LESS

Is the secret to a happy life buying lots of things? I think we all know that the answer is no, but shopping has become a kind of escapism for many people. It's not called retail therapy for no reason! Buying something new gives us a bit of a buzz – because our body releases the feel-good hormone dopamine in anticipation of the 'reward' we're getting. But it's a quick fix, and doesn't bring us happiness in the long run.

Unfortunately, companies play on the feel-good nature of buying something new with their marketing strategies. It's estimated that we are exposed to between 6,000 and 10,000 adverts a day! It's crazy when you think about it.

And we Brits do love a bargain. Whether it's a discounted dress or a BOGOF offer on multipacks of crisps, if we can get something cheap or for free, then we often can't resist. Remember my obsession with 'free' mini bottles of shampoo and conditioner you get in hotels?! I'm a sucker for three for two offers. I'll buy the one thing I actually need and then think, 'If I just buy one more I can get another one free.' So I'll spend ages choosing the two things I don't really need. It's often food from the supermarket that can go off, and a lot of the time it does – adding to the huge problem of food waste (see page 93).

And don't even get me started on that middle aisle in Lidl. I'll pop in for some milk and bread, then spend ages eyeing up all the bargains like, 'Ooh look at this, we could get this sunlounger on offer.' Luckily my husband (the sensible/tight one) is on hand to guide me away. It's so easy to fall for the marketing.

Even when we decide not to buy, there's no escape from internet marketing these days. A quick search for a garden table online or even talking about it within earshot of your phone means you'll be bombarded with adverts for outdoor furniture on every social media platform and web page you visit during the next few days (maybe even weeks)… until you finally give in and buy the table!

Plus buying things is just so easy now. Most of us have our payment cards linked to our phones along with PayPal and Amazon accounts, so we can quite literally buy something in one click of a button.

Recently I found the joy of Apple Pay on my phone. I sometimes leave the house without my wallet and then discover I need to buy something, so it's saved my bacon on many occasions. But it's dangerous too – tapping your phone to buy something means you're barely thinking about what you're buying and the money it has cost. I need to follow my own advice and unsync it from my phone!

> **'RECENTLY I FOUND THE JOY OF APPLE PAY ON MY PHONE – BUT IT IS DANGEROUS!'**

We are now so used to next-day deliveries too – talk about instant gratification! But express deliveries have a knock-on effect on the planet. In order to get things to us sooner, delivery vans will be sent out before they are full, meaning far more trips need to be made. More trips means more emissions. I'm so disorganised, so next-day deliveries have come in handy in the past, but I am making a conscious effort to be more organised. Last Christmas, I made a big order of photo prints well ahead of time with slow delivery, which is better for our planet and cheaper. But then I got an email to say every piece was coming separately so I could get them as soon as possible! Argh! I called

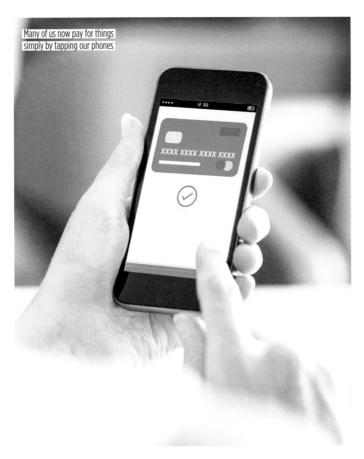

Many of us now pay for things simply by tapping our phones

to ask for the order to come together but was told that wasn't an option – I couldn't believe it. Then, one by one, my parcels arrived – sometimes two in one day from separate drivers! Think of all the extra emissions released on the journeys.

It is time to slow things down and rethink how and why we purchase things. Every single thing we buy needs energy and resources to produce it, then it has to be packaged and transported. And when we are done with it, it needs to be disposed of. The impact of our existing consumer habits is unsustainable. We are running out of resources and the space to dispose of them. It's estimated that by 2030 we could run out of landfill space in the UK. So the actions we take in this next decade are really important.

Put simply, buying less will save you money, reduce waste and benefit the environment. So how can we start to live a more minimal life in a world that tells us we need more?

I've already mentioned the Eight Rs hierarchy on page 56. But there's another one we can use to help us make better decisions when buying. Introducing… the BUYERARCHY of needs, based on a design by Sarah Lazarovic.

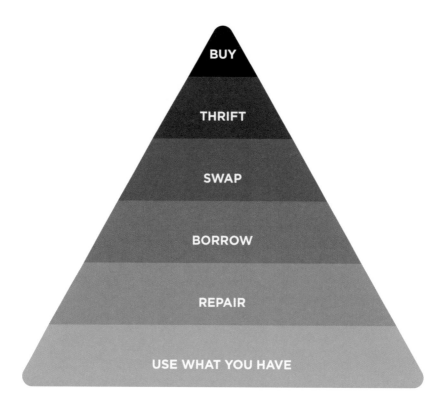

You start at the bottom with using what you have, and work your way up until you have exhausted all options and buying (with intention) is the only choice left. This framework can be applied to almost anything you would normally buy, and it is a great way of saving money. I've been using it the most for clothes shopping – there is more on that later in this chapter.

- ***Use what you have.***
  It sounds obvious, but the first thing we should always do is use what we already have. Whether that is food, clothes, toiletries, appliances, furniture or tools, make good use of what is already in your possession, and look after things well to make them last as long as possible.

  But first you need to know what you actually have. It's hard to retrieve an item if you don't know whether it's in the loft, garage or stuffed in a cupboard in your spare (junk) room!

Just like in the bathroom and in your kitchen cupboards, it's a good idea to do a stocktake of what you have. If, during your stocktake, you find lots of items you don't want any more, give them a new life by repurposing them or giving them to other people. Old sheets can be cut up to become reusable paper towels, empty jam jars can be used as vases and worn-out wellies can make unique plant pots. But if you really have no use for something, here's what you can do instead of throwing it away (remember there is no such place as away!).

- Give them to friends or family who will actually use them.

- Sell them on eBay or at car boot sales.

- Offer them for free on sites such as Freecycle or on Facebook Marketplace – you can also sell on Facebook too.

- Take them to a charity shop – but make sure the items are in good nick and check that the shop can actually sell them, rather than dumping the bags outside when the shop is closed. If a charity shop has more than they can sell, the items might end up going to landfill anyway, and they have to pay to get rid of the rubbish.

- **Repair.**
  If something you own breaks or wears out, what do you do? Chances are you throw it out and buy a new one, because that's so easy to do these days. In fact, many items are not made to last. This is known as planned obsolescence – where items have a predetermined shelf life so we have to buy more. Companies don't make it easy to find out how to fix a product that is broken, either – but there is good news!

In June 2021 the Right To Repair Act came into force. This means manufacturers will have to make spare parts available for items such as washing machines, fridges and TVs and the repairs need to be possible using everyday tools rather than tools specific to that company.

When our vacuum cleaner broke a couple of years ago, my husband tried to fix it. He is pretty handy, but he couldn't suss it out. We looked on YouTube for a video, which is usually a winner but he still couldn't fix it and we thought we'd have to buy a new one. Then we had a brainwave – maybe the manufacturer could help! He called Dyson and a really helpful lady video-called him to troubleshoot the issue. That saved the vacuum – and saved us the £250 cost of a new one! I know we are all busy people, but a 10-minute phone call saved us hundreds of pounds and lots of time. We would have had to research a new one online or go to the shops to find one.

I don't know about you but I love the idea of bringing something old and tattered back to life. We are fans of Drew Prichard's show *Salvage Hunters*, where he finds antiques hidden in people's sheds and his team bring them back to their former glory – it's amazing. I'm pretty good at sewing, so I can mend clothes, toys, make cushion covers and, at a push, I could produce a pair of curtains. But if you don't feel confident in your skills, you can usually find a 'dummy's guide' to pretty much anything (apart from our hoover issue, it seems!) on YouTube. My husband finds video tutorials all the time for plumbing issues, tiling, repairing phones and other appliances.

Alternatively, how about visiting a repair cafe to learn new tips or tricks? These events are starting to pop up around the UK. They usually take place once a month, and skilled volunteers go along to help people with repairs – from sewing on buttons to fixing toasters. In 2018, repair cafes around the world prevented an estimated 350,000 products from going to waste! Visit repaircafe.org to find out if there is one near you.

- **Borrow.**
If you need something for a one-off use, can you borrow it from a friend or neighbour? We've fallen out of this habit over the years – instead feeling like we need to own things ourselves. But we already 'borrow' without really thinking about it when we book holidays via Airbnb – we are literally borrowing someone else's house for a bit to experience a different part of the country or the world. And, of course, we are all familiar with borrowing books from a library. So it's not so strange to apply this concept to household tools or appliances.

For example, if you need a drill to do a bit of DIY, do you really need to go out and buy one? Most drills cost upwards of £35 (and let's be honest, the best ones are a whole lot more than that) so, if you are only using one every now and again, you'll save yourself money by borrowing from a friend or neighbour – not to mention the resources used to make, transport and package the drill.

We often borrow things from our own neighbours, especially socket sets, blades for saws and things like ladders and strimmers. I've even borrowed paint before! Choosing paint colours is hard, and tester pots cost money. So if you like the colour of your neighbour's hallway or kitchen walls, ask if they have any leftover paint that you can try.

I've been known to borrow food too. I'm good at planning meals but not great at checking what we have in the cupboards. I'll be halfway through making a Quorn spag bol and realise I have no spaghetti. I won't drive to the shop to get some, I'll just ask a neighbour. One day we will repay the favour – promise!

> **'I'VE BORROWED LADDERS, SOCKET SETS, PAINT AND FOOD FROM NEIGHBOURS'**

As more people aim to live sustainably, sharing 'libraries' are beginning to pop up all over the country. They allow you to borrow a huge range of items for free or for a small daily or weekly fee. These can include wood-working tools, tents, sewing machines and pasta makers. This saves you loads on the purchase price of the product, ensures that the item gets a full lifetime of use – and it also frees up space in our homes. Search online (using 'share shop', 'library of things' and 'borrow not buy') to see what is available in your local area.

This is also a great way to try out appliances if you are considering investing in something second-hand or new. I'm obsessed with watching videos of people having their sofas and carpets cleaned and want to buy my own machine. But I shall resist and hire one instead. It's the same with patio cleaners. People buy them, but use them only once a year – if that!

- *Swap.*
  Swapping can seem more accessible than borrowing for some people because it feels like a more equal exchange of goods. When you have finished a book, can you swap with a friend rather than buying a new one? See page 190 on swapping clothes, too.

Buying preloved items gives them a new life

• ***Thrift (buy second-hand).***

Inevitably, there will be a time when you need to replace something that can't be fixed. Rather than buying new, could you source something second-hand? Or pre-loved, as I like to call it! Spread the love.

Buying second-hand keeps items in the system for longer, saving them from going to landfill, and it cuts back on the resources needed to make new items. Charity shops, eBay, Freecycle and Facebook Marketplace are all great places to buy and sell things (or get them for free).

Many people say to me, "Well, the new item has already been made so I might as well buy it," but if we all shifted the way we shopped, the demand for new things would fall and manufacturers wouldn't produce so much.

'We've never bought a new car and never will!'

We've never bought a new car, for example. As you know, my husband doesn't like to splash the cash, and he always says that new cars lose 20% of their value the second you drive off the forecourt. He'd also never lease a car either, he'd rather pay outright for a second-hand one. If the price is right, our next car will be an electric one. For more on this, see the transport section on page 214.

My husband is a fan of second-hand cars

- ***Buy (with intention).***
  When you do need (or want) to buy something new, see if you can choose the most eco-friendly option. Think about where it came from, the materials used to make it, how long you will be able to use it for, and if it can be reused later on. Sometimes this may mean spending a little more on furniture or an appliance, but you are doing so in the knowledge that it will last you for many, many years – hopefully forever.

  I did this for my phone cover. It's only a tiny thing but the majority are made of plastic and will end up in landfill, taking years to decay. I spent a long time looking at reviews for products made from bamboo, recycled plastic and other eco materials and eventually chose 'the world's first compostable phone case' from a brand called Pela. It was more expensive than other phone covers but it was worth it to not feel guilty about buying unnecessary plastic.

  You can imagine how difficult it is for me to buy new things in our house anyway, so I am well practised in making do with what we have!

I am really impressed with my compostable phone case

THINK BEFORE YOU BUY

Whether it is clothes, gadgets or home accessories, here are some tips that have helped me pause for thought before buying anything new...

Give yourself 24 hours.

Just like any big decision, sleep on it. It's so easy to buy with the click of a button these days. So wait 24 hours to see how you feel about your purchase. Often, what seems like a must-have item in the moment won't be that important in a day or two.

Unsubscribe from marketing emails.

Seeing your favourite company offering a discount is a sure fire way to feed that pleasure part of the brain. Unsubscribe from their mailing lists (there is usually a very small 'unsubscribe' button at the bottom of the message) This will also reduce emissions from the email being sent – more on that on page 164.

Remove payment methods from your phone.

Having to physically input card details helps you to make more conscious decisions when buying. So unlink your card from your phone.

Say no to free things if you don't actually need them.

Just because someone is giving away a 12-foot trampoline on Facebook Marketplace, does NOT mean you have to go and take it. Only say yes to free things if it is actually something you can make good use of.

Could you buy nothing new for a week?

Set yourself the task to only buy food and essentials for a week. If you get through a week, could you extend it to two?

REDUCE YOUR FASHION FOOTPRINT

I wanted to dedicate a whole section to our wardrobes because we all need to wear clothes – so it's an area of our lives where we can make big changes to help the planet. You might be familiar with the term 'fast fashion' – which is defined as inexpensive clothing produced rapidly by mass-market retailers in response to the latest trends. Fast fashion has made shopping for clothes much more affordable, but these bargain buys come at a huge cost to the planet and the health of the workers making them.

The environmental impact of what we wear might not be as obvious as that of the transport or agriculture sectors, but the fashion industry actually accounts for 10% of all greenhouse gas emissions. It's also the second-largest consumer of water in the world (after agriculture) and pollutes water with microplastics, chemicals and clothing dye.

China and Bangladesh are the two largest fashion manufacturing hubs in the world, and most of the clothes made there end up in Western-world fashion stores. Unfortunately, many of the factories are sweatshops – defined as factories that violate labour laws. They have poor working conditions, unfair wages and hours, and some use child labour. When you realise the true 'cost' of fast fashion, buying that £12 top doesn't seem quite so appealing.

These cheaper items of clothing are not made to last either. The average life of an item of clothing these days is 2.2 years in the UK, but I'd say many thin tops don't last even that long. Some tops go out of shape after one or two washes! The fact that they are so cheap means we don't value them as much as more expensive items, so may think nothing of throwing them away.

They really don't make clothes like they used to. For my 30th birthday party I had an 80s-theme fancy-dress party and the best outfit by far was my Grandma's. She still had clothes from the 80s that were in tip-top condition, so she wore a black velvet jacket with awesome shoulder pads. I made my outfit – a Rubik's cube – from a cardboard box and my twin brother came as Zippy from Rainbow (an outfit he has repurposed for almost every fancy dress party since – Halloween Zippy, fairy Zippy, lion Zippy…)

?

DID YOU KNOW?

- The fashion industry accounts for 10% of all emissions.

- Global emissions from textile production are equivalent to 1.2 billion metric tons of CO_2 – more than the carbon footprint of international flights & shipping combined!

- 150 million trees are cut down every year to make our clothes.

- The fashion industry uses 93 billion cubic metres of water every year – enough to meet the consumption needs of five million people.

AROUND 350,000 METRIC TONS OF CLOTHES, WITH AN ESTIMATED VALUE OF £140 MILLION, GO TO LANDFILL EVERY YEAR IN THE UK.

It's thought that we now own five times the amount of clothes that our grandparents did and that clothing production has roughly doubled since 2000. That's partly because clothes are now so cheap, but also because brands release new 'collections' several times a year. We are encouraged to buy more and more to keep up with the latest trends.

Contrary to what many people believe, having a sustainable wardrobe doesn't have to mean paying more for expensive ethical brands (although that is one option). Instead, you focus on keeping the clothes you do have for longer and buying second-hand – which actually saves you money.

Let's start to put the brakes on fast fashion with these tips...

- ***Shop your wardrobe.***
  Get familiar with all the clothes you own. We often think we've exhausted all outfit options, but the truth is, we wear only a fraction of the clothes we have in our wardrobes.

  Have a sort through yours and see what is hiding away in drawers or at the back of your wardrobe – you might be pleasantly surprised. In mine I've even found brand-new clothes with the tags still on. Usually they're bargains that I have hidden away from my husband and then forgotten about!

  While looking through, you might find things that no longer fit you (we all have that pair of trousers that is two sizes too small that we 'might' fit into one day!) or clothes that you just don't like any more. Whatever you do, don't throw them in the bin. 350,000 metric tons of clothes end up in landfill in the UK every year!

?

DID YOU KNOW?

- British people buy more clothes per person than any other nationality in Europe.

- If we carry on as we are, it is estimated that by 2030 clothing consumption will have increased globally by 63% (from 62 million metric tons to 102 million metric tons).

- We wear 20% of our clothes 80% of the time.

- ***Unwanted doesn't have to mean unworn.***
  Donate good-quality clothes to a friend or charity shop. Or sell them at car-boot sales or online on sites such as eBay, Vinted or Swopped so they have a second life.

'Donate any clothes you no longer want to a friend, a charity shop or sell them on so they have a second life'

Let's also normalise re-wearing outfits! Fast fashion has created the belief that we need a new outfit for every occasion. But how often do you remember what your friend wore last time you saw them? Almost never. And if you did notice and they happened to wear the same thing again, would you care? No.

I used to be guilty of this – I always felt like I had to have something new every time I went to a birthday party or wedding. I'd wear it once then it would sit in my wardrobe wondering if it was ever going to be worn again. I realised how crazy this was. One year I went to five weddings. They were all different friendship groups so I wore the same outfit to all five – saving me money and also helping to save the planet! You may have spotted me wearing the same outfit multiple times on TV too.

Once you are familiar with what you have in your wardrobe, you can get creative with how you pair items and look for new ways to style old clothes. Let's not forget shoes here either! I keep mine in boxes and write what they are on the outside so I don't forget what I have. One of my friends has a great tip – she takes photos of her shoes and sticks them to the inside of her wardrobe door so she can see what she has. I have to confess that I still have boots I haven't worn because I always resort to my old faithfuls.

- ***Borrow from a friend.***
  Let's be honest, what we already own might not always cut it for a special occasion. If you need a one-off item for a wedding or big party, or even just a night out with friends, why not ask a similar-size friend (or sibling, colleague or neighbour!) if you can have a rummage through their clothes and borrow something? It's still 'new to you', and means the outfit is getting more wear than it might do normally. You can offer the favour back when they are after something 'new' to wear too. I've borrowed shoes, bags and clothes from friends and I often lend my lovely evening dresses to friends.

'I often lend my lovely evening dresses to friends'

When I am in the studio, I usually wear clothes that are borrowed from brands and then sent them back. If the clothes are bought in, we make sure as many as possible are from sustainable and ethical brands.

'WHEN I AM IN THE STUDIO, I USUALLY WEAR CLOTHES THAT ARE BORROWED FROM BRANDS AND THEN SEND THEM BACK. IF THE CLOTHES ARE BOUGHT IN, WE MAKE SURE AS MANY AS POSSIBLE ARE FROM SUSTAINABLE AND ETHICAL BRANDS'

- *Swap shop.*

We're so used to switching up our clothes that we can feel like something is 'old' long before it has actually worn out.

If you're not a fan of wearing the same outfit over and over, then swapping is a great way to get something new without spending any money. How about arranging with a friend to swap an item of clothing every few months? That way, you're encouraging someone else to think more sustainably when it comes to their wardrobe, too.

There are also online platforms that offer the option of swapping – it's sometimes called swishing – clothes with strangers. On apps such as Swopped or Nuw, you earn credit from the clothes that you 'sell' to use on clothes from other users that they have in their online wardrobe. There's also a fantastic new subscription swap site for children's clothes called The Little Loop (thelittleloop.com) – you may have seen them featured on *Dragons' Den*! Prices start at £18 a month for 6-7 items to start, then you keep them for as long as you need them (which often isn't that long because kids grow out of clothes so quickly!) before swapping the items an unlimited amount of times. This saves SO many clothes from being thrown away or just sitting in the loft unworn.

> **33% OF WOMEN CONSIDER AN OUTFIT OLD AFTER ONLY THREE WEARS.**

- *Hire.*

When you think about hiring clothes, you might conjure up images of Hollywood celebrities wearing designer gowns on the red carpet, but it's becoming a more mainstream affair these days – and affordable too. I think it is a great option for one-off events, when you want something special but you know you might not wear it again.

Check out online rental stores such as Hirestreet, where you can find well-known brands such as ASOS, French Connection and Lavish Alice. You can rent items for as little as £8 for four days, which saves you money on the RRP and helps save the planet. On the app By Rotation, you can rent clothes from other people, as well as loaning out your own.

If you are someone who enjoys wearing lots of different outfits, then subscribing to a rental service could be a great eco-friendly idea for you. You can pay monthly subscriptions and you'll be sent different items to wear and return each month.

If you want a designer outfit for a really special occasion, then Hurr is a great site. We often use it for hiring in clothes for my TV appearances.

- ***Choose preloved clothes.***
  Inevitably, there will be times when you want or need to buy more clothes, especially everyday items. When you do, could you opt for second-hand instead of new? This used to be a niche market but it has become much more mainstream in recent years, and you can now find 'preloved', 'retro' or 'vintage' clothing in far more places than your local charity shops.

  Buying second-hand is the antidote to fast fashion. It gives clothes their full life – which saves on resources to make new ones and keeps them out of landfill for longer. The clothes are still new to your wardrobe, and it can be just as exciting to buy something preloved as something brand-new – not to mention cheaper!

  Also, if we all start to buy more second-hand items, it will push brands to make longer-lasting clothes. If what we look for in clothes is longevity, then the demand for flimsy, fast-fashion items won't be so high. Remember, if we all do our bit, we can make a big difference!

GREAT NEWS!

Some high-street stores, such as Asda, have started to include preloved clothing collections as part of their commitment towards sustainable fashion. Higher-end fashion chains such as Cos and Selfridges also have second-hand stores online.

A quick reminder here that the idea is to buy only when you actually need something, and not just for the sake of it, but try some of these options when you go looking for something that's 'new to you'…

– Charity shops.
They get a bad rap, but if we are happy to offload bags of our unwanted clothes at charity shops, then we should shop from them too. How about every time you drop something off, you buy something in return? You never know what you might find. When I presented the weather on the BBC, I bought a lot of my on-screen wardrobe in charity shops. Smart jackets can be really expensive – I managed to find an LK Bennett one for £20 instead of £200! And I once found a pair of trainers for Charlotte (the exact ones she had) one size up and they were £5 rather than £35.

'I managed to find an LK Bennett jacket for £20 instead of £200!'

– Vintage or retro stores. The special thing about vintage shops is you can find totally unique pieces – the opposite of fast fashion.

– Shop online. Technology has made second-hand clothes shopping much easier than it used to be. What would have taken hours of trawling through charity shops can now be done in minutes. Plus you can search for specific items that you've seen from well-known brands. Some great options are eBay, Etsy, Preloved, Vinted and Depop, as well as Facebook Marketplace. Kidswear Collective is a lovely website I've used to find beautiful clothes for Charlotte. They stock a lot of designer items, which I would never pay full price for.

I'm not saying never buy from fast-fashion stores again, but do stop to think before you do, and weigh up if there might be a more sustainable option. Maybe you will choose to buy second-hand 25% of the time. That kind of change still makes a big difference if we all chip in and do our bit.

THE 30-WEAR TEST

Okay, so you've got your eye on a dress from a high-street store. It's not made from a particularly sustainable material but you love it – should you buy it? Ask yourself if you will wear it 30 times. If you won't, then it would be better to go through the buying options listed above instead. If you will wear it at least 30 times, then buy the dress and don't feel too guilty about it!

- **If buying new, try to choose the most sustainable option.**
Just like when buying any 'new' item in your life, do your research and see if you can choose the most sustainable option within your budget. Clothes from sustainable brands are understandably more expensive than fast-fashion brands because of the materials used and how much the workers are paid to make them. If you spend a little more, you will love it more and look after it more, meaning it will last longer.

If you can, support local small businesses, and choose natural or recycled fabrics that are free from chemicals and dyes (see below).

Material matters.
Let's look at some of the most common fabrics that our clothes are made of...

- **Synthetic fabrics such as polyester, nylon and acrylic.**
The problem with synthetic fabrics is that they are made from fossil fuels (just like plastic). Producing polyester releases two to three times more carbon emissions than cotton, and the production of nylon releases nitrous oxide, which causes 300 times more warming than carbon dioxide and stays in the atmosphere for 100 years.

Because synthetic fabrics are a type of plastic, it also means they take years to break down in landfill and they contribute to the shocking amount of plastic in the sea (more on microfibres on the next page).

Consider investing in a GuppyFriend Washing Bag. This is a bag that you put your synthetic fabrics in before you wash them. Tests show that the bag stops 99% of microfibres entering the water system. Fibres that build up in the bag should be thrown away in your normal rubbish.

? DID YOU KNOW?

- Half of clothes sold by online fashion brands are made from 'virgin plastic' such as polyester, nylon and acrylic.

- Washing clothes releases 500,000 tons of microfibres into the ocean each year, the equivalent of 50 billion plastic bags.

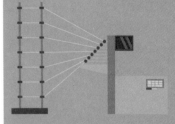

MICROFIBRES

Microfibres from synthetic clothes, such as nylon, polyester and acrylic, are a major cause of ocean pollution. Every time we wash these materials they shed millions of tiny plastic fibres that get through the water treatment plants and into the sea. In fact, microfibres from clothing account for 35% of all microplastics found in the ocean. Just like microplastics (see page 52), they are ingested by sea creatures and can make their way up the food chain and end up in human bodies, too.

- **_Cotton_**

  The production of cotton releases far fewer emissions than synthetic fabrics and, because it is a plant-derived fabric, it's also biodegradable. But it comes with its own environmental impact – the huge amount of water, pesticides, fertilisers and insecticides needed to grow it.

  Cotton uses more pesticides and insecticides to grow than any other single major crop in the world

- **_Denim_**

  Jeans are a staple of our wardrobe and never go out of fashion. In the UK, 70 million pairs are sold every year. Denim is made of cotton, which uses crazy amounts of water to grow, and the dye used to colour the jeans also pollutes water systems.

- **_Viscose (rayon)_**

  Viscose is the most popular type of rayon – a fibre made from regenerated cellulose, such as wood pulp (usually from eucalyptus trees). It's natural rather than synthetic, but turning the cellulose into fibre requires a lot of energy, chemicals and water. Another major issue with this type of fabric is deforestation. Only a small percentage is made from sustainable sources (see Lyocell, right).

COLOURFUL CLOTHES

They may look bright and breezy, but our coloured clothes are harming the planet. Textile dyeing and 'finishing' is one of the biggest water polluters on our planet. Clothes are repeatedly dunked in vats of dye to ensure the colours bind to the fabric and don't fade out, then chemicals or treatments are applied to give them a certain feel or look. In countries where regulations aren't as strict as ours, toxic waste water from clothing factories is dumped directly into rivers, posing a danger to aquatic life as well as the people living along the river banks.

- **Which fabrics get the thumbs up?**

  - **Linen** is made from flax, which needs only rainwater to grow and it doesn't require lots of chemicals in the production. In its undyed state it is biodegradable, so will break down when the item has come to the end of its life.

  - **Organic cotton** uses 71% less water to grow than conventional cotton (see left) and no harmful pesticides, fertilisers or insecticides are involved in the process.

  - **Bamboo** is a popular sustainable fabric but it is not quite as eco-friendly as some people think. It grows quickly and easily, and doesn't need lots of pesticides or fertilisers. But turning the hard bamboo canes into fibres takes a lot of energy and strong chemicals, which are harmful to workers and waterways.

  - **Lyocell** (Tencel) is a way of producing rayon (see left) that is more eco-friendly because it uses sustainably sourced wood and operates a 'closed loop' system – all the chemicals used in the process are recycled. Because it is a plant-derived fabric, it is biodegradable and doesn't need bleaching because it is naturally white. You may have heard of Tencel, which is the name used for Lyocell by the company Lenzing AG.

- **Recycled materials**

  As they try to become more sustainable, many brands are using recycled plastic to make fabrics such as recycled polyester. It's a great way to divert plastic bottles from landfill or the ocean, and requires far fewer resources to make, which generates fewer greenhouse gases. But it is still a non-biodegradable fabric that will take years to break down, and it will still contribute to microplastics in the ocean.

?

DID YOU KNOW?

- It takes over 2,700 litres of water to make a cotton shirt – the amount you would drink in around 3.5 years.

- It takes about 10,000 litres of water to produce a pair of jeans.

- Producing one pair also creates as much greenhouse gas as driving a car for 80 miles.

- *Keep clothes around for longer.*
  To get the most out of the clothes you own, you have to take good care of them. From washing less frequently to buying better hangers, there's a lot we can do…

  – *Wash clothes only when you need to.* Washing too often can cause damage to the fibres and decrease the lifespan of your clothes. Most things, apart from underwear, don't need to be washed after one wear. Jeans, for example, do not need to be washed every time you wear them. I usually wear leggings and I don't wash them unless they're actually dirty. I could probably go a month without putting a wash on because I have a lot of clothes – but because my husband is so tall, he has fewer clothes.

  – *Spot-clean stains.* If you get a mark on a top, can you spot-clean it rather than washing the whole item? Washing-up liquid is great for cutting through grease stains!

  – *Wash at a lower temperature.* This is not only better for the environment, but it is kinder to the fabric and reduces colour fading.

  – *Air-dry rather than tumble-dry.* As long as it's not pouring down, it's always a better idea to hang your washing on the line rather than using a tumble-dryer. The heat impairs the quality of the fabric and it's one of the ways in which microfibres are shed from our clothes and make their way to the ocean (see page 194).

Line-drying your clothes will reduce their carbon footprint

Try to fix rather than throw away!

— Fix rather than throw away.

It's time that mending our clothes came back into fashion! This could mean anything from sewing a button back on to taking your shoes to a cobbler to get them re-heeled. As I said earlier, I am pretty nifty with a needle! If you don't feel confident about sewing, could you ask a friend or family member with the skills? Or you can find some great tutorials on YouTube. See page 180 for info on repair cafes.

— Repurpose.

If an old T-shirt really has seen better days, can you turn it into cotton pads for removing your make-up or use it as a cleaning cloth? You can also keep hold of an old battered pair of jeans and use the fabric to patch up other pairs.

— Invest in better hangers.

Now, the idea in this book is NOT to buy more things, but if you notice that your plastic or wire hangers are misshaping the shoulders of your clothes and causing droopy collars, then it could be a good idea to invest in some padded hangers. Donate unwanted hangers to charity shops, or give them to retailers who might be able to recycle them.

For info on eco laundry detergents, see page 157.

DID YOU KNOW?

- Washing laundry at 60°C and drying it in the tumble-dryer produces the equivalent of 3.3kg of CO_2. If you switch to washing at 30°C and line-drying, that amount goes down to 0.6kg.

8.

CELEBRATIONS

Who doesn't love a party? I know I do. Whether it is a birthday bash, Christmas celebration or a baby shower, it's so much fun to get people together and have a good time, especially after the last couple of years! But these celebrations – especially Christmas – can be some of the most wasteful times of the year.

Think about a 'classic' party. We've got bunches of balloons on plastic ribbons, presents wrapped in sparkly wrapping paper and shiny bows, disposable plates, cups and cutlery, plastic trays full of store-bought, pre-cut fruit, veg and nibbly bits. And at the end of the

day, it all gets thrown into one big black bin bag and sent to landfill. And that's not even thinking about the unwanted presents that might be wrapped up inside the sparkly paper!

Planning a party takes a lot of work, and making it eco-friendly adds a little bit more pressure – but it is totally doable. When I organised my 40th birthday party last year, I tried my best to not create unnecessary waste. I hired a venue that also did the catering, so I ordered the minimum amount of food to make sure we weren't left with loads leftover at the end of the night. I also decided not to have decorations because I didn't want to buy anything new or single-use. And for the kids, I bought huge bags of pick 'n' mix from the cash and carry and decanted them into glass jars that I'd saved at home. It kept the little ones happy while the adults partied, and it really cut back on the plastic used up if you buy loads of little bags of sweets.

That's just a few examples of the things you can consider when it comes to celebrations, but there are lots of other actions we can take to minimise our impact on the environment, while still having an amazing time with friends and family…

- ***Send virtual invites.***
  Think of the trees and invite people by email or text. Doing things digitally does have its own environmental impact (see page 160 for more) but significantly less than printing invites on paper then sending them in the post. The first time I did this was for Charlotte's christening because I'd left it too late to design an invitation, get copies printed then post them out. Initially, it felt a bit impersonal to send a virtual invite, but it was so much easier – and a lot of my friends now do the same. I design mine using a picture collage app. All you have to do is find a nice picture, add the words you want, then you can send it out over WhatsApp or email it to people. It takes 10 minutes max, and it's easier for people to RSVP and for them to find the event details nearer the time. I've done it for all Charlotte's birthdays and for my 40th.

- ***Say bye-bye to balloons.***
  I will never buy another single-use balloon ever again. There, I've said it! I know a balloon arch looks great and it's hard to imagine a party without balloons, but do you ever think

DID YOU KNOW?

- An extra 30% of rubbish is produced and discarded over the festive period.

- The average British adult spends £500 on Christmas gifts.

- At Christmas, 54 million platefuls of food are wasted – see page 93 for tips to reduce food waste!

I had sweets in glass jars at my 40th to cut back on plastic

REUSE JAM JARS TO HOLD SWEETS, BREAD STICKS, CARROT AND CELERY STICKS, TEA LIGHTS OR SMALL BUNCHES OF FLOWERS.

about what happens to them and the ribbons they're attached to once the party is over? They get thrown straight in the bin or, if they're filled with helium, they can float off into the atmosphere and end up polluting our natural world. Latex balloons CAN be composted, but not many people do this. If foil balloons end up in landfill it's likely they will be blown away because they're so light. Then they can end up in rivers or oceans, where aquatic life can mistake them for food. It's best to avoid balloons altogether, but if you do get a foil balloon, either keep it to be reused again (yes, you can reuse them!) or recycle it properly (see page 252). Great eco-friendly alternative decorations are…

- Paper fans
- Paper bunting
- Honeycomb balls
- Paper chains
- Tissue paper pom-poms
- Fresh flowers

'I'm never buying another single-use balloon ever again.
There, I've said it!'

For Charlotte's birthday last year, we had colourful bunting and paper flowers, which I have packed away nicely ready to be used next year. My husband had been getting really moany about me keeping hold of them because he says it clutters up the cupboards, but I pointed out that it saves us money (always a winner with him!) It's no different than putting up Christmas decorations then taking them down and packing them away until the next year. The important thing is to remember where you put them. It's no good putting them in a 'safe place' and then forgetting where that place is…

Any decorations we use that have a birthday age on, or are themed (such as Peppa Pig or Postman Pat) I'll pass on to a friend so that they can reuse them.

DID YOU KNOW?

- A party for 30 people can send more than 100 single-use items to a landfill site.

- It is estimated we use 4.7 billion plastic straws in England every year.

- ***Avoid single-use paper or plastic plates, cups and cutlery.***
  By now we all know that single-use plastic items are bad! But you might be thinking that paper plates are surely better? Unfortunately, as soon as paper plates come into contact with greasy or wet food, they can't be recycled because the residue on them would contaminate the paper recycling, so they have to be thrown out with the general waste. Consider using your own plates if you have enough, but if you are worried about them being broken you can invest in a set of child-safe plastic party dishes to be used again and again. Yes, they're plastic, but they can be reused for years, are hard to break and they're much easier to eat and drink from than paper versions.

I make an effort to not buy any single-use plastic items, but if you are searching for themed plates, cups and tablecloths, it's actually really hard to find anything that isn't disposable. I will buy one set of themed paper plates for the kids, then everyone else uses a plastic reusable set I found in IKEA, or real plates. I know the paper plates still can't be recycled if they have food residue on them, but at least they don't take hundreds of years to break down like plastic does.

We use reusable plastic plates for parties!

- ***Hire out party supplies.***

  A great planet-friendly idea is to rent plastic party plates, trays, bowls and cups. This encourages people to buy less and means the items get used to their full capacity. A friend of mine started doing this a few years ago. She bought some of the IKEA plates and bowls and then hired them out to people for kids' parties. It's a no-brainer really. You can rent them from as little as £10, which is the same or even less than you'd end up paying for single-use items. And you can still match them to your party theme by choosing pastel colours if it's princesses or unicorns and red or blue for football teams.

- ***Use reusable straws.***

  Plastic straws are one of the top 10 most commonly found items on coastal litter clean-ups around the world! Thankfully, you can't buy plastic straws in England now (apart from in pharmacies, for medical reasons) because of a ban that was introduced in October 2020.

  If you really want straws at a party, then you can get really nice paper ones – but they're still single-use and have to be thrown in the normal rubbish once they're wet. The best option is to choose reusable straws. We have a set of bamboo ones and Charlotte loves drinking fruit smoothies through them. You can also buy sets of 12 reusable silicone or metal ones, which come with a handy thin cleaning brush, for around £6.

Only choose biodegradable glitter

GOODBYE GLITTER

Glitter is not just annoying because it literally gets EVERYWHERE, it's also a real hazard for our natural world. It's made of lots of teeny, tiny bits of plastic, which means it's a microplastic in its original form – a huge problem for ocean life (see page 52). For the last couple of years, some UK retailers, including Morrisons and Waitrose, have pledged to not use glitter in any of their store-brand Christmas items, such as crackers and wrapping paper. If you do want glitter at a kids' party, or to use as make-up, look out for biodegradable versions. Glitter made from plant cellulose (rather than plastic) will decompose naturally in a compost bin, food-waste bin or even in soil.

- ### Ditch the party bags?

Sending people home with a little bag of 'treats' is a nice tradition, but one that is not really necessary. I have never made party bags for Charlotte's birthdays. Mainly because my husband thinks they're a waste of money (no surprise there, then), but also because they take lots of organising – parties are hard work at the best of times without the added stress!

'I give books instead of party bags at Charlotte's parties'

And, of course, they're usually just full of plastic that gets discarded. Perhaps a bottle of bubbles, a plastic toy that breaks within five minutes, a balloon, some sweets (wrapped in plastic, no doubt) and a piece of cake. Who really needs that? I now give books. I buy them in bulk, so it keeps the cost down, and it's a gift you know will get used. Some other eco alternatives are…

- Paper bags or cardboard boxes instead of plastic bags.
- A pack of seeds. This is a really lovely idea and will help kids connect with nature too. Charlotte absolutely loves helping me in the garden and at our allotment. For more on this, turn to page 121.
- Chocolate or sweets wrapped in foil or paper instead of plastic.
- Cardboard/wooden craft sets. For example, make your own cardboard aeroplane or a wooden bead jewellery kit.

Another idea is to arrange an 'experience' party, where kids (or adults!) take part in a craft activity – such as decorating a ceramic plate or designing their own T-shirt. That then becomes their gift to take away.

- *Planet-friendly party food.*

  Classic store-bought party food comes in lots of packaging (usually plastic), so the best thing to do here is to make your party food from scratch if you can. There are loads of tips on how to make more sustainable food choices and about supermarket shopping on page 80. But some party-friendly ideas are...

  - Buy loose fruit and veg and chop it up as finger food instead of buying the pre-cut versions which come in plastic tubs.
  - Make your own sandwiches. I organised an afternoon tea for Charlotte one year and we made the sandwiches, the scones and the cakes together. It was a really fun activity, reduced the amount of plastic packaging we would have used from store-bought sandwiches and cakes, and it was much cheaper.
  - Make your own dips instead of buying them in plastic tubs.
  - Buy large sharing bags of crisps to minimise the amount of packaging.
  - Choose drinks in glass bottles or cans instead of plastic.

  If you do end up buying the odd item in plastic packaging, make sure you recycle it properly. Similarly, dispose of any food waste (although try to limit this!) in your food-waste or compost bin to reduce your impact on the environment.

> **'I'VE BEEN KNOWN TO GO THROUGH PEOPLE'S BINS AT PARTIES TO SEPARATE THEIR RUBBISH'**

- *Have clearly labelled rubbish bins.*

  We may have the best intentions to create no rubbish at all, but a party is always going to create some waste. Make it easy for people to know where to put their food waste and anything recyclable to avoid it all going in one bin and ending up in landfill. I have three bin bags at a party and make a loud announcement about which is for rubbish, which is for food waste and which is for recycling (yes, parties at my house are fun!). I have even been known to go through other people's bins at parties to separate their rubbish.

THE GIFTS

We've covered the celebrations themselves, but what about the presents? So many gifts are bought for the sake of it (because we think we can't possibly go to a party empty-handed!) and go unused or end up in the bin. The prospect of this actually used to make me feel quite anxious in the run-up to celebrations because I just didn't want to end up with lots of 'stuff' that's not wanted, can't be returned and ends up in the 'regift drawer' (yes, we've all got one!). If it's your birthday or celebration, I think the best approach is to…

- ***Make a gift list.***
  It can feel really uncomfortable asking for things for your birthday, but I've become a bit of a pro at it now. In fact, people often joke that they're scared to go 'off-list' if they do see something they think I might like, just in case I don't! I think gift lists make total sense – you know you are getting something you want, and the person giving the gift knows you'll love it. So can you get into the habit of sending a list to family and friends? If you feel awkward about it, then explain that you want to start the conversation about creating less waste – and this is one way of doing it. It only takes one person in a group of friends or family to start this and I bet everyone will get on board. And if they don't, then at least you tried.

  I did this for Charlotte's fourth birthday too. She has so much stuff already, so I asked people to stick to a list of selected things (basically, not plastic tat!), or to get vouchers or experience days.

UNWANTED GIFTS?

Here's what you can do with them... First up, please, PLEASE, don't throw them in the bin. As I've said in many chapters of the book, one person's trash is another person's treasure!

Exchange it for something you DO want.

If you have a gift receipt, you can take the item back to the store it came from and exchange it for something of equal value that you will actually use, or a gift voucher/card. If you don't have the receipt, some shops will exchange an item without a receipt (at the price it is currently on sale at). Or, you could be brave and ask the person who bought it for you for their proof of purchase...

Regift.

Would that brightly coloured scarf your aunt gave you better suit a friend? If so, pass it on to them when it is their birthday – or just to make their day! In my antenatal group, one mum suggested we regift items that our children no longer wanted or played with. It's giving a new life to the toy and also clearing some space at home. Win-win.

Give to charity.

If you donate your present to a charity shop, there is more chance that someone will actually buy it because they want it, and the money from the sale will go towards a good cause. Now doesn't that make you feel good?

Donate to a refuge.

Bottles of lotions and potions are among some of the most unused presents we get (see the bathroom section on page 124 for more!). Charities such as Refuge and Women's Aid will usually take everyday essential toiletries, such as shampoo, shower gel and make-up – as well as new underwear, pyjamas and clothes – to help women and children escaping violence. Visit Refuge.org.uk and Womensaid.org.uk to find your local centre.

When it comes to buying gifts for other people, here are a few ideas to make present-giving a little bit more planet-friendly…

- **_Give gifts you know people want._**
  We have enough pressures in life, why make 'choosing the perfect present' one of them? I know this can seem like it takes the magic out of celebrations, but next time it is someone's birthday, can you ask them what they actually need or want? That way there is less chance of your carefully-thought-out-but-possibly-unwanted gift sitting in a cupboard unused or, even worse, being thrown in the bin.

  My husband, who we all know is super-grumpy, never wants anything when I ask him. In the past I'd buy him things just for the sake of it and he would complain. So now I'll get something small, like a fancy bottle of booze I know he will enjoy, and then give him an IOU. Even if he does want something, he will NEVER let me buy it before Christmas – we have to wait for the sales!

  If you really do prefer to buy a surprise gift, then ask yourself these questions before purchasing:

  - Will they use the gift or am I buying it for the sake of it?
  - Is the item on sale and therefore appears more attractive?
  - Is it made well so it will last?
  - What is it made of and how is it packaged? (Try to avoid plastic!)

  For more tips on 'buying less', see page 174.

- **_Make your own gifts._**
  Add a personal touch to your gift-giving and help the planet at the same time – homemade presents use less energy and resources than mass-produced products. You could make anything from cookies to candles. Think about what skills you have and put them to good use! A few years ago, one of my friends saved jars then filled them up with layers of the ingredients needed to make a cake. She tied a fancy ribbon around the jar and the gift tag had the instructions to make the cake, plus anything extra you'd need. It was so simple, but really effective. I've since seen these kits in shops and they cost around £10 – so it is much cheaper to make your own.

- **_Get 'green' gifts._**
  If you do want to purchase something, then what about an item that will help someone be more environmentally friendly? There are many suggestions throughout this book, from reusable metal water bottles to a set of reusable make-

up pads. You could even gift a copy of this book to someone to help them on their eco-journey!

'Charlotte asked for a litter picker for Christmas!'

For Christmas, I asked for a metal razor – no more plastic for me! And guess what Charlotte wanted… a litter picker! We've been on a few litter picks near our home, and you'd be surprised how much rubbish you find in a one-mile radius. Please either put your rubbish in the bin, or take it home to recycle!

- *Pre-loved presents.*
Second-hand doesn't have to mean second-rate. You can pick up some lovely preloved items from vintage stores, charity shops, local Facebook selling pages or online on selling sites such as eBay and Vinted. Often, the items are actually new but they're being sold on because they're unwanted.

'We bought Charlotte a second-hand princess castle from Facebook Marketplace for less than half its original price'

I'm very happy for Charlotte to have preloved items. She had a big plastic princess castle for her birthday one year which I found on Facebook Marketplace. It was less than half the original price, well looked after and the family were happy it was going to be loved again. Another year, we got her a second-hand bike, which was a quarter of the price! For more info on buying preloved, see page 182.

- *Favour small businesses.*
I know life is busy and Amazon is SO convenient for buying presents, especially when you need them the next day, but it's important that we support small and local businesses. Small brands put so much time, effort and money into creating their products, and if we don't support our local high street shops, they'll be at risk of shutting down.

- *Think outside the box…*
There are some unique gifts you can give people which don't have to involve a physical present…

  - *Adopt or sponsor an animal in the wild.* You can pay a monthly or yearly subscription to organisations such as Born Free and the World Wildlife Federation to adopt animals like penguins, lions and snow leopards. That way, you are helping support habitats around the world and the species that rely on them.

- *Buy a tree as a gift.* You can buy an actual tree for the person to plant in their own garden, or you can pay for a tree to be planted somewhere around the world. For the last two years I've bought a tree for everyone at *Good Morning Britain*. The first year they got an avocado tree planted in Africa, and last Christmas a mangrove in Madagascar. To be honest, when I decided to do this I thought there might be about 100 people at *GMB* but there are actually 280!!

Trees have many benefits to the planet. They provide oxygen, help to absorb carbon, provide food, give shelter to animals (and humans), help prevent soil erosion and can help to cool towns and cities.

'I bought everyone at Good Morning Britain a tree for Christmas'

I've also always given the gift of a physical tree to my friends' children when they are christened. Traditionally, it is an apple tree for boys and a pear tree for girls. It was really lovely to see one of my friend's boys eating an apple from their tree a few years later!

- *Say it with flowers.* For the last few years, rather than trying to think of something to buy my grandma for Christmas (because she doesn't really need anything!), all the grandkids have chipped in and we've sent her flowers at the start of every month. We get hers from M&S because she used to work there and wouldn't want them from anywhere else, but there are lots of companies that now send flowers in completely plastic-free packaging, such as Freddie's Flowers and Bloom And Wild. It's a really lovely way to let someone know you are thinking of them throughout the year.

- *Experience days and meals out.* Spending a day with friends and family can be much more meaningful than buying a physical gift. My husband and I started doing this for our birthdays about 10 years ago. We'll go to the theatre, have a night in a hotel or enjoy a lovely afternoon tea instead of buying presents. It's a nice way to extend your birthday celebrations too! Could you club together with friends to buy a spa day voucher, or pay for a fancy meal out?

IT'S A WRAP!

It's not just the gifts themselves that can cause a lot of unwanted waste – glittery wrapping paper, sparkly ribbons and shiny bows can be a disaster for the environment! They're single-use items (unless you save gift-wrap and bows from presents you've been given and use them later on – obviously I do!) and a lot can't be recycled because they contain glitter, foil or plastic. That means they end up in landfill, or they're mistakenly put in the recycling bin where they can contaminate whole batches of recycling.

Keep hold of gift bags you're given to use again

You may now be looking at your rolls of shimmering wrapping paper and fancy bows and thinking, uh oooh, this doesn't look recyclable. But don't panic – as always, the best thing to do is…

- **_Use what you have first._**
  Even if the paper and ribbons you have aren't recyclable, it's better they are used to wrap a gift beautifully than being put straight in the bin. Remember, don't waste anything! Once you've used up what you have, you can make more sustainable choices…

- **_Reuse!_**
  Save any gift bags, boxes, fancy paper or ribbon that your gifts are wrapped in to reuse on other people's presents. I keep all my gift bags and use them to give presents. I always leave the tags on when I store them away so I know I'm not giving a friend the same bag they gave me! When it's time to use them, snip off the old tag, add a homemade gift tag (see page 213) and ta-da, it's as good as new.

- **Find alternatives to wrapping paper.**
  Presents can look just as smart by using these to wrap them…

  - **Newspaper and magazine pages.** These can look really chic – in fact, a colleague wrapped all her presents in the pages of magazines and they looked great.

  - **Fabric.** I think it is a lovely idea to wrap presents in a satin scarf or other nice fabric that can be worn or reused by the recipient. Like getting two presents in one!

  - **Recycled brown paper.** You can get this from most post offices. It is easily recyclable and it doesn't have to be boring…

    Instead of using sparkly ribbons and bows, go for the rustic look by tying twine or reusable ribbon around your parcels. Add embellishments such as leaves, berries or dried oranges and cinnamon sticks. If you prefer patterned paper then you can create your own by using stampers and paint. I once wrapped presents in paper that Charlotte had drawn pictures on and painted. I've also used old boxes that Charlotte has painted. It's a fun activity to do with her, personalised and reduces waste.

- **Use tape sparingly…**
  Standard sticky tape, such a sellotape, is plastic and can't be recycled. Use as little as you can when wrapping presents. And always remove it from wrapping paper before you recycle it, as it can contaminate the paper recycling. Sellotape has now released a zero plastic, fully compostable tape, which is amazing, but you still have to take it off wrapping paper before you put it in the recycling. The best options are to use brown tape, which is paper recyclable, or ribbon which can be reused.

Remember, sticky tape is plastic so can't be recycled – make sure you take it off wrapping paper before you put it in the recycling bin!

> **CAN IT BE RECYCLED? DO THE SCRUNCH TEST!**
>
> The best way to check if wrapping paper can be recycled is to crumple a piece into a ball in your hand. If it stays scrunched up when you open your hand then it can be recycled. If it bounces back open then it can't be recycled. If your paper has glitter on it, then it can't be recycled, even if it scrunches. And the same goes for paper that is laminated or has gold or silver foil embellishments.

Me and Charlotte make our own gift tags from Christmas cards

CARDS

Sending cards is a lovely way to let people know you are thinking of them, but be careful what type of card you choose. As with wrapping paper, if a card has foil embellishments or glitter it can't be recycled, so opt for ones that are paper only. Even better, choose one that can be given a second life – you can buy 'plantable' cards that contain seeds and will grow into anything from carrots to wildflowers.

- ***Make your own gift tags***.
  If you are sent glittertastic cards then don't fret – they can be reused as gift tags for presents! Every year after Christmas, Charlotte and I cut up our cards to make really cute gift tags for the following year. If the cards have snowmen and Christmas trees on, for example, we'll cut around those shapes, then use a hole punch to make them into tags. If the card has more of a general festive scene, we'll cut out a triangle shape instead.

> ### SAVE YOUR STAMPS!
>
> Did you know you can donate used postage stamps to charities so they can be turned into funds? Simply cut around the stamp on the envelope (it doesn't matter if it has a postmark on it) leaving 1cm of envelope around the edges. Search online for charities that accept them (Amnesty, RNIB and Oxfam are a few that definitely do) then order a free, pre-paid envelope to be delivered to your house and then send them off.

9.

TRANSPORT

We all need to travel. Whether it's to the local shop, to work, to school, to visit family or to go on holiday. But how we get around makes a huge difference to our carbon footprint.

Transport accounts for 27% of the UK's total emissions – making it the most polluting sector! – with 99% of the emissions from the transport sector coming from road travel. It's also perhaps the most obvious way (to us) that we pollute our natural world, because we can physically see the exhaust fumes coming from the vehicles. We all know how horrible it is to walk down a busy road and breathe them in.

DID YOU KNOW?

- Carbon dioxide emissions from transport in the UK totalled 97.1 million metric tons in 2020.

- Transport produces 27% of the UK's total emissions. Of this, 91% comes from road transport vehicles.

- 77% of households in Great Britain have a car.

- Four out of every five miles travelled in the UK happens in a car.

- Just under half the population of England and Wales travel less than 3.1 miles to work. This would take 45 minutes to walk or 15 minutes to cycle.

While some of the emissions from transport come from the manufacture of the vehicles, the majority is from their use once they are on the road.

In 2020, emissions from the transport sector totalled 97.2 million metric tons. A huge amount, but that was actually 19.6% less than in 2019, largely due to the travel restrictions that came with the pandemic. We were told to work from home and to travel less, so we walked and cycled more, and we adjusted to not travelling abroad so easily. So we know that we are capable of travelling less when we need to…

So, what measures can we take to cut down our emissions from transport even further?

- ***Reduce the amount of car journeys you make.***
  Around 77% of households in Britain have a car, and it is by far the most popular form of transport. In 2019, 84% of journeys were made by car, van or taxi. By comparison, just 1% of trips were made by bicycle.

As vehicles become more efficient, the emissions from passenger cars have actually gone down in the last couple of decades. In 2002, cars produced 78 million metric tons of carbon dioxide equivalent, whereas in 2019, they produced 67.7 million metric tons. But they are still a major source of pollution – accounting for more than half of the total greenhouse gases from transport in the UK.

THE INTRODUCTION OF E10 PETROL AT UK FORECOURTS COULD CUT TRANSPORT EMISSIONS BY 750,000 METRIC TONS A YEAR – THE EQUIVALENT OF TAKING 350,000 CARS OFF THE ROAD, OR ALL THE CARS IN NORTH YORKSHIRE.

A huge part of our carbon footprint comes from the way we travel – so we should try to cut down on the journeys we make

'WE MADE A CONSCIOUS DECISION TO HAVE ONLY ONE CAR IN OUR FAMILY'

We made a conscious decision to have only one car in our family because I just couldn't justify having two based on the impact they have on the environment. And, well, you can probably guess why my husband didn't want two cars... it's cheaper! Our car is diesel and we will use it until it needs replacing, because as with all things on this eco-journey, it's not a case of getting rid of what you have and buying something new, it's better to wait until you NEED something new. When we do, our next car will be an electric or hybrid (see more on electric cars later in this chapter).

It takes a bit of planning (like many things on an eco journey), but we manage totally well with one. On a normal day, my husband uses it for work and I walk or get the bus if I need to go anywhere with Charlotte. If there are days when I need the car for longer journeys, my husband cycles to work or will catch a lift with someone else (see the points further on about public transport and car sharing). I do travel by hybrid

DID YOU KNOW?

- In England, 56% of the trips we make in the car are under five miles – which could easily be done on foot, by bike or on public transport.

- Nine out of 10 people breathe polluted air that exceeds WHO guidelines.

- In the UK, between 28,000 and 36,000 deaths a year are linked to air pollution.

- Cars in the UK emitted 67.7 million metric tons of carbon dioxide equivalent in 2019 – enough to power more than 8 million homes for a year.

car to and from work every day, but all the journeys are offset by ITV (meaning they pay money to schemes which remove the equivalent carbon dioxide from the atmosphere) and the company is starting to use fully electric cars, so lots of steps in the right direction.

It can be so easy to overuse the car. We've all had those times when we're feeling a bit tired and the weather isn't great, so we hop in the car to drive to the local shop instead of walking. You might think one little journey isn't going to make much difference, but it's these small journeys that all add up when we all do it all of the time. About 20% of all journeys in the UK are less than one mile – if we do them by car when we are able to walk or cycle then that's unforgivable!

Of course, I'm not going to suggest you give up your car – unless you live in a city where there are really good transport links, it's hard to get around without your own vehicle. But what if you reduce the number of journeys you make? Here are some suggestions…

– *Walk more.*

Another really obvious one! Research suggests that one in five car journeys we make are unnecessary. So whether it's that quick trip to the local shop to get bread, or dropping your kids off at school, could you leave the car at home for at least one of these journeys per week and walk instead? I promise you, once you start, you'll instantly feel the benefits of getting outside more and exercising too.

I walk one mile to pick up Charlotte from school, no matter the weather. You know what they say – there is no such thing as bad weather; just the wrong clothes! So the key is to be prepared. It takes me around 20-30 minutes each way, and it's become a really lovely bonding time with Charlotte. When she was younger, we'd look out for buses or 'nee-naws' or name the colour of cars. Now we look at the door numbers of houses or the number on the front of the buses, so it's also an educational time for her. We get to talk about her day too and more recently we have started litter-picking.

'I walk one mile to pick Charlotte up from school, no matter the weather!'

Charlotte kept pointing out the rubbish on the walk home, and she'd ask why people hadn't put it in the bin. I'd say, "I don't know, darling, some people are just a bit naughty!" and I told her we could get a litter picker to help tidy it up. So she added one to her Christmas list and was so happy when Father Christmas delivered it. The first time we used it, we picked up a whole bag of rubbish on our one-mile walk, and Charlotte said, "Mummy we are saving our planet!" I

Walking to and from school cuts our emissions – and we try to make the journey fun!

was so proud of her wanting to make a difference. Everyone who walked past said thank you, so this helped Charlotte feel like she was doing something good. I've never understood why people don't put their rubbish in the bin. And if it's recyclable, please take it home to recycle it properly! See page 244 for recycling tips.

The average distance from home to primary school in the UK is 1.6 miles. If your journey to school (or even to work) is similar and you usually drive, could you walk one day a week instead? It does mean you have to be ready to leave the house earlier, but it is worth it…

Let's use the average journey to primary school as an example (1.6 miles, so there and back is 3.2 miles), but I could just as easily be talking about a trip to the local shop or the train station. An average car emits approximately 228g of CO_2e per mile. If you walked 3.2 miles once a week, you'd save 37.93kg CO_2e a year that would have been released into the atmosphere. That's the same as 24 bags of rubbish being recycled instead of going to landfill, or 68,616 smartphones being charged.

Doesn't sound a lot? Think about how much it would be if EVERYONE walked one 3.2-mile journey a week instead of driving. There were 32 million cars registered in the UK in 2021. If every single one of those cars drove 3.2 miles less each week, it would be the equivalent of taking 263,968 cars off the road for a year! See, when we work together we can make a HUGE difference. So why stop at one day? Could you walk a short journey two or three days a week?

As with so many of the changes in the book, the benefits of walking over driving extend way beyond reducing carbon emissions. It will save you money in fuel (plus wear and tear on your car), it will make the air cleaner and the additional exercise will boost your health. It's recommended that we do a minimum of 150 minutes of moderate intensity (such as walking) exercise a week. That works out at around 22 minutes every day. This will reduce the risk of dementia, depression and stroke by 30%, breast cancer by 25%, bowel cancer by 45%, and type 2 diabetes by a whopping 50%. Walking 1km more, along with eating less meat and insulating more homes, is also one of the ways that could save the NHS up to £17 billion a year.

It takes around 25 to 30 minutes to walk 1.6 miles (let's call it an hour for a round trip), so you can easily exceed the daily target. If you prefer to count steps, then a 3.2-mile trip is around 6,200 steps – a good chunk out of the 10,000 many people aim for.

So, whether it is to get your morning paper, take the kids to school or head to your gym class, could you walk at least one of those journeys each week?

– *Ride a bike…*
…or a scooter or skateboard! Anything that gets you there that little bit faster than walking. If time is an issue for you, or your journey to work or into town is a bit too long to walk, could you cycle? Biking is around three times quicker than walking. So, using the 1.6-mile example from above, you could do it in 8 minutes (16 minutes there and back).

'MY HUSBAND TAKES CHARLOTTE TO SCHOOL ON THE BACK ON HIS BIKE EACH MORNING'

We love getting out on our bikes

We all bought bikes for a cycle campaign I was supporting in 2021 and we have really enjoyed going out as a family. We couldn't go far with Charlotte on her own bike because she is quite slow, so my husband bought a seat for her to go on his, and she loves it. They have a big horn to let people know they are coming – and everyone always smiles as they ride past. That's actually how my husband takes her to school in the morning. Then I collect her on foot in the afternoon.

We were not the only people to buy bikes last year. During the height of the pandemic, bike sales rose by 22%, so that means far more people now have bikes they can use instead of a car. In fact, we had to wait for ages to get ours because there were none in the shops and ordering online took weeks.

Think of the benefits of cycling over driving. Reduced emissions, cleaner air, saving money on fuel and you don't need to find a parking space. And, of course, cycling is a fantastic form of exercise. It can burn double the amount of calories as walking. My calves definitely noticed the difference. Word of warning: for longer journeys, invest in a padded seat!

DID YOU KNOW?

- Just under half the population of England and Wales travel less than 3.1 miles to work – a 15-minute bike journey.

- Taking the train rather than driving can cut your emissions by 75%.

- A journey via bus emits 40% less carbon dioxide than driving the same route in the car.

- A 15% increase in coach journeys each year could lead to approximately 47 million fewer cars on the road, saving over a quarter of a million metric tons of carbon dioxide and significantly reducing congestion on our roads.

– Take public transport.

If you are travelling on your own, then taking public transport will reduce your carbon emissions per journey. This is because emissions are worked out per passenger mile. So while a bus or train is bigger and produces more emissions than a car, the emissions split between the amount of people on board is less because far more people can fit on a train or bus than in a car.

Of course, there are lots of variables here, such as the number of people travelling in your car or whether a bus or train is at full capacity, and the type of fuel it uses. But as a general rule, if you are travelling alone or with one other person, it is better for the environment if you take public transport. Take a look at the chart (right) to see how each mode of transport compares.

CARBON FOOTPRINT OF TRAVEL PER KILOMETRE

The carbon footprint of travel is measured in grams of carbon dioxide equivalents per passenger kilometre. This includes carbon dioxide, but also other greenhouse gases, and increased warming from aviation emissions at altitude.

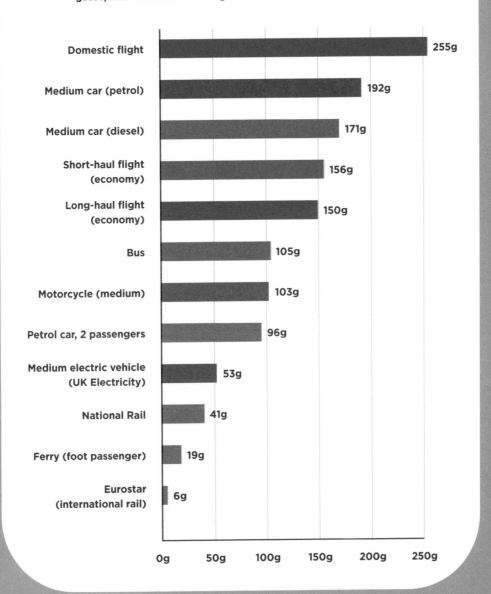

Travel type	Carbon footprint
Domestic flight	255g
Medium car (petrol)	192g
Medium car (diesel)	171g
Short-haul flight (economy)	156g
Long-haul flight (economy)	150g
Bus	105g
Motorcycle (medium)	103g
Petrol car, 2 passengers	96g
Medium electric vehicle (UK Electricity)	53g
National Rail	41g
Ferry (foot passenger)	19g
Eurostar (international rail)	6g

Source: UK Department for Business, Energy & Industrial Strategy. Greenhouse gas reporting: conversion factors 2019.

There's also the joy of just sitting back and relaxing while someone else does all the hard work. You can use the time you would have spent driving to call a friend, read a book or sort some of your life admin. Here are your options…

– Buses.

If you live in a city or large town then buses are plentiful and the easiest way to get around. If you live in a village or the countryside, however, then it might not be so easy. I live in Berkshire, where the bus into town is once an hour, but I still make use of it as often as I can. Because my husband has the car for work, I'll walk into town (about 2.5 miles) with Charlotte and then get the bus back, especially if I have bags to carry too. Charlotte absolutely loves the whole experience – looking out for the bus number when it is approaching, getting on and buying a ticket, looking out the window and feeling like a big girl in the seat. Although, there have been quite a few times that I've misread the timetable, which has meant a long walk home with a very tired four-year-old.

> **'There have been quite a few times that I've misread the bus timetable, which has meant a long walk home with a very tired four-year-old'**

In London, a single bus journey for an adult costs £1.55 no matter how far you go. You can even take multiple buses (and trams) within one hour and pay no extra. But outside of London fares are dearer and vary depending on where you are in the country. My bus journey is around £2.50 for a single. On average, cars cost 14.6p per mile for fuel, so in terms of price per mile, cars are cheaper, but they emit 40% more carbon per person, per journey (if you are travelling alone) and you also have to take into consideration the cost of wear and tear on your car per journey and the general upkeep of the vehicle.

- *Trains.*

If you're travelling slightly further away, then getting the train is a great way to reduce your emissions. A car journey with one person in the vehicle is four times more polluting than taking the train. There are 11,000 miles of train lines in the UK, 2,500 stations and 1,500 trains each day, so there are so many options!

While Britain is notorious for having some of the most expensive train fares in Europe, if you plan ahead and buy advance tickets, the prices can be quite reasonable. We cannot escape the fact that train travel is always going to be more expensive than driving in terms of fuel cost, though. But can you look at the positives? You are helping the planet, you get to sit back and relax on a train rather than having to deal with the busy UK roads, and you can maybe even have a little drink on board!

'You get to sit back and relax on a train, rather than dealing with the busy UK roads'

When I went to Glasgow for COP26 last year, I chose to travel by train rather than drive or fly. It was a five-and-a-half-hour journey and I honestly loved it. I had lots of research and prep to do for the conference and general house admin to sort, so it was a really productive time. Another thing I love about train journeys is being able to look out of the window at the beautiful British countryside. Much nicer than looking at the road. And let's not forget that you can rest! I was able to sleep on the way back. Bliss.

When we took Charlotte on her first train trip locally, it was more expensive and it took us longer to get to our destination but it was such a great experience for her. She loved the whole process – from getting the ticket, helping us read the board, getting on the train and talking to people on the train. It was such a lovely day out for us. It's easy to forget how much fun it can be when we are so busy looking down at our phones or racing around in our cars all the time (more on trains versus planes further on).

– *Coaches.*

Coach travel is actually one of the cleanest ways to travel, aside from an electric car. The average emissions per passenger per coach journey are around five times lower than travelling by car. You can travel via coach from most major cities and airports, and prices are often much cheaper than the train. I went by coach to one of my friends' hen parties and we all raced to sit at the back to be one of the 'cool kids' – because I wasn't one back in my school days! Also, having a toilet on board was a big win for the hung-over journey back…

- ***Plan ahead and combine journeys.***

  If you have an appointment at the dentist, can you do your food shop on the way back, instead of making two separate trips in the car? We do this kind of thing all the time. In fact, we try to not make any unnecessary journeys. We have our food shopping delivered, and I can walk to the local butcher or grocers. But if I have an appointment in town and need to use the car, I'll try to fit in other things on that same journey – such as getting any supplies I might need for Charlotte, or grabbing a few extra food bits.

  We've always done this because we have only one car, but also because when I am with Charlotte, I don't like to be running errands. I'd rather do them all in one go while she is at school. If I have to do them during our time together, then we will make an afternoon out of it and walk instead. For example, there is a lovely cafe next to the post office, so we'd walk there and stop and have some lunch too.

IDLING CARS

Not sure about you, but I was always under the impression that leaving your engine running for a short period was more fuel-efficient than turning your engine off and on again. Turns out I was wrong! An idling engine can produce up to twice the emissions of a car in motion. And, did you know that it is actually an offence to leave your engine running when the car is parked? Local authorities have the power to fine someone £20 if they refuse to turn off the engine of their stationary car. Where I live, they have signs that say 'Billy Never Idles – Neither Should You!' with a big picture of pop singer Billy Idol!

- ***Car share.***

  If you've seen Peter Kay's *Car Share* then you know what this one is all about! If you buddy up with someone for a journey then it reduces the amount of cars on the road and therefore the greenhouse gas emissions. Is there someone who takes a similar route to work that you could share a lift with? If you're unsure, how about putting a notice up at work, or asking around? Or maybe school mums can get together and arrange to take it in turns to take kids to school (if school really is too far to walk or cycle!).

If you'd feel comfortable sharing with people you don't know, then you can connect with people on car-sharing websites such as Liftshare. These allow you to find people who will be travelling in the same direction as you so you can travel together to cut down on costs, traffic congestion and emissions. It's great for people who have similar commutes to work, or for one-off events such as football games. The site works a little bit like Airbnb, where users are verified with passport details in order to ensure everyone's safety.

> *'If I need the car for a day, my husband will get a lift to work with someone'*

Car sharing doesn't have to mean with someone from another household though. Could you car share within your household? That's what we do, and as I said in the introduction of this chapter, if I need the car for a day, my husband will get a lift to work with someone, or he will cycle. English households have an average of 1.3 cars at their disposal. How many does yours have? Ask yourself whether you really NEED a car if someone else in your household already has one. You'll not only save on emissions, but you'll save on the cost of another vehicle, the insurance, tax, MOT and general maintenance. The average cost of owning a car in the UK is £256 per month. So you could save over £3,000 each year!

• *Hire a car.*
   If you can get by in your day-to-day life without a car, then hiring one is a great option for those odd times when you do need one. You can rent cars from £12 a day (depending on the size of the car) through well-known car hire companies, who often have brand-new fleets of cars – which include electric cars – so are more fuel-efficient.

   Alternatively, you can rent another person's car on sites such as Turo. It's a form of car sharing, really, because you are sharing someone else's car for a few hours, a day, a week or however long you might need it.

   If you have a car that you hardly use but really don't want to get rid of it, then maybe consider registering it with a car-sharing site like Turo, so that other people can make use of it. Obviously, the more your car is used, the more emissions it creates, but making cars available to share means fewer people own vehicles, which equals fewer emissions in the long run.

TIPS FOR MORE EFFICIENT DRIVING

When you do need to drive, there are things you can do to use less fuel, which means your car won't emit so much greenhouse gas and you'll save money!

Remove anything you don't need from inside or on top of the car.

This might seem really obvious but if you have a roof rack attached, take it off until you need it. If you have boxes of stuff in the boot, store them elsewhere. The heavier your car, the more energy (fuel) it needs to travel.

Regularly check your tyre pressure.

Under-inflated tyres reduce your vehicle's drag, which increases the amount of fuel you use.

Slow down.

Driving at speeds over 70mph will burn fuel quicker and increase your emissions – not to mention it's illegal! It will cost you around 25% more in fuel to drive at 70mph than 50mph. Unsurprisingly my husband already knows this. He says that 57mph is the optimum speed, but it feels frustratingly slow. I leave him to it though, as he does the driving on long journeys.

Set yourself a challenge!

Make a note of how many miles per gallon you use (the info will be on your dash) and see if you can beat it next month.

- ***Go electric!***

Electric cars are becoming more and more popular in the UK, with 11.6% of new car sales in 2021 being electric. They're better for the environment than conventional diesel and petrol cars and they're much cheaper to run. They're also going to be super important in our bid to meet the climate targets set out at COP26 (see page 44).

I know that switching to an electric car from a conventional car (if you haven't already) is not a simple or cheap decision to make, but it is something to think about when your current car needs replacing. Even Charlotte seems to be on board with the idea. She's really good at pointing out things that are bad for the environment, and every time she sees a car with an exhaust now (including ours!), she will say, "Look, Mummy, that gives out smoke!" and she starts coughing. I don't know where she gets her drama from!

'Charlotte starts coughing every time she sees a car with an exhaust – I don't know where she gets her drama from!'

And soon, we won't have much choice – from 2030, the government has banned the sale of new petrol and diesel cars in the UK. And hybrid cars will be phased out by 2035. Many car manufacturers are aiming to beat this target, with Peugeot saying they'll be fully electric by 2025 and Vauxhall by 2028.

There are two main reasons electric cars are better for the environment than petrol or diesel cars. The first is that, unlike conventional cars, which will always require fossil fuels to run them, electric cars have the ability to run on clean, renewable energies such as wind and solar.

DID YOU KNOW?

- An electric car has about half the climate impact over its lifetime compared to an average petrol or diesel car.

- Electric cars get more than twice as many miles out of the same amount of energy than conventional cars.

- As of December 2021, there were an estimated 370,000 electric cars on the road in the UK and 710,000 plug-in hybrids.

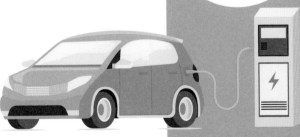

The second reason is that their engines are far more efficient than conventional engines, so they use less energy. Even the most efficient petrol cars use only 12-30% of the fuel's energy to create movement (and other useful functions). The rest is wasted in heat and noise. Whereas electric cars use around 77% of the energy they produce to move the car. That means you can drive more than twice the number of miles on the same energy.

As well as this, they also drastically reduce air pollution from exhaust fumes. Electric cars do, however, still produce air pollution from tiny particles that get scraped off the tyres and brake pads through friction, as all vehicles do.

While electric cars are far greener than petrol and diesel cars, nothing is ever 100% green. The car still needs to be manufactured, and the mining of cobalt needed for the creation of the batteries in electric cars (as well as the batteries used in smartphones, laptops etc) can be problematic because of worker exploitation. Because of this, electric car manufacturers are moving away from the use of cobalt in their batteries and ensuring they work with producers who regulate workers' rights to the highest possible standard.

As research for the book, I tried out an electric car for six months so I could hopefully answer any questions you might have. I also wanted to know if it was a swap I could see our family making, and the answer is YES, 100%. I loved it. I drove a Honda e, a small runaround that me and Charlotte decided had a 'smiley face' on the front. (Look it up online, you'll see what we mean!)

Was it an easy adjustment?

Yes. To be honest, the weirdest thing for me was that it appeared, at first, to have no wing mirrors! But the car has cameras on the sides and the view from those is cleverly displayed inside the car on small screens. Who knew! It had a lot of other impressive technology too, which is one way companies are drawing people in. There was even a display where you could feed fish – that kept Charlotte engaged for hours!

DID YOU KNOW?

- Electric cars cost more than £1,300 less to run each year than an equivalent car with a petrol or diesel engine.

- There are now more than 42,000 (and counting!) charge point connectors across the UK in more than 15,500 locations – that is more than the amount of petrol stations.

How much do they cost to buy?

This varies depending on the type you buy and whether it is new or second hand. You might want to sit down for this, because the average price of a new electric car in the UK is £44,000, but they range from around £17,000 to upwards of £138,000. The car I had, the Honda e, would have cost £35,000 to buy. Electric cars are more expensive than an equivalent car with a petrol or diesel engine because it's a relatively new technology. But prices are already coming down and are expected to reduce more in the next few years as the demand for electric cars increases. Research also suggests that electric cars work out cheaper over a seven-year period, because they cost around £1,300 less to run each year. That's because electricity is cheaper than petrol and diesel, electric cars require less maintenance than conventional cars and they are exempt from road tax. And, as time goes on, there will be more second-hand electric cars on the market.

...and to charge?

Again, this depends on the type of car you have and the size of the battery, plus the energy tariff you have at home. It can range from around £2.36 up to £15.49 to fully charge.

Are there enough charging points and how easy is it to charge?

I never struggled to find one, but then I wasn't driving long distances and could charge at home. There are now more than 42,000 (and counting!) charge point connectors across the UK in more than 15,500 locations – which is more public places to charge than there are petrol stations! In my car, I could press a button that would tell me the nearest charging point, whether it was slow or fast, and if it was free, so it was actually really easy. Every time I searched I was amazed there were so many. You can also get apps and visit websites that will tell you the same information.

All cars have two types of charging plugs. One is to plug into the house mains, which is called a trickle charge and took my car around 12 hours for a full charge. That sounds like a long time but it rarely needed a full charge, and I could put it on overnight. Then there is a different plug that you can use at charging points around the UK. Normal charging points take around 4 hours for a full charge, whereas fast charging points will do it in about 30 minutes. I could get mine to 80% charge in 30 minutes at a fast charging point.

I used the car to drive to work while I was testing it, and because there are no electric charge points there but lots of plugs, I'd usually take the trickle plug with me, to make sure I wouldn't get caught out. But sometimes I'd forget it because my car would be plugged into a socket in the garage, and opening the large garage door at 4am in the morning (the time I have to leave) is quite a faff… and noisy! If we decide to buy an electric vehicle when our current car needs replacing, I would get a charging point installed at home. On average, these cost between £800 and £1,100, but the government is currently offering grants to cover up to 75% of the cost of new chargers being installed, with a maximum contribution of £350 to homeowners who live in flats or people who live in rental accommodation.

How far can you get before you need to recharge?

It depends on the car. Mine could do up to 130 miles on a full charge, but some electric vehicles, such as the larger Tesla models, can travel up to 220 miles. So you have to buy one that suits your needs. Mine was perfect for getting me to and from work, which is around 30 miles each way. I won't lie though, 'range anxiety' was a real thing when I first started driving it. I miscalculated once. I travelled to a weather broadcast an hour away and used 55% of my battery getting there. I hadn't packed my trickle charger either and I knew I would never make it home. Luckily, someone else had an electric car so I borrowed their charger and plugged it in at a gift shop. Apart from Tesla chargers, all electric car chargers are compatible with other makes.

Is it realistic that you could drive long journeys, say, to the south of France for a holiday?

Yes. You will just need to plan! I didn't need my car for long journeys but it could drive for up to two hours, which is actually the recommended time you should have a rest from driving. It takes around 30 minutes to fully charge at a fast charging point. During that time you can stretch your legs, have a comfort break and a bite to eat, then return to your fully-charged car feeling refreshed. You can, of course, buy electric cars that can travel for longer distances.

I tried out the Honda-e and loved it

Flying produces the most emissions per person of any mode of transport

LET'S NOT FORGET FLYING

We all know that flying is bad for the environment. Aviation alone is responsible for 2.5% of global emissions, and while that number may seem low compared to other sectors (for example, food waste accounts for 10-12% of emissions), one return flight can generate the same emissions as 40% of the average person's annual carbon footprint. Flying produces the most carbon emissions per person of any mode of transport.

On top of the carbon released by planes, there are other environmental factors to consider when it comes to flying. Aircraft contrails – the white streaks planes leave in the sky – result in the formation of clouds which trap heat in the Earth's atmosphere. Although these heat traps are only temporary, it is thought they can have as much of a warming impact on the planet as the carbon emissions themselves.

And while many other modes of transport are able to switch to using electric energy (which can be generated from renewables such as wind and solar), aviation is currently reliant on fossil fuels.

?

DID YOU KNOW?

- Short-haul flights emit more CO_2e per person per mile than long haul.

- A single journey from London to Paris by plane costs from £64, and takes on average a total time of 4 hours 40 minutes (depending on how far you live from the airport) and emits 59kg equivalent of carbon dioxide. By train, the same journey will cost from £49, take an average of 2 hours 55 minutes and emit 2kg equivalent carbon dioxide.

I have to admit that I love planes, I think they are amazing. I used to work as a forecaster for the RAF and I loved working at RAF Brize Norton. It's the airport for the RAF and I used to see all the different planes coming in from all over the world. There's a really lovely airbase near us where we go to watch the comings and goings. You can sit and get some food and watch the planes come in.

I'm also a fan of flying, although I don't do it very often. I love being in the air and seeing how the weather changes as you travel through the clouds. I also like predicting when we will get turbulence based on the clouds. If you're the poor person next to me, you'll get a full lesson! So, I will never say don't fly, but could you fly less?

DID YOU KNOW?

- One return flight from London to Sydney will use around 40% of the average person's annual carbon footprint.

- Travelling by coach instead of plane can cut your carbon emissions by 90%, while a train journey can reduce your emissions by 75%.

> *'I love being in the air and seeing how the weather changes as you travel through the clouds, so I'll never say don't fly'*

These days, I only fly if I need to for work. My husband and I have only flown on holiday once in the last 10 years because we prefer to go on cruises, which leave from Southampton (this, of course, has its own environmental impact, more on this on page 237) and Charlotte has never been on a plane. Because she was born prematurely, we were advised against flying for two years because of her weakened immune system. Then, when she would have been able to, we went into the Covid-19 lockdowns. I'd happily take her on a plane now, but once a year maximum.

One of the silver linings of Covid is that we have all cut down on the amount of travelling we do – especially abroad. Now that things are opening up a little more, I can understand that people want to go abroad in search of guaranteed sunshine. But what if we start to see air travel as a luxury rather than our first option for getting about? Here are some alternatives…

- *Fall in love with staycations.*
  The UK has some of the most wonderful countryside in the world. From the rugged mountains of the Scottish Highlands to the beautiful beaches in Cornwall, there is so much to explore on our idyllic isle. And you can get around the UK easily without jumping on a plane. While we want to cut down on the amount of driving we do, the emissions from travelling via car are slightly less than flying. The most environmental way to travel is via train or coach, though…

- *Travel via coach or train.*
  As discussed earlier in the chapter, train and coach travel is much better for the environment than driving, but it has an even bigger impact when you compare it to flying. Arriving at your destination by coach instead of plane will cut your emissions by a whopping 90% – and if you choose a train over a plane, you'll knock your emissions down by 75%. It's a no-brainer really, especially when it comes to domestic travel. As mentioned earlier, I took the train to Glasgow for COP26 instead of flying or driving. Even though I love flying, I didn't have a second thought about how I would get there.

IN FRANCE, MPs VOTED TO SUSPEND DOMESTIC AIRLINE FLIGHTS ON ROUTES THAT CAN BE TRAVELLED BY DIRECT TRAIN IN LESS THAN TWO AND A HALF HOURS.

'Slow travel is about making the journey as much a part of your holiday as the destination'

You can even travel quite easily throughout Europe on trains and coaches. 'Slow travel', as it is called, is about making the journey as much a part of your holiday as the destination. I've never been on a sleeper train but it's on my bucket list. One of the things I love about cruising is going to sleep and then waking up in a different destination, so it would be just the same, but on a train.

- *Video calls to the rescue!*
  It's hard now to think that before the pandemic began, people would fly around the UK or even to Europe and America just for a business meeting. But if Covid has shown us one thing, it is that a lot can be achieved over Zoom! It's hard to say how things will go once travel is less restricted, but I think that businesses have seen how much time and money they can save from conducting meetings online, let alone the saving on carbon emissions.

And if you do fly…

- *Offset your flights.*
  If you have to fly for business or you decide to fly for pleasure (occasionally!) then you can offset your flight. This is when you pay towards a scheme that helps to capture carbon. You work out the emissions your flight would have released, then pay to take the equivalent amount out of the atmosphere. This could be done through planting trees or the creation of man-made carbon traps. Research where you put your money though. World Land Trust and Cool Earth are endorsed by Sir David Attenborough, and work to maintain existing rainforests, which is more beneficial to the environment than planting new trees.

'When I flew to Belfast to film Mastermind, I personally paid to offset that flight'

In 2020 I had to fly to Belfast to film *Mastermind*. (By the way, my chosen topic wasn't clouds or climate change – it was Bon Jovi! I scored 8/9 and I'm still gutted that I dropped a point!) I personally paid to offset that flight. I'd asked to be put in economy but they booked me into business (there were two seats in a row instead of three). I wasn't sure which company to use, so I went with Carbon Footprint™, the one Elton John used when he flew Harry and Meghan in a private jet to his French home!

When I flew to Svalbard to report on the impact of climate change, I flew economy and ITV offset the flight.

- *Choose one long-haul trip over lots of short-haul flights.*
  This may seem counter-intuitive, because surely the longer the flight the more greenhouse gases released? But domestic and short-haul flights are actually the worst offenders in terms of CO_2e per mile travelled. That's because it's the take-off and landing that use the most fuel. Take a look back at the chart on page 223 to see how long-haul and short-haul planes compare in terms of emissions.

- *Fly direct.*
  For the same reason as above, flying direct creates fewer emissions because you have only one take-off and one landing, rather than several.

- *Fly economy.*
  Business and first class seats take up a lot more room than economy, which increases the carbon footprint per passenger. I've only ever flown 'proper' business class once, on a trip to Dubai organised by their tourist board. I went

with my husband and it was the best thing that has ever happened to us. It had huge reclining seats – it was insane! It was almost better than the hotel and the whole holiday! But that was enough for me, I don't need that all the time. So if you have a big anniversary or special occasion and want to experience first or business class then do it… I won't tell anyone! But it can't be the norm or the go-to. Choose economy for regular flights!

- **Travel light.**
  Heavier planes require more fuel to take off and stay airborne than lighter planes, so the less luggage you take, the less fuel needed. You might think that your luggage won't make that much difference, but it's one of those situations where if we all do our little bit, collectively we make a big difference. For example, if every passenger who took a flight from Heathrow to Frankfurt in a typical year (pre-Covid) packed one fewer pairs of jeans, they would have saved 59 metric tons of CO_2e – the equivalent of the energy used to power seven homes for a year.

CRUISE CONTROL

You might assume that a ship would produce fewer emissions than a plane, but that's not actually the case. A cruise liner such as Queen Mary 2 emits 0.43kg of CO_2e per passenger mile compared to 0.257kg on a long-haul flight. Considering cruising is something I have done for years, I was pretty shocked to find this out. However, progress is being made in the cruising sector. P&O, who we usually cruise with, have recently launched their Iona ship. It's the greenest member of their fleet because it is powered by liquified natural gas. And Norway was the first country to launch the first hybrid electric-powered cruise liner, which lowers CO_2e emissions by 20%.

The Queen Mary 2 cruise ship

TAKING THINGS FURTHER

If you've now read through all of the chapters of the book, you'll see that there are so many things we can do to help save our planet. My original title for this book was going to be 101 Ways To Save Our Planet, but I realised I shouldn't put a number on it – the list is endless. Once you get the ball rolling in one area of your life, you can easily make changes in others to live more sustainably. And if you're anything like me, you'll start to see the world through different eyes and wonder why you ever lived any other way – and you'll want to tell everyone about it!

Many of the suggestions in this book are about swapping, reducing or rethinking things in our lives, but there is one powerful tool we can still use, and that's our voices! Whether it's telling friends about how some of the changes could really benefit their lives as well as helping the planet, or implementing proper recycling at your workplace, it all makes a difference. Here's how you can keep the conversation going…

STAY INFORMED

If you found this book useful, then look up other resources too. There are so many shows, books and social media accounts that can help you along on your journey.

Here's a list of documentaries, TV shows and films that have really opened my eyes.

I went to The Green Planet premiere

Blue Planet II BBC iPlayer
The Green Planet BBC iPlayer
Our Planet Netflix
Cowspiracy Netflix
Seaspiracy Netflix
Before The Flood Amazon Prime Video
One Strange Rock Disney+
Breaking Boundaries Netflix
The Need To Grow Theneedtogrow.com
Greta Thunberg: A Year To Change The World BBC iPlayer

Don't Look Up Netflix.
The Story Of Stuff Storyofstuff.org
Kiss The Ground Netflix
Down To Earth With Zac Efron Netflix
An Inconvenient Truth Amazon Prime Video
The Breakdown Earthrise.studio/projects
Seat At The Table YouTube series by Jack Harries
Climate Crisis: Our Changing World ITV.com

There are also some great kids shows that teach children about sustainability too:

Octonauts, Peppa Pig, Go Jetters, Sesame Street, Biggleton, Hey Duggee

You can read more about the impact of climate change in Svalbard in the Arctic Ocean and watch video clips here:
itv.com/goodmorningbritain/articles/laura-tobin-reports-on-the-devastating-impact-of-climate-change

And a short series on climate change here: *itv.com/climateaction/climate-change-the-facts.html*

Books that inspired me to write my own include:

Climate Majority by Leo Barasi
The Sustainable(ish) Living Guide by Jen Gale
The Sustainable(ish) Guide To Green Parenting by Jen Gale
How To Save Your Planet One Object At A Time by Tara Shine
Give A Sh*t: Do Good, Live Better, Save The Planet by Ashlee Piper
Who Cares Wins: How To Protect The Planet You Love by Lily Cole
Zero Waste Home: The Ultimate Guide To Simplifying Your Life by Bea Johnson

And those that are great for introducing kids to a sustainable way of living:

What The World Needs Now: Trees, Less Plastic, Bees by Cheryl Rosebush
Someone Swallowed Stanley by Sarah Roberts
What A Waste: Trash, Recycling And Protecting Our Planet by DK
Charlie And Lola: Look After Your Planet by Lauren Child
Peppa Pig: Peppa Loves Our Planet
Little People, BIG DREAMS: David Attenborough by Maria Isabel Sanchez Vegara

Charlotte actually quite likes watching nature, farm and zoo programmes with us, as well as David Attenborough shows.

Because I love all things science and weather, I follow Carbon Brief, at CarbonBrief. org. They have a daily newsletter that keeps me up to date with the latest environment and climate stories from around the world. You can find lots of other accounts to follow on Instagram that provide tips on sustainable living. Look up the hashtags #zerowaste #sustainableliving and #savetheplanet to make a start. Even if there is no one in your actual local community championing the same causes as you, you can guarantee you'll find like-minded people online.

SPREAD THE WORD

We are easily influenced by what people around us are doing. If you've enjoyed this book and the process of the eco journey, talk to your friends and family about it. You'll be amazed how many people start to follow your lead. While I've been writing this book, I've encouraged friends to put food scraps into a food waste bin/compost, to walk more (instead of driving), to have plastic-free parties, switch to shampoo bars and reusable sanitary pads, to start making gift lists and to look seriously at electric cars. If you use social media, can you post some of your sustainable switches there to inspire others? The more people see, the more they'll be interested in finding out more.

LEAD BY EXAMPLE

Throughout the book you will have seen how much Charlotte has picked up just by watching me. As she grows up, she will be very aware of the need to be sustainable and to think about the planet in a way that wasn't possible for my generation while we were growing up. We eat healthily hoping our children will do the same, and we speak kindly to each other so they will follow suit. So it makes sense to lead as green a lifestyle as possible, so this becomes the norm for our kids. Charlotte is very aware of recycling things properly. She never wants me to throw things away – I've even sewed up two pairs of tights with holes in them because she didn't want them to go in the bin. It took me five minutes and they were as good as new. Plus I saved myself £5 and a trip to the shops. Charlotte's also been leading by example with her litter picker – now all her friends want to join in!

But what about when you're out and about with strangers? One way I try to lead by example is to refuse things I wouldn't buy myself. For example, when I'm out on location presenting the weather, people will often offer me and the crew a tea or coffee (I don't usually drink them but on a cold morning it's a must!). If I haven't got my reusable cup with me, I always ask if the drink will come in a mug or a takeaway cup. If they say takeaway cup I'll reply, "Oh, I'm okay, thank you." I'm usually met with a confused look and "Oh okay… it can be recycled." It does feel a little awkward (and possibly rude) to say no to a kind offer, but I explain that I want to be more sustainable and not use items that will need to be recycled or thrown away.

Sometimes they will return with tea in a real mug for me AND the crew, which means me saying no has reduced the amount of waste that needs to be recycled! This also makes the crew think twice about using takeaway cups in future too. So you never know when your choices might influence someone else.

Take reusable cups with you when out and about

TALK TO YOUR BOSS ABOUT IMPLEMENTING GREENER MEASURES AT WORK

It can be frustrating trying your best at home and then getting to work and finding they don't even have recycling bins or they have single-use plastic cups at the water dispenser.

Where I work at ITV there is a commitment to achieving net zero, zero waste and having a 100% sustainable supply chain by 2030. ITV has a green team, and I've been to some of their meetings. They have made some huge changes and there are more to come, including introducing storylines on soaps about air pollution, not having plastic bags and takeaway cups. Again, leading by example.

Our canteen isn't managed by ITV, so there were a few things I wanted to make more sustainable there. I managed to get them to change their takeaway containers to compostable ones rather than ones that have little plastic windows by saying I wouldn't have breakfast. Again, refusing things really does work! And I also campaigned for them to install food-waste bins and more recycling bins, and this happened.

There are lots of other ways you could make your workplace more environmentally friendly, such as using recycled paper in the printer, starting a TerraCycle collection for those hard-to-recycle items like pens and crisp packets (for more, see page 252), and encouraging car sharing and cycle-to-work schemes.

SEE WHAT CAN BE DONE IN SCHOOLS

If you have children, check out what measures their school is taking to make it a more planet-friendly place. A lot of these may cross over with things that can be done in the workplace, such as introducing recycling bins and making sure all the children have reusable water bottles. You could also suggest that they set up a second-hand clothes sale for school uniforms so people don't have to buy new. We have one at Charlotte's school and I got the majority of her uniform there. The clothes were less than half the price and hardly worn, as kids grow so quickly! Charlotte's school does a lot of outdoor learning too, which I think is great. If your child's school hasn't got one already, could you suggest a kitchen garden to them?

WRITE TO YOUR MP

If there is something in your local area that you think could be improved, such as needing more recycling bins in parks, organising litter picking or campaigning to keep green spaces green (rather than building on them), can you write to them? Sometimes the best way to get the attention of an MP is to start a petition and get as many people in your local area to sign it. You can start petitions online at Change.org or Parliament.uk/get-involved/sign-a-petition.

SIGN PETITIONS

If you are following eco-conscious people on social media, it's likely you will see them post their own petitions for you to sign – get involved if it is something you also feel passionate about. I follow Greenpeace and sign lots of their petitions.

PUT YOUR MONEY IN A GREEN BANK

It's all well and good spending our money (or not) on sustainable products and greener companies, but if your savings and monthly wages are paid into a bank that invests in industries which are detrimental to the planet, such as fossil fuels, it's almost undoing all our personal hard work. Do your research on green and ethical banks that support and invest in companies that help people and the planet. Triodos bank is currently the most ethical bank in the UK. They promise to finance only those companies that focus on people, the environment or culture. And they are fully transparent and publish the details of all their investments. Other ethical banks include Nationwide, Monzo and Starling.

GO LITTER PICKING

You might not drop litter but unfortunately some people do. And one way we can help to keep our natural world clean (and stop animals getting injured) is to pick it up. I've already mentioned in the book that me and Charlotte go litter picking on our walk back from her school. You don't have to join an organised litter pick, just pick up any when you see it and pop it in the bin (or take it home to recycle!).

Charlotte loves to go litter picking

JOIN A BEACH CLEAN

If you live near a beach, then you can do this just as you would a litter pick. But if you live far away, how about including a beach clean on a day trip to the seaside? It's a great way to reduce plastic pollution and protect sea life (see page 50 for more info). This year, The Great British Beach Clean is taking place between 17-25 September, so that would be a great time to get involved, or you can sign up to one of the National Trust beach cleans at *nationaltrust.org.uk/lists/pitch-in-with-a-beach-clean.*

PLANT TREES

Trees are so important for capturing carbon and providing us with oxygen, yet the world is losing them at a rate of one football pitch of forest every second.

It's easy to think that planting a new tree for every one that is cut down levels out any damage done, but it's not as simple as that. A tree absorbs the maximum amount of carbon when it is fully grown, so it can take 5 to 15 years for the tree to capture the same amount as the one that was chopped down. It's also important that we plant a variety of different trees. Cutting down whole forests and replacing them with only one type of tree will have a negative impact on biodiversity.

The UK government has pledged to plant one million trees between 2020 and 2024, and this year the Queen is inviting people to 'Plant A Tree For The Jubilee' as part of the Queen's Green Canopy to mark her Platinum Jubilee. For advice on the type of tree to plant and the best time of year to plant it visit Queensgreencanopy.org. Once you have planted a tree, you can add it to the 'canopy' map on the website.

RECYCLE RIGHT

Throughout the book, I've suggested ways that you can reduce the amount of packaging you bring into your home, so hopefully you will end up with less waste to get rid of. But unless you become a zero-waste superstar, it's near-impossible to not end up with at least some rubbish to throw out or recycle each week.

Remember that the second to last step on our sustainability pyramid (on page 56) is Recycle. It's our last option before we have to allow things to rot in landfill. Yet every year in the UK, we create 26 million tonnes of waste, and only 45% of that gets recycled.

It's up to us to sort our recycling at home before it is picked up by our local authorities. And in theory, it's pretty straightforward – most paper/card, glass, tins and plastic can go in the recyclable bin, food goes in the food-waste or compost bin, and everything else goes in the general bin. But in practice, knowing what can and cannot be recycled can get pretty confusing – the rules change depending on which local authority area you live in, and we rely on rather baffling recycling symbols on packaging to tell us what to do.

'Knowing what can and can not be recycled can get pretty confusing'

This confusion can lead some people to not bother recycling at all, while others throw everything in the recycling and hope for the best. The latter is known as 'wishcycling' and can be just as bad for the environment as not recycling – but there's more on this later in the chapter.

Getting recycling right is essential for the health of our planet. It helps to conserve the Earth's limited natural resources and saves the energy (and therefore carbon emissions) needed to extract the raw materials and make them into new products. It also helps to protect ecosystems and wildlife in those areas where natural resources are taken from, and it drastically reduces the amount of problematic waste we have on our planet. If that's not enough to convince you, then check out these facts…

- *Recycling a single aluminium can will save enough energy to power a TV for up to three hours or an iPod for up to twenty hours.*
- *Recycling a single glass bottle will save enough energy to power a laptop for half an hour.*
- *Recycling a single plastic bottle will save enough energy to power a lightbulb for three hours or more.*

In this chapter, I've included tips on how to recycle well, a breakdown of what all those recycling symbols actually mean, and where you can recycle some of those so-called 'non-recyclables'. I know that together, we can do better and increase the amount we recycle in the UK!

FIRST UP, HERE'S HOW TO GET THE MOST OUT OF YOUR RECYCLING AT HOME...

- *Empty, wash and dry.*
  Pour away any liquids and scrape out food from containers. Food waste is one of the biggest contaminants of recycling. DO NOT use fresh water to wash your jars and pots (it's such a waste!), use leftover washing-up water instead, and make sure the containers are dry before you put them in the bin. Wet bottles and tins can leave cardboard soggy, which means it can't then be recycled.

- *You don't need to remove labels…*
  …unless the recycling symbol tells you to. Labels on glass jars and bottles are removed as part of the recycling process.

- *Crush and flatten.*
  Crushing metal cans and plastic water bottles will save space in your recycling bin and stop them rolling off sorting belts at recycling centres.

DID YOU KNOW?

- British households create over 26 million metric tons of waste each year – that's the weight of around 260 large cruise ships.

- We recycle an average of 45.5% of our household waste in the UK, whereas Germany recycles 60-70%!

- More than 28 million glass bottles and jars – which can be recycled over and over again – end up in landfill every year. That's the equivalent of the Empire State Building filling up every three weeks.

Crisp packets can now be recycled at most large supermarkets

- ***Nothing smaller than a credit card.***
  Small items including bottle caps, shredded paper, small yoghurt cups and sticky notes are often too small to be picked up by sorting machines at recycling centres. They can become lodged in equipment and create cross-contamination issues. With bottle caps, check whether the recycling label says 'lid on'. If not, it is actually better to throw it in the bin because it could be made of a different type of plastic.

- ***Combined materials are a NO...***
  Composites – a combination of two or more components to make a material that is light, strong and durable – are difficult to recycle, and can't be put in your home recycling collection. Composite items include crisp packets and salad bags. Other items that are made of two or more materials, such as a toothbrush or razor, can not be recycled at home but they can be recycled through TerraCycle (page 252).

- ***Know your plastics.***
  Plastic recycling is where things get quite confusing. So much so that a code was introduced in 1988 to help us understand what type of plastic we are dealing with and whether it can be recycled. You'll find a number between 1 and 7 on most plastics (see chart on the right).

TOP TIP

If you have tin foil, save up the scraps and wait until you have enough to roll into the size of a tennis ball before putting it into the recycling bin.

OUR PLASTIC IN NUMBERS

 1. PETE (polyethylene terephthalate) is widely recycled and most often used in clear plastic bottles such as fizzy drink bottles, ketchup and cooking oil bottles, plus food punnets.

 2. HDPE (high density polyethylene) is found in stiff coloured bottles and tubs such as milk bottles, bottles of bleach and margarine tubs, as well as softer plastics such as some grocery bags. It is widely recycled, but check that your local authority collects it. Grocery bags cannot be picked up in your home collection – recycle these at larger supermarkets.

 3. PVC (polyvinyl chloride) is often used in pipe fittings, window fittings, some meat containers, clingfilm and medicine blister packs. PVC can not be recycled at home. Medicine blister packs can be recycled at some pharmacies and larger supermarkets will accept clean clingfilm as part of their flexible plastic recycling.

 4. LDPE (low-density polyethylene) is a flexible plastic found in bread bags, grocery bags and squeezy shampoo bottles. It can be recycled, but check whether your local authority collects it. Bread bags and grocery bags can be recycled at larger supermarkets.

 5. PP (polypropylene) is a rigid plastic used to make packaging trays, takeaway tubs, outdoor furniture and toys. It is becoming increasingly more recyclable, so check if your local authority collects it.

 6. PS (polystyrene) is not usually recyclable in normal collections. Polystyrene can be made into rigid or foam types of plastic and is found in Styrofoam cups, some yoghurt pots, CD cases plus medical trays and dishes.

 7. Other – this is a miscellaneous category which contains plastics that are not recyclable in your home collection, such as bioplastics and composites (such as crisp packets and salad bags).

THE PLASTIC CODE NUMBERS ARE NOT THE ONLY SYMBOLS AND LOGOS THAT CAN APPEAR ON OUR PACKAGING. YOU MAY ALSO FIND THESE...

MOBIUS LOOP

This is one of the most widely recognised recycling symbols and it means the item is capable of being recycled but not that it is made of recycled materials or that it will be accepted in all recycling collections. If the symbol is accompanied by a percentage, that indicates how much of the item has been made from recyclable materials. Before putting this in your recycling bin, check what other symbols the packaging has.

GREEN DOT

This symbol does NOT mean the item is recyclable (even though I always thought it did)! It indicates that the producer has made a financial contribution towards the recycling and recovery of packaging in Europe.

Widely
Recycled

WIDELY RECYCLED

This means the packaging is collected by at least 75% of local authorities in the UK.

Rinse/Lid On

Widely
Recycled

RINSE / LID ON

The 'widely recycled' symbol can also feature instructions such as 'rinse' and 'lid on'. Rinsing packaging ensures no food waste contaminates the recycling, particularly if it is collected with paper recycling. Caps and lids smaller than 40mm are too small to be captured for recycling. Placing the lid back on the bottle means it will be captured and recycled with the bottle.

Recycle   Don't
               Recycle

RECYCLE/DON'T RECYCLE

This symbol can be seen when part of the packaging can be recycled and part can not. Certain items, such as a film, might have to be removed before recycling. For example, the thin film of plastic on top of a punnet of blueberries needs to be removed from the plastic punnet because only the punnet is recyclable in your home collection. The lid can be recycled at large supermarkets.

Check
Locally

CHECK LOCALLY

This means that only some authorities (20-75%) will recycle this item. Check with your local authority.

WIDELY RECYCLED WITH BAGS AT LARGE STORES

This means it cannot be picked up by your local authority, but the item can be recycled at large supermarkets. Look out for this on carrier bags, bread bags and toilet roll packaging.

WIDELY RECYCLED AT RECYCLING CENTRES

Another item that can't be recycled in your home collection, but can be recycled at your local recycling centre.

NOT YET RECYCLED

This symbol indicates that less than 20% of local authorities recycle this item. It doesn't always mean it can't be recycled at all though, check TerraCycle on page 252.

COMPOSTABLE (INDUSTRIAL)

When you see the seedling logo on items, it means that the item can be composted, but through your food-waste or garden collection, and not in your home compost because it needs a higher temperature to start the breakdown. Never place compostable plastic with your normal household plastic recycling because it is meant to break down, rather than be recycled. For more information on food-waste, see page 93.

HOME COMPOSTABLE

This is a newer symbol and means that the item will break down in your home compost. It can also be disposed of in your food-waste bin. For more information on home composting, see page 119.

GLASS RECYCLING

This is used as a reminder to recycle glass containers, either in your home recycling (if accepted) or at a glass collection site.

ALUMINIUM RECYCLING

Used to indicate aluminium packaging that is fully recyclable, such as fizzy drink cans and tin foil (if clean).

Local authorities don't all collect the same items, so the labels are based on what the majority do. To check your local area, enter your postcode at Recyclenow.com/local-recycling

WHY WE NEED TO STOP 'WISHCYCLING'

Sometimes, in order to recycle more, we actually have to recycle less. Hear me out….

Wishcycling is the act of putting something in your home recycling and 'hoping' it will be recycled. We've all done it. You stand at your bins, look at the packaging and think, "Surely this can be recycled, it'll be fine…" and put it in the recycling bin. But when a non-recyclable item is put into otherwise 'good' recycling, it creates a huge problem for waste recycling centres. It can damage recycling equipment or contaminate the whole batch. Even a very small amount of non-recyclable material can result in tonnes of otherwise reusable waste being diverted to landfill. Just think, you're trying to be 'good' but it's actually making things worse. That's why it's so important to 'recycle right'.

Take pizza boxes, for example. They're cardboard, so it's easy to think they can be recycled, but any greasy residue can render the rest of that batch of recycling unusable. That's because cardboard recycling uses cold water to break up the paper, which can't cut through the grease. Any part of the box that has grease or food on should be torn off and thrown in the general rubbish bin – only put completely clean and dry cardboard in the recycling.

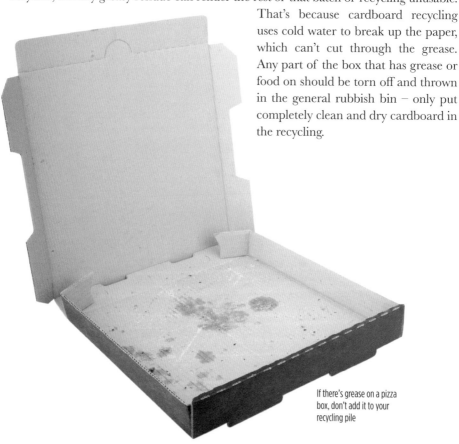

If there's grease on a pizza box, don't add it to your recycling pile

Below is a list of items that can't be recycled in your home collection. Some of these would be better off being thrown in the regular bin, but others can be recycled through other schemes. Read on…

COMMON ITEMS THAT SHOULD NOT BE PUT IN YOUR HOME RECYCLE BINS

- CDs and DVDs
- Clingfilm
- Clothing and textiles
- Crisp packets
- Disposable coffee cups
- Drinking glasses and Pyrex cookware
- Electrical items
- Food waste
- Hand soap pump dispenser tops
- Laminated foil pouches such as baby food or pet food pouches
- Nappies (both used and unused)
- Pet bedding and litter
- Photo paper
- Plastic bags

- Plastic netting on fruit and veg
- Pizza boxes with greasy residue
- Post-it notes
- Receipts printed on thermal paper
- Sanitary products (unused and used)
- Shampoo bottles and food containers that have not been rinsed
- Soft plastic such as bread bags and film lids
- Toothpaste tubes
- Toothbrushes
- Used tissues, kitchen roll or tissues
- Wet wipes

It is not the end of the line for some of these so-called non-recyclables. There are lots of drop-off points and schemes around the UK that will take them off your hands, so they don't end up in landfill…

Recycle flexible and soft plastics at large supermarkets.
Many local authorities will not collect flexible plastics such as grocery bags, bread bags, freezer bags, plastic film lids, clingfilm, cheese packets, cereal bag inserts and crisp packets. But the great news is that many of these can now be recycled at large supermarkets around the country. Look out for the 'Widely recycled with bags at large stores' symbol on packaging, and keep your eyes peeled next time you visit your local supermarket to see what drop-off points they have.

We have SO many bags full of all of these items in the garage. I rarely go to the supermarket because we get deliveries, and when I do I often forget to take them! My husband keeps threatening to throw them away if I don't take them soon…

Batteries can be taken to recycling centres or any shop that sells more than 32kg of batteries a year (that's around 345 4-packs of AA batteries). Even though batteries should never be put in the bin, it is estimated that Brits throw away over 600 million batteries every year. In landfill, they release harmful toxins into the environment. There's no excuse – save them up at home and take them to a shop near you!

Spectacles can be donated or recycled at opticians, and you can recycle soft contact lenses and their packaging through TerraCycle (see below).

Small electrical items can be donated or recycled at many local libraries (that's right, where you go to get books!). This includes hair dryers, straighteners, mobile phones, toys, toasters, coffee machines and drills. Larger electric items can usually be taken to your local recycling centre.

DID YOU KNOW THAT ALMOST ANYTHING CAN BE RECYCLED?

It's just that some things are harder than others. Local authority recycling schemes usually only accept items made from one material – these are more common, easier to recycle and make money when they are recycled. TerraCycle is a fantastic organisation that specialises in dealing with those hard-to-recycle items such as coffee capsules, foil balloons, food pouches, razors and personal protective equipment (PPE). Think about a razor, for example – it's made of plastic and metal. Together, they can't be recycled, but when separated they can.

BEAUTY, HEALTHCARE AND WELLNESS PRODUCTS CAN BE RECYCLED AT BOOTS…

…and you earn Advantage Card Points in return! This includes make-up containers, items that are too small for home recycling such as mini travel bottles, and toothpaste tubes and dental floss packets. You can also find Maybelline make-up drop-off points in Tesco, Superdrug and Sainsbury's stores, which accept all brands of make-up. Some cosmetics can also be recycled through TerraCycle (see right).

TerraCycle is funded by brands, manufacturers and retailers all over the world, so that the recycling programmes are free for the customers (that's us). There are more that 1,600 public drop-off points around the UK. In fact, there is one within 4 miles of 80% of UK households. Visit terracycle.com/en-GB to see a list of everything they can recycle, and to find your nearest drop-off location for that item.

If there isn't one near you, you can request to start one yourself from your home, school or office using their Zero Waste Boxes. You can choose an All-In-One box, which allows you to throw in all those items you can't usually recycle at home, such as CDs, hair brushes, plastic toys, pens and sweet wrappers, or you can choose a box for something specific, such as coffee pods or disposable face masks. Once you've filled up your box, you ship it to TerraCycle (free of charge) for them to recycle. All shipments are carbon-neutral, meaning the transport emissions are offset.

This option does come with a cost. Box prices start from £100, so it's a good thing to do with a group of mates or people in your local community so you can spread the cost. One of the mums in my antenatal group started collecting baby pouches through this scheme. And during the pandemic I was saving up soap dispenser lids to send off too. Yes, it cost a bit of money, but it was so much easier than having to find drop-off points near us, and it gave us peace of mind knowing these items were not going to end up in landfill. Also, the boxes are large, so it takes a while to fill them up!

Visit terracycle.com/en-GB for more information.

COULD YOU MAKE ECOBRICKS?

Ecobricks are a fantastic way to turn your plastic waste into something good. You just need an empty single-use plastic bottle and you fill it with clean, dry plastic. When the plastic is packed densely enough, you end up with a solid block which can be used as reusable building blocks in walls, garden furniture and other projects. By cramming the plastic into the bottle, you reduce the net surface area of the plastic packaging, which reduces the chance of it degrading and producing toxins and microplastics. It also means that the plastic that would have gone to waste is being put to good use. I made some with friends before sending them off. See *ecobricks.org* for more.

AFTERWORD

You've reached the end of the book and I really hope you've found it full of useful and practical advice on living a more sustainable life. I hope you now feel ready to get started on your own journey to help save our planet! There are just a few things I want to remind you of before you get going.

Many people believe that caring for the planet means going vegan, never flying again and being completely zero-waste. But that's just not realistic for most of us. Whether you make one or one hundred of the changes in this book, you will still be having a positive impact on the world around you. Repeat after me: No one can do everything but everyone can do something!

There will be times when life gets in the way and you can't make the most sustainable choices. And that's okay. It's not about perfection – it's about progress. In the words of zero-waste chef Anne-Marie Bonneau, "We don't need a handful of people doing [it] perfectly. We need millions of people doing it imperfectly."

If you forget to take your reusable cup with you one day, it's (literally) not the end of the world. Just try to remember it next time and make it a habit! It's about becoming a conscious consumer in general.

And don't forget that it's not a race. Start with the changes that seem most doable to you, then work your way through a few more. If you need inspiration, then turn the page for my Top 10 tips.

One last piece of advice is to spend as much time as you can outdoors. It's easy to lose sight of the very thing we are trying to save – our beautiful planet. So put down this book and take a wander. Look at the trees, the fields, the animals, the wildlife, the sky. We have so much to thank the Earth for, so it's time we do something in return.

Now there's not much left for me to say apart from I hope you enjoy this journey as much as I have. Oh hang on, my husband just shouted something from the other room...

What did he say? Oh, just the usual question he likes to tease me with: "How will you be saving the planet this week?"

But that's actually a good way for me to sign off. By asking that very question...

How will YOU be saving the planet this week?

TOBIN'S TOP 10

Remember, no one can do everything, but everyone can do something. There are more than 200 ideas in this book, but these are the 10 that I think are most important....

1 **Reduce food waste.** Brits throw away an alarming six meals' worth of food each week. This is made up of food scraps, food that goes out of date before we eat it and foods we simply decide we don't want. Food waste accounts for 8-10% of all greenhouse gas emissions – which is four times more than flying! – and it releases harmful methane into the atmosphere. This gas warms the Earth up to 80 times more than CO_2. Reducing the amount of food you throw away will not only reduce emissions, it will save you money on your shopping bills too! For tips on limiting food waste as well as how to recycle it properly, see page 93.

2 **Insulate your home.** Taking energy-saving measures such as turning down your thermostat, setting your heating on a timer and installing a climate-friendly heat pump is only going to go so far if the heat you generate is going to escape from the house. British houses lose approximately 35% of heat through walls, 25% through the roof, 25% through doors and windows and 15% through floors. See page 66 for what insulation measures you can take to save your energy and money!

3 **Recycle right.** We want to reduce the amount of waste we generate full stop, but it is so important that we recycle what we can. Only 10% of plastic is recycled worldwide. If I see someone with a single-use plastic bottle and ask them why they aren't using a reusable one (yes, I am that person!) they'll often say "Oh, but I can recycle it…" but how many people actually do? We create 26 million metric tons of waste each year in the UK, yet only 45% of that gets recycled. See page 244 for recycling tips and page 46 for the mounting problem of plastic.

4 **Reduce your meat intake.** Livestock farming is responsible for 14.5% of global greenhouse gas emissions, so cutting down on the amount of meat you eat will make a big difference. Around 14% of adults in the UK now follow meat-free diets, but it doesn't have to be all or nothing. Not eating meat on just one day a week will still have a positive impact. In fact, if everyone ate one less red-meat meal a week, it could cut the UK's greenhouse gas emissions by 45 million metric tons. That's the equivalent of taking 16 million cars off the road! If/when you do eat meat, aim to buy it locally and sustainably sourced. For more information, see page 86.

5 **Go plastic-free one item at a time.** Cutting down on the plastic items in my life has been one of the biggest things I have done on this eco journey – and dare I say, the most fun! Once you start with this, you really can't stop. For sustainable bathroom switches see page 124, and for how to reduce plastic in the kitchen, turn to page 80. And for a reminder of why plastic is so bad, take a look at page 46.

6 **Walk more...** instead of driving! Transport produces 27% of the UK's total emissions and 91% of this comes from road transport vehicles – our cars! If you can replace even one short car journey a week by walking, you'll make a dent in those emissions. For example, if every car in the UK drove three miles fewer each week, it would be the equivalent of taking 263,968 cars off the road each year. You'll also reap the benefits elsewhere, such as getting more exercise, reconnecting with nature and saving money on fuel. For more on how to reduce transport emissions, see page 214.

7 **Buy less stuff!** Whether it's clothes, appliances or cosmetics, ask yourself whether you really need something new before you buy it. Even though there are suggested items to buy in this book as replacements for single-use plastics, the idea is to always use what you have first. After that, look at other options such as borrowing, hiring or buying second-hand before you choose something new. You'll find tips on buying less on page 174. Which leads me on to…

8 **Think twice before you throw things away.** Could that item you no longer want be given a second home somewhere else? One person's trash is another person's treasure. If it's broken, could it be fixed? And if it's packaging, can it be recycled? I think we forget that anything we throw away will sit in landfill for years. Remember, there is no such place as away!

9 **Invest your money wisely.** It's all well and good making an effort to cut down on plastic, drive less and reduce your food waste, but if your money is in banks or pensions that are investing it in fossil fuels, then it's almost undoing all your hard work. For ethical and green banks, see page 242. It's important to look at the energy supplier you use too. Can you switch to one that uses renewable sources of energy? For more information, see page 71.

10 **Spread the word!** If you've been inspired to make changes after reading this book, then tell your friends and family. When you share your own journey with others, it won't be long before they want to get involved – trust me! You can use your voice to see if you can implement greener measures at work or at your kid's school, as well as speaking to your local MP and signing petitions that you care about.

TICK LIST

You can find all the suggestions from the book in the list below. Tick off the ones you have done, cross off the ones that are not relevant to you, and add any other ideas to the blank space at the end. Good luck...

HOME ENERGY

Reducing the amount of energy you use by...
- ☐ Lowering your thermostat by 1°C (then keep going to see how low you can go...)
- ☐ Setting timers on your heating.
- ☐ Turning radiators off in rooms you don't use.
- ☐ Swapping to energy-saving light bulbs.
- ☐ Turning the lights off when you leave a room...
- ☐ Investing in smart bulbs.
- ☐ Installing a smart meter.

Use more renewable energy by...
- ☐ Getting a Green Light Signal bulb.
- ☐ Switching to a green energy company.
- ☐ Getting solar panels installed.
- ☐ Switching to a heat pump.

Keep heat in by...
- ☐ Closing your curtains at night.
- ☐ Draft-proofing doors and windows.
- ☐ Getting cavity wall insulation.
- ☐ Insulating your loft.
- ☐ Getting under-floor insulation.

IN THE KITCHEN

Switch to a planet-friendly diet by...
- ☐ **Reducing your meat consumption.**
  - ☐ 1-2 meat-free days a week.
  - ☐ 3-4 meat-free days a week.
  - ☐ 5-6 meat-free days a week.
  - ☐ Meat free!
- ☐ Buying local, sustainably produced meat.
- ☐ Switching dairy milk to plant-based milk.
- ☐ Cutting down on the amount of fish you eat.
- ☐ Choosing fruit and veg that's in season.
- ☐ Going organic where you can.
- ☐ Cutting down on products containing palm oil.

Reduce food waste by...
- ☐ Doing a stocktake of what you already have then using it.
- ☐ Planning your meals, making a shopping list and sticking to it.
- ☐ Don't shop hungry!
- ☐ Freezing leftovers and any food that will go out of date before you use it.
- ☐ Making soups or smoothies from things on the turn.
- ☐ Buying wonky fruit and veg.
- ☐ Shopping in the reduced section at supermarkets.
- ☐ Disposing of any food waste in your home food-waste caddy or garden compost.

Reduce plastic packaging by...

- ☐ Buying in bulk.
- ☐ Buying products packaged in paper, cardboard or glass.
- ☐ Choosing loose fruit and veg.
- ☐ Saying no to receipts.
- ☐ Buying fresh bread.
- ☐ Choosing wine with a real cork.
- ☐ Taking your own containers to deli counters.
- ☐ Going big on crisps.
- ☐ Making food from scratch.
- ☐ Going to a refill store for store-cupboard staples.
- ☐ Finding alternatives to clingfilm and foil.
- ☐ Switching baking paper for silicone sheets.
- ☐ Buying recycled kitchen roll in paper packaging.
- ☐ Choosing loose leaf or biodegradable tea bags.

Save water and energy when making a cuppa by...

- ☐ Watching your kettle!
- ☐ Only boiling what you need.
- ☐ Using a thermos flask.
- ☐ Descaling regularly.

Reduce your pet's carbon footprint by...

- ☐ Choosing wet food in tins instead of pouches.
- ☐ Giving them chicken and fish over beef and lamb.
- ☐ Buying dry food in bags that can be recycled.
- ☐ Using cat litter that is made from wood or grains that are biodegradable or compostable.
- ☐ Choosing biodegradable poop bags.
- ☐ Avoiding flimsy plastic toys that can fall apart more easily.

GARDENING

Create healthy green spaces by...

- ☐ Choosing real grass over fake.
- ☐ Using an electric or cordless lawn mower instead of a petrol one.
- ☐ Planting trees and shrubs strategically.
- ☐ Using peat-free compost.
- ☐ Setting up a compost bin.
- ☐ Growing your own fruit, veg and herbs.
- ☐ If you only have a balcony, growing plants in pots or up the wall.

Help wildlife by...

- ☐ Leaving some of your lawn 'wild'.
- ☐ Making a bee hotel.
- ☐ Clearing a path for hedgehogs.

IN THE BATHROOM

Reduce the amount of 'stuff' in your cupboards by...

- ☐ Using up the products you already have.
- ☐ Saying no to freebies – like the little bottles you get in hotels.
- ☐ Switching to eco products.

Reduce plastic by...

- ☐ Buying in bulk.
- ☐ Getting products in glass or metal.
- ☐ Using shampoo, conditioner and soap bars.
- ☐ Refilling your own bottles at a zero-waste

store or signing up to an online refill service.

☐ Switching cotton wool rounds for reusable make-up pads.

☐ Ditching cotton buds or use a reusable one.

☐ Using a flannel instead of a wet wipe, or choose biodegradable wipes.

☐ Getting a refillable deodorant.

☐ **Switching from standard sanitary products to:**

    ☐ Reusable pads.

    ☐ Reusable pants.

    ☐ Menstrual cup.

☐ Choosing a bamboo toothbrush.

☐ Buying silk or bamboo dental floss.

☐ Trying toothpaste tabs.

☐ Getting a metal safety razor.

☐ Buying toilet paper in bulk, and looking out for ones made from recycled paper as well as in paper packaging.

SAVE WATER

Cut down on the water you use in the bathroom by...

☐ Turning off the tap when you're brushing your teeth.

☐ Choosing a shower over a bath.

☐ Reducing your shower time by singing your favourite song!

☐ Having a 'Navy shower'.

☐ Fixing a water-saving device to your shower head.

☐ Thinking before you flush!

Save water while washing clothes and dishes by...

☐ Washing only full loads in the washing machine.

☐ Using a dishwasher instead of washing by hand.

☐ Not rinsing your plates before you put them in the dishwasher.

☐ Always fully loading the dishwasher before putting it on.

☐ Using the eco setting.

☐ **Washing up in the sink more efficiently:**

    ☐ Scraping off leftovers immediately.

    ☐ Soaking the plates in a couple of centimetres of water.

    ☐ Never washing them under running water, always in a bowl.

    ☐ Washing the cleanest things first.

    ☐ Making sure the water is as hot as it can be to kill germs.

Reduce plastic in your cleaning products by...

☐ Switching plastic sponges for a wooden brush, loofah or compostable sponge.

☐ Choose biodegradable washing up gloves – or don't use any!

☐ Buying your washing detergent either in bulk, in cardboard boxes, taking your own containers to a refill store or using laundry strips.

Avoid using the hose pipe by...

☐ Washing your car using a bucket of water and a sponge.

☐ Using a watering can to water plants.

☐ Not watering your lawn.

☐ Getting a water butt to collect rainwater.

Reuse water by...

- ☐ Washing recyclable packaging in old washing up water.
- ☐ Saving pasta and rice water to water plants with.
- ☐ Using the water from cooking vegetables to cook rice and pasta in.
- ☐ Collecting water in a tub when you are waiting for it to get hot /cold and reuse.

DIGITAL

Reduce carbon emissions from technology by...

- ☐ Clearing out your email inbox.
- ☐ Unsubscribe from marketing emails and newsletters.
- ☐ Sending fewer emails.
- ☐ Using a green web browser.
- ☐ Putting your phone on low-power mode.
- ☐ Turning off your gadgets and unplug them from the wall.

Cut down your screen time by...

- ☐ Setting a usage limit on apps.
- ☐ Disabling notifications on apps that don't need your attention immediately.
- ☐ Avoiding using your phone first thing in the morning or last thing at night.
- ☐ Having screen-free times/zones.

Reduce the impact of streaming by...

- ☐ Using WiFi rather than 4G.

- ☐ Watching on a smaller screen.
- ☐ Watching in lower definition.
- ☐ Keeping hold of your phones for longer.

Avoid electrical waste by...

- ☐ Switching to rechargeable batteries.
- ☐ Keeping hold of your phones for longer.
- ☐ Recycling electrical equipment.
- ☐ Trading in your old mobile when upgrading.
- ☐ Donating your old phones or tablets to charities that supply them to people in need.
- ☐ Selling your items on eBay or Facebook Marketplace.
- ☐ Giving fully-working electrical goods to charity.

BUY LESS

You can avoid buying new things by...

- ☐ Using what you already have.
- ☐ Repairing what you do have.
- ☐ Borrowing.
- ☐ Hiring.
- ☐ Swapping.
- ☐ Buying second hand.

Stop buying things on a whim by...

- ☐ Giving yourself 24 hours before deciding to buy something new.

- ☐ Unsubscribing from marketing emails.
- ☐ Removing payment methods from your phone.

Reduce what you bring into your house by...

- ☐ Saying no to free things if you don't actually need them.
- ☐ Buying nothing new for a week (other than food and essentials).

FASHION

Reduce the amount of new clothes you buy by...

- ☐ Borrowing from a friend.
- ☐ Swapping items with family, friends or online.
- ☐ Hiring an outfit.
- ☐ Buying preloved clothes.
- ☐ Doing the 30-wear test before buying new.
- ☐ Choosing the most sustainable option.

Keep clothes in good condition for longer by...

- ☐ Only washing them when you need to.
- ☐ Spot-cleaning stains.
- ☐ Washing at a lower temperature.
- ☐ Air-drying rather than tumble-drying.
- ☐ Fixing rather than throwing away.
- ☐ Repurposing them into something else.
- ☐ Investing in better hangers.
- ☐ Choosing the most sustainable option.

CELEBRATIONS

Keep parties planet friendly by...

- ☐ Sending virtual invites.
- ☐ Saying bye-bye to balloons.
- ☐ Avoiding single-use paper or plastic plates, cups and cutlery.
- ☐ Hiring out party supplies.
- ☐ Using reusable straws.
- ☐ Not using glitter unless it is compostable.
- ☐ Ditching the party bags or making them less wasteful.
- ☐ Avoiding party food in plastic packaging.
- ☐ Having clearly labelled rubbish, recycling and food-waste bins.
- ☐ Making a gift list.

If you don't want a gift you've been given, get rid of it responsibly by...

- ☐ Exchanging it for something you DO want.
- ☐ Regifting it.
- ☐ Giving it to charity.
- ☐ Donating it to a refuge.

When giving gifts, reduce the likelihood of waste by...

- ☐ Giving gifts you know people want.
- ☐ Making your own gifts.

- ☐ Getting 'green' gifts.
- ☐ Buying pre-loved presents.
- ☐ Favouring small businesses.
- ☐ **Thinking outside the box by...**
  - ☐ Adopting or sponsoring an animal in the wild.
  - ☐ Buying a tree as a gift.
  - ☐ Saying it with flowers.
  - ☐ Choosing experience days and meals out.

Make gift wrapping less of an environmental nightmare by...

- ☐ Using the wrapping paper you already have first.
- ☐ Reusing paper, gift bags and bows that were on presents you have been given.
- ☐ Finding alternatives to wrapping paper, such as newspaper, fabric and brown paper.
- ☐ Using tape sparingly...
- ☐ Doing the scrunch test to see if wrapping paper is recyclable.
- ☐ Making your own gift tags from cards.
- ☐ Saving your stamps and sending them to charity.

TRANSPORT

Reduce the amount of car journeys you make by…
- ☐ **Walking more.**
  - ☐ 1-2 short journeys per week.
  - ☐ 3-4 short journeys per week
  - ☐ 5-6 short journeys per week.
- ☐ Riding a bike.
- ☐ Taking public transport.
- ☐ Combining journeys.
- ☐ Car sharing.
- ☐ Hiring a car.
- ☐ Getting an electric car.

Make your car more fuel efficient by….
- ☐ Removing anything you don't need from inside or on top of the car.
- ☐ Regularly checking your tyre pressure.

- ☐ Slowing down.

Cut down on the amount of flights you take by…
- ☐ Going on staycations.
- ☐ Travelling via coach or train.
- ☐ Having video calls instead of flying to meetings.

If you do fly, reduce the impact by…
- ☐ Offsetting your flights.
- ☐ Choosing one long-haul trip over lots of short-haul flights.
- ☐ Flying direct.
- ☐ Flying economy.
- ☐ Travelling light.

TAKING THINGS FURTHER

Keep up the good work by…
- ☐ Staying informed – watch documentaries, read books and follow social media accounts about saving the planet.
- ☐ Spreading the word.
- ☐ Leading by example.
- ☐ Talking to your boss about implementing greener measures at work.

- ☐ Seeing what can be done in schools.
- ☐ Writing to your MP.
- ☐ Signing petitions.
- ☐ Putting your money in a green bank.
- ☐ Going litter picking.
- ☐ Joining a beach clean.
- ☐ Planting trees.

ANY EXTRAS…

- ☐
- ☐
- ☐
- ☐
- ☐
- ☐
- ☐
- ☐
- ☐

- ☐
- ☐
- ☐
- ☐
- ☐
- ☐
- ☐
- ☐
- ☐

ACKNOWLEDGEMENTS

There are many people who have made *Everyday Ways To Save Our Planet* possible. The most important is my daughter Charlotte. She is my reason for wanting to write this book. For her and the future generations, we are passing the baton that is our planet on to them and I want to give them a fighting chance. Thank you, Charlotte, for being so amazing, kind and funny. For your strength and inspiring me every day. Yes, you're only four, but you were born three months early and had to fight from day one. You defied all the odds and have kept that fighting spirit with you – it's you who gives me hope for the future.

Thank you to my incredible agent, Professor Jonathan Shalit OBE, the chairman and founder of InterTalent Rights Group – the best in the business! He has a superb eye for people and ideas that will connect with the public and he believed in me and the book idea from day one. Thank you for your fantastic ideas, help and guidance along the way. And my heartfelt thanks to InterTalent's Meisha Kelly, who has dealt with the huge amount of correspondence needed for this book, as well as being there for the fantastic cover shoot (a 'pinch me' moment).

Of course, I couldn't have done this without my publisher, Mirror Books, who fell in love with my idea for the book from the moment they heard about it. I remember our initial meeting, where I just talked and talked and you just listened – not because you had to but because you wanted to. Special thank-yous to the managing director Steve Hanrahan for saying YES, to Paul Dove, Roy Gilfoyle and Chris Brereton for editing the text, to Rick Cooke, Chris Collins and Adam Ward for the amazing design, and to Claire Brown for helping me promote the book.

I also want to thank Mirror Books for introducing me to a superstar called Melanie Hancill, who helped me write, organise and edit this book. We found an instant connection with matching beliefs and goals for the project. Thank you for the many hours of Zoom chats going over every section of the book in fine detail and for turning huge amounts of research and notes into a coherent and well-structured whole. I'm a fan of why say one word when 100 will do, so this book would have been twice as long (but probably half as interesting) if I'd had my way.

I'm so grateful to the many people in my science community for their guidance. Thank you firstly to Mona Lukha, head of ITV Weather, for supporting me and kindly volunteering to read over the manuscript. Thank you to Professor Liz Bentley, Chief Executive of the Royal Meteorological Society, Clare Nullis from the World Meteorological Society,

Leo Barasi, the author of *Climate Majority*, Professor Ed Hawkins from the University of Reading and Leo Hickman, the Director and Editor of Carbon Brief, for your help and advice (and graphs!). Plus a thank you to the Met Office for their continued support throughout my career, and to the many scientists there for taking the time to talk to me and sending through the most up-to-date science. I'd also like to thank the Royal Meteorological Society for making me a fellow with unanimous vote! And I'm so grateful to Emily Dixon for helping with the research for this book.

For getting me to where I am today, a special mention for my parents, Paul and Carol. They pushed me (just enough), believed in me (more than I did), loved me (more than is humanly possible) and were there for me every step of the way as I followed my dreams. I'd also like to thank my teacher, Mr Hannant, who made me fall in love with the weather when I was just 14. Thank you to all my teachers along the way at Duston Upper School and at the Meteorology and Physics department at the University of Reading.

I'm grateful for all the work experiences which got me to where I am today. Thank you to my boss Duncan Tudor at the Met Office, RAF Brize Norton and to the BBC Weather Centre for all the amazing opportunities. And a big shout out to the fantastic team on *Good Morning Britain* at ITV for giving me what I genuinely think is the best job in the world. Thank you to my incredible editor Neil Thompson for always championing me and my passion for the weather, the environment and climate change and for allowing me to add a little sprinkle of science along the way. The trips to Svalbard, COP26 and the Isles of Scilly were so important and allowed me to show viewers the reality facing our planet. Thank you to Emma Gormley, managing director of ITV Daytime, who was there for my interviews at ITV and saw something in me that she thought the viewers would love, and for pushing the climate change message through our shows.

There are so many people I am grateful for that I am not able to list them all here. But if you have had to endure my constant 'book chat' many times over (yes, that's you Kevin), thank you – you know who you are.

Nearly last and by no means least, my husband! He's the butt of a lot of jokes in this book because he is genuinely the tightest man on our planet. But he is also the loveliest. Thank you for supporting me to do the job that I love and for being there during the many hours, days and weeks writing this book.

Finally, a massive thank you to YOU, for buying and reading this book. I've poured my heart and soul into it and the fact you have bought it means there is hope for our planet. I really do believe we can all make a difference. I have hope for the future, for my Charlotte and the generations to come.

Laura xx

REFERENCES

INTRODUCTION

Nine out of 10 of us will mention it at least three times a day: bbc.com/future/article/20151214-why-do-brits-talk-about-the-weather-so-much

July 2021 was the hottest month ever recorded for our planet: https://www.noaa.gov/news/its-official-july-2021-was-earths-hottest-month-on-record

The last decade has been our warmest ever: ncdc.noaa.gov/sotc/global/201913

LETTER TO CHARLOTTE

One million of eight million animal and plant species are threatened with extinction: un.org/sustainabledevelopment/blog/2019/05/nature-decline-unprecedented-report/

Since 1970 we have lost 68% of global wildlife: wwf.org.uk/press-release/living-planet-report-2020

By 2050 all the plastic in the oceans will weigh more than all the fish: https://www.plasticsoupfoundation.org/en/plastic-problem/plastic-soup/more-plastic-than-fish/

Animals listed as extinct in the wild: .iucnredlist.org/

WHAT IS CLIMATE CHANGE?

TED talk by climate scientist Dr James Rae in 2018: ted.com/talks/james_rae_climate_change_simple_serious_solvable

In the last 170 years the Earth's temperature has risen by around 1.2°C above average: ipcc.ch/sr15/chapter/chapter-1/

Climatologist Professor Ed Hawkins' Climate Stripes: showyourstripes.info/s/globe

The last eight years have been the warmest on record: scitechdaily.com/2021-continued-earths-warming-trend-the-past-8-years-have-been-the-warmest-in-the-global-record

December 2021 was the 444th consecutive month with temperatures above average: ncdc.noaa.gov/sotc/global/202112

2020 was the joint warmest year on record, tied with 2016: climate.copernicus.eu/copernicus-2020-warmest-year-record-europe-globally-2020-ties-2016-warmest-year-recorded

Scientists say there is a 99% chance that 2022 will be in the top 10 warmest years on recorded: phys.org/news/2022-01-years-hottest-ever.html

Around 99% of the Earth's atmosphere is made up of nitrogen (78%) and oxygen (21%): climate.nasa.gov/news/2491/10-interesting-things-about-air

The level of CO_2 in our atmosphere has risen by 50% since 1750: carbonbrief.org/met-office-atmospheric-co2-now-hitting-50-higher-than-pre-industrial-levels

CO_2 levels in the atmosphere are now the highest ever recorded: metoffice.gov.uk/about-us/press-office/news/weather-and-climate/2021/2021-carbon-dioxide-forecast

The last time the level of CO_2 in the atmosphere was above 400ppm was during the Pliocene Epoch, between 2.6 and 5.3 million years ago: theconversation.com/climate-explained-what-the-world-was-like-the-last-time-carbon-dioxide-levels-were-at-400ppm-141784

During the Pliocene Epoch the sea level was about 23.5 metres higher than today and the average temperature was 4°C higher: nature.com/articles/s41586-019-1543-2

Methane is up to 80 times more warming than CO_2: edf.org/climate/methane-crucial-opportunity-climate-fight#:~:text=Methane%20has%20more%20than%2080,warming%20in%20the%20near%20term.

The concentration of methane in the atmosphere has more than doubled since pre-industrial times, reaching 1,900ppb (parts per billion) in 2021, compared to 722ppb in 1750: ft.com/content/d0ab40a8-aee2-11e9-8030-530adfa879c2; gml.noaa.gov/ccgg/trends_ch4/

Nitrous oxide is 300 times more warming than carbon dioxide: epa.gov/ghgemissions/overview-greenhouse-gases

Since 1750, the amount of nitrous oxide in the atmosphere has increased by 23% – 270ppb in 1750 to 334ppb in 2021: n2olevels.org

Human industry emits about 100 times more CO_2 than volcanic activity: phys.org/news/2019-10-humanity-emissions-times-greater-volcanoes.html

The influence of the orbital changes in the last 125 years have had a negligible impact on the global temperature: bloomberg.com/graphics/2015-whats-warming-the-world/

99.8% of climate scientists say that humans are the cause of the Earth heating: theguardian.com/environment/2021/oct/19/case-closed-999-of-scientists-agree-climate-emergency-caused-by-humans

UK emissions estimated at 454.8 million tonnes of carbon dioxide equivalent (80% from carbon dioxide); Consumption emissions in the UK are 37% higher than UK-based emissions; Our total greenhouse gas emissions for 2019 were 43.8% lower than in 1990: Emissions via sector: assets.publishing.service.gov.uk/government/uploads/system/uploads/attachment_data/file/957887/2019_Final_greenhouse_gas_emissions_statistical_release.pdf

UK's estimated CO_2 emissions for 2020 are 10.7% less than in 2019: assets.publishing.service.gov.uk/government/uploads/system/uploads/attachment_data/file/972583/2020_Provisional_emissions_statistics_report.pdf

The Arctic is warming two to three times faster than the global average on Earth: phys.org/news/2021-05-arctic-faster-planet.html

Since the 1980s glaciers have lost more ice than they have acquired – the equivalent of 27.5 metres being sliced off the top: climate.gov/news-features/understanding-climate/climate-change-glacier-mass-balance

670 million people live in high mountainous regions: news.un.org/en/story/2019/09/1047392

1.5 million Brits travel abroad for ski holidays: lhm-marketing.com/en/uk-ski-market-how-many-brits/

The Arctic lost 6,000 gigatonnes of ice between 1993 and 2019, which caused a global average sea level rise of 17mm: rmets.org/metmatters/diary-svalbard

Glaciers are at their lowest extent in 2000 years: ipcc.ch/report/sixth-assessment-report-working-group-i/

Glacier melt has been responsible for 40% of sea level rise since 1901: ipcc.ch/report/ar6/wg1/downloads/report/IPCC_AR6_WGI_Chapter_09.pdf

If we carry on as we are, there will be a 50% reduction in the volume of ice in glaciers by 2100, and an 80% reduction in small glaciers: sciencedaily.com/releases/2019/04/190409083258.htm

If all glaciers in the world melted the average global sea level rise would be 0.3 metres: nature.com/articles/s41561-019-0300-3

Between 1979 and 2006, summer ice melt increased by 30%: nsidc.org/cryosphere/quickfacts/icesheets.html

If the ice sheet melted completely, sea levels would rise by 7%: climate.nasa.gov/faq/30/if-all-of-earths-ice-melts-and-flows-into-the-ocean-what-would-happen-to-the-planets-rotation

If all glaciers and ice sheets melted, global sea level would rise by more than 60 metres: sealevel.nasa.gov/understanding-sea-level/global-sea-level/ice-melt

In August 2021, rain (instead of snow) fell at the summit of Greenland's ice sheet for the first time in recorded history: theguardian.com/world/2021/aug/20/rain-falls-peak-greenland-ice-cap-first-time-on-record-climate-crisis

Arctic sea ice is at its lowest in 1,000 years: ipcc.ch/report/sixth-assessment-report-working-group-i/

Since 1979 we've lost an area of sea ice that would cover around half of Europe: twitter.com/metoffice/status/1184065129014583296

In the last 40 years, we've lost an average of 87,000 km² per year – that's a total of 3.4 million km²: blog.metoffice.gov.uk/2020/04/21/new-study-highlights-increasing-vulnerability-of-arctic-sea-ice/

In 2020, late-summer Arctic sea ice was at its second lowest in recorded history: climate.nasa.gov/news/3023/2020-arctic-sea-ice-minimum-at-second-lowest-on-record/

If we carry on as we are, the Arctic will be ice-free during summer in 10 to 30 years: nationalgeographic.com/science/article/arctic-summer-sea-ice-could-be-gone-by-2035; theguardian.com/environment/2011/jul/11/arctic-ice-free

Svalbard, it is warming nearly six times faster: norwaytoday.info/news/the-climate-warming-in-svalbard-is-six-times-greater-than-it-is-globally/

In the last 50 years the average winter temperature has increased by 7.7 degrees, from -15.9°C to -8.2°C. And the average summer temperature has increased by 2.5 degrees, from around +3.8°C to +6.3°C. To put that into perspective, in the same amount of time, the Earth has warmed by 0.88°C, the UK has warmed by 1.24°C and Svalbard has warmed by 4.9°C. Nowhere on Earth is heating up this fast: Figures from the Norwegian Meteorological Institute

The world's oceans recorded the hottest temperatures in history in 2021; The heat absorbed by the oceans last year was equivalent to seven Hiroshima atomic bombs detonating each second, 24 hours a day for 365 days a year: thehill.com/changing-america/sustainability/climate-change/589187-oceans-absorbed-heat-equivalent-to-7-hiroshima

Oceans absorb 23% of the annual emissions of CO_2 from the atmosphere: public.wmo.int/en/media/press-release/carbon-dioxide-levels-continue-record-levels-despite-covid-19-lockdown

Between 2006 and 2018, the global sea level rose by 4.4cm: www.ipcc.ch/report/ar6/wg1/#TS

Open ocean surface PH has declined globally over the last 40 years and is now the lowest it has been for at least 26,000 years; Many of the world's oceans experienced at least one 'strong' marine heatwave at some point in 2021: public.wmo.int/en/media/press-release/state-of-climate-2021-extreme-events-and-major-impacts

We've lost over half of the world's coral reefs since 1950: nhm.ac.uk/discover/news/2021/september/over-half-of-coral-reef-cover-lost-since-1950.html

If we reach 2°C of warming, we'll lose 99% of our coral reefs: ipcc.ch/2018/10/08/summary-for-policymakers-of-ipcc-special-report-on-global-warming-of-1-5c-approved-by-governments/

We've seen global average sea levels rise by 21-24cm since 1880: climate.gov/news-features/understanding-climate/climate-change-global-sea-level

The Isle de Jean Charles in Louisiana, USA has shrunk by 98% since 1955 because of rising sea levels and coastal erosion: nrdc.org/stories/people-isle-jean-charles-are-louisianas-first-climate-refugees-they-wont-be-last

The Tuvalu archipelago will be the first nation in the world to disappear due to rising sea: theguardian.com/global-development/2019/may/16/one-day-disappear-tuvalu-sinking-islands-rising-seas-climate-change

It's predicted that the Marshall Islands could be lost to climate change as early as 2080: agupubs.onlinelibrary.wiley.com/doi/full/10.1029/2020EF001525

The carbon emissions of the richest 1% are more than double the emissions of the poorest half of humanity: oxfam.org/en/press-releases/carbon-emissions-richest-1-percent-more-double-emissions-poorest-half-humanity

By 2050, 300 million people's homes will fall below the current level of coastal flooding: climatecentral.org/news/report-flooded-future-global-vulnerability-to-sea-level-rise-worse-than-previously-understood

Isles of Scilly most impacted by climate change in the UK: itv.com/news/2021-07-20/why-climate-change-is-more-dangerous-for-isles-of-scilly-than-anywhere-in-uk

For every 1°C rise in warming the air holds 7% more moisture: carbonbrief.org/explainer-what-climate-models-tell-us-about-future-rainfall

The July 2021 floods in Germany were the deadliest in almost 60 years: yaleclimateconnections.org/2021/07/central-europe-staggers-toward-recovery-from-catastrophic-flooding-more-than-200-killed/

China's Henan province experienced a year's worth of rain in just four days in July

2021: public.wmo.int/en/media/press-release/water-related-hazards-dominate-disasters-past-50-years

The floods in China resulted in 302 deaths and more than 92,000 homes damaged or destroyed: upi.com/Top_News/World-News/2021/08/02/china-Chinese-flood-death-toll-302-Henan-Province/4071627922306/

In the city of Zhengzhou, 644.6mm of rainfall was reported in just 24 hours: yaleclimateconnections.org/2021/07/extreme-rainfall-in-china-over-25-inches-falls-in-24-hours-leaving-33-dead/

During Storm Ida in September 2021, 80mm of rain fell in New York in one hour: https://www.statista.com/chart/25690/new-york-city-hourly-rainfall-records/

Siracusa, Sicily reached 48.8°C on 11 August 2021: https://www.newscientist.com/article/2286967-sicily-hits-48-8c-the-highest-temperature-ever-recorded-in-europe

Death Valley, California reached 54.4°C on July 9, equalling a similar 2020 value as the highest recorded in the world since at least the 1930s; Cizre in Turkey, set a national record with a temperature high of 49.1°C; Tbilisi in Georgia had its hottest day on record at 40.6°C: meteorologicaltechnologyinternational.com/news/climate-measurement/past-seven-years-set-to-be-warmest-on-record-finds-wmo-report.html

Lytton in British Columbia, Canada, reached a sweltering 49.6°C in July 2021: rmets.org/metmatters/record-breaking-heat-canada

Lapland recorded a temperature of 33.6°C in July 2021 highest in 100 years: lifeinnorway.net/arctic-region-bakes-in-record-heatwave/

In January 2022, Australia equalled its hottest day on record with a temperature of 50.7C: bbc.co.uk/news/world-australia-59977193

Giraffes have seen their population decline by 40% in the last 30 years: bornfree.org.uk/articles/giraffes-in-crisis

The global polar bear population is expected to decline by 30% by 2050: geographical.co.uk/nature/polar/item/2076-polar-bear-populations-to-decrease-by-30-percent-by-2050

In 2019, a 42°C heatwave in Australia killed one third (at least 23,000) of the country's spectacled flying fox bats: nrdc.org/onearth/heat-wave-australia-killed-23000-spectacled-flying-foxes

It's estimated that 1 billion small sea creatures died during a heat wave in the Salish Sea in 2021: globalnews.ca/news/8008202/billion-sea-creatures-die-bc-heat-wave/

In the UK, 34°C has been recorded in seven of the last 10 years, whereas it happened only seven times in the 50 years before that: carbonbrief.org/met-office-the-uks-august-2020-heatwave

April 2021 was the sunniest on record: metoffice.gov.uk/about-us/press-office/news/weather-and-climate/2021/lowest-average-minimum-temperatures-since-1922-as-part-of-dry-april

Since 1884, the top 10 warmest years on record have all occurred in the last 20 years: metoffice.gov.uk/about-us/press-office/news/weather-and-climate/2019/state-of-the-uk-climate-2018

It's now 10 times more likely that the UK will record a temperature of 40°C in the coming decades (once in every 100 years instead of once in every 1000): metoffice.gov.uk/about-us/press-office/news/weather-and-climate/2020/chances-of-40c-days-in-the-uk-increasing-due-to-human-influence

metoffice.gov.uk/research/climate/understanding-climate/uk-and-global-extreme-events-heatwaves

During the 2018 heatwave in the UK, a sharp increase in the daily death count coincided with exceptionally high temperatures: assets.publishing.service.gov.uk/government/uploads/system/uploads/attachment_data/file/942648/PHE_heatwave_report_2018.pdf

Since 1862, six of the 10 wettest years in the UK have happened in the last 24 years: rmets.org/news/climate-change-continues-be-evident-across-uk

Winters have been 12% wetter over the last decade compared to the period 1961-1990: metoffice.gov.uk/binaries/content/assets/metofficegovuk/pdf/research/ukcp/ukcp-headline-findings-v2.pdf

In 2020, we had the wettest day the UK had recorded since 1891: blog.metoffice.gov.uk/2020/10/16/rainfall-on-uks-wettest-day-on-record-could-have-more-than-filled-loch-ness/

It's three times more likely that we will see an event like Storm Alex (once every 100 years rather than once every 300): metoffice.gov.uk/about-us/press-office/news/weather-and-climate/2021/climate-change-shifting-uks-high-impact-weather

The rate of sea level rise was 1.5mm per year from the start of the 20th Century but between 1993 and 2019, it has increased to more than 3mm per year: post.parliament.uk/research-briefings/post-pn-0555/

The sea level has risen by nearly 2cm per decade over the 60 years up to 2018: metoffice.gov.uk/about-us/press-office/news/weather-and-climate/2021/climate-change-continues-to-be-evident-across-uk

It's estimated that 1.5 million properties will be at risk from flooding in England by 2080, and 100,000 homes at risk from coastal erosion: theccc.org.uk/2018/10/26/current-approach-to-protecting-englands-coastal-communities-from-flooding-and-erosion-not-fit-for-purpose-as-the-climate-changes/

Around 30 million people were displaced by extreme weather events such as storms and floods in 2020: ifrc.org/press-release/red-cross-red-crescent-report-reveals-extent-impact-people-forced-flee-their-homes

We are on track for a temperature increase of nearly 3°C by 2100: reuters.com/article/us-climate-change-un-idUSKCN1NY186

Almost 167 million homes could be lost to disasters by 2040: reliefweb.int/report/world/climate-crisis-destroy-167-million-homes-next-20-years

The latest IPCC report showing predictions for 1.5°C low, high etc https://climateactiontracker.org/global/cat-thermometer/

Forests absorb 2.6 billion tonnes of CO₂ every year: iucn.org/resources/issues-briefs/forests-and-climate-change

An area of forest the size of a football pitch is destroyed every second; Microscopic marine algae and bacteria in oceans absorb about as much carbon as all the plants and trees on land combined: clientearth.org/latest/latest-updates/stories/what-is-a-carbon-sink/

Trees absorb around 30% of the greenhouse gases we emit into the atmosphere: iucn.org/resources/issues-briefs/forests-and-climate-change

More than half the world's forests have been destroyed: theworldcounts.com/challenges/planet-earth/forests-and-deserts/rate-of-deforestation/story

Peatlands cover just 3% of the world's land area: weforum.org/agenda/2021/06/peatlands-worldwide-emissions-carbon-environment-climate-change

Peatlands store twice as much carbon as all the trees on the Earth combined: iucn.org/resources/issues-briefs/peatlands-and-climate-change

The latest pledges and targets show that with current policies the Earth will warm by 2.9°C by 2100 compared to pre-industrial levels (with a range between 2.1°C to 3.9°C): nytimes.com/interactive/2021/10/25/climate/world-climate-pledges-cop26.htm

An optimistic best-case scenario, implementing all targets, could limit warming to 1.8°C (with a range between 1.5°C to 2.4°C): iea.org/commentaries/cop26-climate-pledges-could-help-limit-global-warming-to-1-8-c-but-implementing-them-will-be-the-key

THE PROBLEM WITH PLASTIC

Half of all plastic is designed to be used only once and then thrown away; Every year, we produce more than 300 million metric tons of plastic waste worldwide: unep.org/interactive/beat-plastic-pollution

The average household in the UK throws out 128 items of plastic every week: wsrecycling.co.uk/news/post/household-plastic-waste-increases-during-lockdown

Of the 8.3 billion metric tons (and counting) of plastic created since the 1950s, 6.3 billion metric tons became waste plastic; Most plastics take upwards of 400 years to decompose; Globally, 91% of waste plastic is not recycled: nationalgeographic.com/science/article/plastic-produced-recycling-waste-ocean-trash-debris-environment

In 2018, a plastic bag was discovered at a depth of 10,975 metres in the Mariana Trench in the Pacific Ocean: nationalgeographic.com/article/plastic-bag-found-bottom-worlds-deepest-ocean-trench

In 2020, microplastics were discovered in snow near the summit of Earth's highest peak, Mount Everest: nationalgeographic.com/environment/article/microplastics-found-near-everests-peak-highest-ever-detected-world-perpetual-planet

The UK is responsible for 3.7 million metric tons of plastic waste each year: statista.com/topics/4918/plastic-waste-in-the-united-kingdom-uk/#dossierKeyfigures

The UK is the second biggest producer of plastic waste per person in the world, behind America: theguardian.com/environment/2020/oct/30/us-and-uk-citizens-are-worlds-biggest-sources-of-plastic-waste-study

In the UK, we actually recycle around 47% of our plastic waste: assets.publishing.service.gov.uk/government/uploads/system/uploads/attachment_data/file/1002246/UK_stats_on_waste_statistical_notice_July2021_accessible_FINAL.pdf

88% of people changed their lifestyles to reduce the amount of plastic they used after watching Blue Planet II: globalcitizen.org/en/content/88-blue-planet-2-changed-david-attenborough

A rubbish truck's worth of plastic gets dumped into the ocean every single minute: greenpeace.co.uk/news/why-is-there-so-much-plastic-in-the-ocean

Approximately 19 billion disposable face masks headed to landfill in 2021: bbc.co.uk/news/uk-wales-57687261.

More than 1 million seabirds and 100,000 marine mammals die from plastic pollution every year: worldwideboat.com/knowledgebase/plastic-pollution-and-marine-life

The Great Pacific Garbage Patch covers 1.6 million square kilometres; It's estimated that there is around 80,000 tons of plastic waste in it; Sea turtles swimming around the Patch have up to 74% of their diets composed of plastic: theoceancleanup.com/great-pacific-garbage-patch/

If we carry on producing and using plastic in the way we are now, it's estimated there will be more plastic than fish in the sea by 2050: plasticsoupfoundation.org/en/plastic-problem/plastic-soup/more-plastic-than-fish/

The amount of plastic going into the oceans every year weighs as much as 10 times all the blue whales alive today: uk.whales.org/our-4-goals/create-healthy-seas/impact-of-plastic-pollution-on-whales-and-dolphins/

We eat a credit-card sized amount of plastic every week: plasticsforchange.org/blog/category/new-study-shows-people-eat-a-credit-card-size-worth-of-plastic-each-week

It's estimated that the average person eats 70,000 pieces of microplastic each year: globalcitizen.org/en/content/microplastics-in-food-eating-plastic-waste/

35% of microplastics found in the sea come from the clothes that we wear: phys.org/news/2018-09-microplastics-world-oceans-synthetic-textiles.html

Microplastics and fibres have been found in fish, honey, beer, sea salt plus bottled and tap water: ncbi.nlm.nih.gov/pmc/articles/PMC6132564/

Between 400,000 and one million people die every year from diseases and accidents relating to poorly managed plastic waste in developing countries; It's estimated that plastic pollution kills one person every 30 seconds: climateaction.org/news/plastic-killing-up-to-one-million-people-a-year-says-sir-david-attenborough

WHAT CAN WE DO?

Only 45% of the waste we create in the UK gets recycled: recyclingbins.co.uk/recycling-facts

The UK average carbon footprint is about 13 tonnes of CO₂e per person each year: carbonindependent.org/23.html

That's double the global average carbon footprint: pawprint.eco/eco-blog/average-carbon-footprint-globally

Around 75% of our carbon footprint comes from transport, housing and food: assets.publishing.service.gov.uk/government/uploads/system/uploads/attachment_data/file/957887/2019_Final_greenhouse_gas_emissions_statistical_release.pdf

100 companies are responsible for 71% of greenhouse gas emissions: cdp.net/en/articles/media/new-report-shows-just-100-companies-are-source-of-over-70-of-emissions

20 firms are behind more than half of single-use plastic waste: bbc.co.uk/news/science-environment-57149741

Climate Change Committee report showing the role of individuals in reaching net zero (43% using new technologies, 16% behavioural changes and 41% low carbon technologies and fuels): theccc.org.uk/wp-content/uploads/2020/12/The-Sixth-Carbon-Budget-The-UKs-path-to-Net-Zero.pdf

HOME ENERGY

40% of carbon emissions in the UK come from our homes: theccc.org.uk/wp-content/uploads/2016/07/5CB-Infographic-FINAL-.pdf

We could achieve 11% of the UK's 2050 carbon emissions target by just taking household energy efficiency measures: edfenergy.com/for-home/energywise/6-tips-go-net-zero-starting-today

A study in 2020 showed that almost two-thirds of Brits had their thermostats turned up to more than 20°C: energylivenews.com/2020/10/28/uk-homes-could-save-1-4bn-by-turning-thermostats-down-by-just-1c/

Over the course of a year, if you turn down your thermostat by 1°C, you could save up to £40 off your annual energy bill, and cut your carbon footprint by around 300kg CO₂e: theguardian.com/environment/ethicallivingblog/2007/nov/09/savecarbonwhilekeepingwarm

Carbon equivalent calculator: epa.gov/energy/greenhouse-gas-equivalencies-calculator

Approximately 35% of heat is lost through walls, 25% through the roof, 25% through doors and windows and a further 15% through floor: rbkc.gov.uk/environment/climate-change/prevent-heat-loss-your-home

Closing your curtains at dusk can reduce heat loss by 15-17%: thisismoney.co.uk/money/bills/article-2644012/Energy-House-scientists-Make-rain-snow-test-energy-efficiency.html

A window left open overnight in winter will waste enough energy to drive a small car more than 35 miles: environment.admin.cam.ac.uk/facts-figures

If you properly draught-proof your home, you could save £60 on your energy bills every year; If every home in the UK properly draught-proofed their homes, it would save enough energy to heat 400,000 homes, and a total of £190 million a year: thegreenage.co.uk/tech/draught-proofing/

Loft, wall and floor insulation costs and savings: onehome.org.uk/your-home/19-warm-and-cosy-homes/265-how-much-could-you-save-by-insulating-your-home

Lighting is responsible for 15% of the energy we use in our homes: energy.gov/energysaver/lighting-choices-save-you-money

Traditional incandescent bulbs use only 10% of the energy they use to produce light, with the rest lost as heat inside the bulb: ovoenergy.com/guides/energy-guides/energy-saving-light-bulbs

Switching from halogen to more energy-saving bulbs could cut 1.26 million tonnes of carbon emissions a year – the equivalent to removing half a million cars from the UK's roads: gov.uk/government/news/end-of-halogen-light-bulbs-spells-brighter-and-cleaner-future

CFLs use 75% less energy than a filament bulb and they last 10 times longer: everycrsreport.com/reports/RS22807.html

https://www.energy.gov/energysaver/led-lighting

LEDs use 90% less energy than a traditional bulb, and 90% of the energy they do use goes towards producing light: scienceabc.com/innovation/why-are-led-lights-so-energy-efficient.html

They also have an exceptionally long life, with many promising 50,000 hours of light – around 50 times longer than a traditional bulb, 25 times longer than a halogen bulb and 8 times longer than a CFL bulb: bulbs.com/learning/ledfaq.aspx

If you replace all the bulbs in your home with LEDs, you could reduce your carbon emissions by 65kg per year. That's the equivalent of driving your car 220 miles: energysavingtrust.org.uk/top-tips-to-reduce-your-carbon-emissions

It's estimated that if everyone installed smart meters – both homeowners and businesses – it could reduce UK carbon emissions by 45 million tonnes – the equivalent of taking 26 million cars off the road for a year: gov.uk/government/news/government-sets-out-plans-to-drive-up-smart-meter-installations

In order to meet the Paris Climate Agreement goals, 70% of electricity generation needs to come from solar and wind by 2050: iea.org/reports/net-zero-by-2050

In order to meet net zero by 2050, the UK needs to quadruple offshore wind capacity: gov.uk/government/publications/the-ten-point-plan-for-a-green-industrial-revolution/title

Renewable energies outperformed fossil fuels for the first time in 2020, providing 43% of UK electricity compared to 37.7% from fossil fuels: offshorewind.biz/2021/03/25/renewable-energy-outperforms-fossil-fuels-in-uk

As of May 2021, around 900,000 UK homes have solar panels installed: theswitch.co.uk/energy/guides/renewables/solar-energy

Around 25% of houses in the UK are on top of former mines: theguardian.com/environment/2021/aug/10/abandoned-pits-former-mining-town-seaham-county-durham-fuel-green-revolution

As of 2020, nuclear power generated 20% of the UK's electricity: world-nuclear.org/information-library/country-profiles/countries-t-z/united-kingdom.aspx

Getting solar panels can reduce your home's carbon footprint by 80% in one year; Solar panels last for around 50 years: renewableenergyhub.co.uk/main/solar-panels/why-are-solar-panels-good-for-the-environment

It costs an average of £4,800 to fit a standard home with solar panels: moneysavingexpert.com/utilities/free-solar-panels/

Solar panels could save you between £90 and £240 off your energy bills a year: solartogether.co.uk/bolton/blog/how-much-do-solar-panels-cost

43% of Swedish homes have a heat pump: standard.co.uk/news/uk/european-greenpeace-uk-norway-finland-government-b954954.html

Heat pumps use 75% less electricity to heat your home than conventional electric heaters: evergreenenergy.co.uk/heat-pumps/are-heat-pumps-environmentally-friendly/

Heat pumps can cost between £6,000 and £45,000: renewableenergyhub.co.uk/main/heat-pumps-information/a-guide-to-heat-pump-prices-in-2019/

If you are switching from a new gas boiler, then you may not save on running costs, but you will be drastically cutting your carbon emissions. If you are switching from an electric heating system, then you could save up to £920 a year on your energy bills.

evergreenenergy.co.uk/heat-pumps/will-i-save-money-by-installing-a-heat-pump

The top three countries in Europe to have heat pumps installed in almost half of their homes are Norway, Sweden and Finland: theecoexperts.co.uk/air-source-heat-pumps/top-countries

IN THE KITCHEN

Food production accounts for around 26% of global greenhouse gas emissions: ourworldindata.org/food-ghg-emissions

Agriculture is the largest consumer of fresh water in the world: fao.org/3/i7959e/i7959e.pdf

Agriculture takes up half of the world's habitable land: ourworldindata.org/global-land-for-agriculture

It is actually better, emissions wise, to eat tomatoes grown from the natural heat of the sun in Spain then transported here than tomatoes grown in artificially heated greenhouses in the UK: winacc.org.uk/downloads/STAP/Food%20transport%20full%20version.pdf

Around 14% of adults in the UK now follow meat-free diets, and the number of people who gave up meat in 2020 (470,000) was double that of 2019. In 2022, a further 8.8 million Brits say they plan to go meat-free: finder.com/uk/uk-diet-trends

Livestock farming is responsible for 14.5% of all greenhouse gas emissions: fao.org/news/story/en/item/197623/icode/

Farming animals uses and pollutes vast amounts of water: fao.org/3/i7754e/i7754e.pdf

And takes up 83% of agricultural land on earth: ourworldindata.org/agricultural-land-by-global-diets

The storage of manure and the use of synthetic fertilisers are also responsible for 65% of all human-related emissions of nitrous oxide: cowspiracy.com/facts

If everyone swapped one more red-meat meal a week for a plant-based alternative, it could cut the UK's greenhouse gas emissions by 45 million tonnes. That's the equivalent of taking 16 million cars off the road: meatlessfarm.com/meatless-consumption-target

The number of animals raised for slaughter on Earth now outweighs wildlife by 15 to 1: interactive.carbonbrief.org/what-is-the-climate-impact-of-eating-meat-and-dairy

Going vegan for two-thirds of meals could cut food-related carbon emissions by 60%: economist.com/graphic-detail/2019/11/15/how-much-would-giving-up-meat-help-the-environment

A 50g portion of red meat is linked to at least 20 times more greenhouse gas emissions and 100 times more land use than a 100g portion of veg: worldinfigures.com/highlights/detail/257

Globally, a frightening one acre of land is cleared for animal farming every second: worldanimalfoundation.com/advocate/farm-animals/params/post/1280000/animal-agriculture-causing-extinctions

All protein calculations: fdc.nal.usda.gov; .bhf.org.uk/informationsupport/heart-matters-magazine/nutrition/protein/how-to-get-protein-without-the-meat

Plant-based meals cost 40% less than those containing meat and fish and take a third of the amount of time to prepare: veganuary.com/vegan-meals-cost-40-percent-less-than-meat-fish

Replacing half of UK meat and dairy consumption with a combination of fruits, vegetables, and cereals could reduce dietary emissions by 19% and avert roughly 37,000 premature deaths from cardiovascular disease and cancer per year: ncbi.nlm.nih.gov/pmc/articles/PMC7190375/

It's estimated that people who eat meat spend £645 extra a year than those on a meat-free diet: plantbasednews.org/opinion/meat-free-diet-cheaper-ps600-year

If the UK went vegan it could save the NHS more than £30 billion: plantbasednews.org/news/economics/nhs-save-money-vegan-doctor

Greenhouse gas emissions from UK beef are about half the global average: nfuonline.com/archive?treeid=141504

Producing a glass of dairy milk results in almost three times the greenhouse gas emissions of any non-dairy milks: bbc.co.uk/news/science-environment-46654042

Plant-based milk chart: sciencefocus.com/science/which-vegan-milk-is-best-for-the-environment

46% of the plastic in The Great Pacific Garbage Patch is made up of fishing gear: nationalgeographic.com/science/article/great-pacific-garbage-patch-plastics-environment

Fishing boats that trawl the bottom of the ocean release as much carbon per year as the aviation industry: theguardian.com/environment/2021/mar/17/trawling-for-fish-releases-as-much-carbon-as-air-travel-report-finds-climate-crisis

Every year, there is 25 million acres of deforestation but ocean floors are destroyed by trawlers at a rate of 3.9 billion acres a year: greenpeace.org/aotearoa/story/seaspiracy-netflix-movie-take-action

Longline fishing lays enough lines a day to wrap around the world 500 times: independent.co.uk/life-style/seaspiracy-netflix-fishing-cowspiracy-b1824343.html

UK households throw away an average of six meals a week: bbc.co.uk/news/uk-24846612

5.8 million whole potatoes are thrown out every day; 24 million slices of bread go to waste every day; 5.8 million glasses of milk are poured away every day; 1.4 million bananas are binned every day; 178 million bags of salad a year are chucked out every year: ukharvest.org.uk/news-and-media/events-and-news/news/the-most-commonly-wasted-foods-in-british-households-and-how-to-rescue-them

Food waste alone produces 8-10% of all global greenhouse gas emissions; 70% of food waste comes from our homes: wrap.org.uk/media-centre/press-releases/wasting-food-feeds-climate-change-food-waste-action-week-launches-help

9.5 million tonnes of edible food is thrown away by households every year in the UK: lordslibrary.parliament.uk/food-waste-in-the-uk

Over a year, the average family throws away around £700 of food shopping: https://wrap.org.uk/media-centre/press-releases/food-waste-falls-7-person-three-years

If we all stopped wasting the food which could have been eaten, it would have the same CO₂ impact as taking one in four cars off UK roads: wrap.org.uk/resources/guide/waste-prevention-activities/food

41% of food is thrown away because we don't use it on time, 28% is wasted because we don't like it, 25% ends up in the bin because we cooked, prepared or were served too much and the last 6% for other reasons: viva.org.uk/planet/the-issues/food-waste/
The average UK household throws away 20% of all food purchased: recyclingbins.co.uk/recycling-facts

Globally, 931 million tonnes of food is wasted. That's the weight of 23 million loaded 40-tonne trucks. Put bumper to bumper, that's enough to circle the world seven times: unep.org/news-and-stories/press-release/un-17-all-food-available-consumer-levels-wasted

More than 4.5 million metric tons of fruit and veg is thrown out every year in the UK: dailymail.co.uk/news/article-6076325/More-4-5million-TONNES-fruit-vegetables-thrown-away-UK-year.html

Brits get through an average of 209 crisp packets per person in a year: circularonline.co.uk/news/poll-reveals-typical-brits-annual-waste

Only 5% of the world's supply of palm oil is certified as 'sustainable': sustainability.iceland.co.uk/our-planet/palm-oil

96% of people who drink tea in the UK use tea bags rather than loose leaf: theguardian.com/food/2021/feb/12/fancy-a-proper-brew-why-you-wont-regret-ditching-the-teabags

Brits drink around 100 million cups of tea a day: rd.com/article/why-british-drink-tea
Billions of particles of microplastic are released from teabags into each cup: newscientist.com/article/2217483-plastic-tea-bags-shed-billions-of-microplastic-particles-into-the-cup

All pet carbon footprint stats from: agriapet.co.uk/hub-agria-blog/2021/november/7-steps-to-reduce-your-pet-s-carbon-pawprints

745,000 miles of cling film is used by households across Britain every year – enough to go around the circumference of the world 30 times over: beebeewraps.com/blogs/news/what-is-the-problem-with-cling-film

Every day, 51,000 trees are felled to meet the daily demand for single-use paper towels: bettergoods.org/reusable-paper-towels

IN THE GARDEN

92% of people said their gardens were important to them in terms of health and wellbeing during 2020: ngs.org.uk/new-report-gardens-and-coronavirus-2020

You can burn up to 300 calories an hour doing light gardening: gardenbenches.com/blog/gardening-burn-calories/

Gardens in Britain cover an area larger than all of the country's nature reserves combined: hiwwt.org.uk/sites/default/files/2018-04/150318%20Wildlife%20gardening%20Butterfly%20border%20NB.pdf

Alarming figures show that 7,000 people are dying every year from living in areas with a lack of green space because of toxic pollutants: uk.newschant.com/health/more-than-40000-people-die-every-year-in-europe-because-of-a-lack-of-green-space-research-reveals/

Most people who live to 100 or more all do some kind of gardening: bbc.com/worklife/article/20181210-gardening-could-be-the-hobby-that-helps-you-live-to-100

Around 80% of the UK population live in urban areas: assets.publishing.service.gov.uk/government/uploads/system/uploads/attachment_data/file/1028819/Rural_population__Oct_2021.pdf

Gardens take up 25% of land in most cities: ons.gov.uk/economy/environmentalaccounts/bulletins/uknaturalcapital/urbanaccounts

On a hot day, the average temperature of real grass in the sun is 38.1°C, whereas fake grass soars to a scorching 62.3°C: facebook.com/page/119000758289594/search/?q=artificial%20grass (@daisyfirstaid)

A 2,500 square foot area of real grass produces enough oxygen for a family of four to breathe: stma.org/eight-benefits-of-natural-grass

An average sized lawn can capture as much as 136kg of carbon every year: mass.gov/doc/supporting-document-j/download

For every 1°C the mean temperature rises by the end of winter, grass will start growing six days earlier in spring; Between 2012 and 2019 there were 15% more growing days compared to 1961-1990: rhs.org.uk/science/pdf/RHS-Gardening-in-a-Changing-Climate-Report.pdf

Petrol lawnmowers produce 11 times more polluting emissions than a car; The average petrol lawnmower emits as much CO_2 in one hour as driving a car just under 100 miles: onlynaturalenergy.com/grass-lawns-are-an-ecological-catastrophe

Studies have shown that more than 200 species of wildflower would grow on lawns if we would only let them: plantlife.org.uk/about-us/news/no-mow-may-how-to-get-ten-times-more-bees-on-your-lockdown-lawn

In the UK, we have 275 species of bee: beepalace.com/about_palace.php
Only 10% of bees are social bees, such as the honeybee and bumblebee, the vast majority are solitary bees: lancaster.gov.uk/assets/attach/5999/Solitary%20Bees.pdf

More than 90% of global crop types are visited by bees: friendsoftheearth.uk/nature/why-do-we-need-bees

An estimated 97% of wildflower meadows disappeared from England and Wales between the 1930s and 1980s: independent.co.uk/climate-change/news/nature-studies-meadows-are-the-wildflower-experience-taken-to-the-ultimate-power-8655761.html

Peat bogs store twice as much carbon as all the world's forests: unep.org/news-and-stories/story/peatlands-store-twice-much-carbon-all-worlds-forests

Around 50% of the food we throw away can be composted; Composting for just one year can save the same amount of greenhouse gases as your kettle produces annually, or your washing machine produces in three months: recyclenow.com/reduce-waste/composting/why-compost

Every 20,000 people who compost can divert more than 10,000 tonnes of organic waste from landfill while growing 400-plus tonnes of fresh food every year: subpod.com/pages/the-vision

One full allotment (250 square metres) should feed a family of four for one year: croydon.gov.uk/libraries-leisure-and-culture/parks-and-open-spaces/allotments/croydon/allotments

IN THE BATHROOM

The average household in the UK uses 216 plastic hair-care bottles a year; A typical household also goes through 24 bottles of shower gel, 24 tubes of toothpaste, 12 bottles of moisturiser and 108 loo rolls each year: dailymail.co.uk/sciencetech/article-8647127/Average-British-household-used-216-plastic-haircare-bottles-YEAR.html

Globally, 80 billion plastic shampoo and conditioner bottles get thrown out every year: climateaction.org/news/zero-waste-beauty-brand-ethique-launches-in-uk

Recyclable bathroom waste accounts for up to 40% of total landfill waste in the UK: circularonline.co.uk/insight/whats-your-bathroom-waste-legacy

The average person spends £400 on beauty products each year in the UK: professionalbeauty.co.uk/site/newsdetails/brits-spend-400-pounds-on-beauty-products
Phthalates, paraben, bisphenol A and triclosan being suspected endocrine disruptors: pubmed.ncbi.nlm.nih.gov/25216151/

Liquid soaps require five times more energy for raw material production and nearly 20 times more energy for packaging production than bars of soap; People use six times the amount of liquid soap (by weight) than bar soap: conservationmagazine.org/2013/05/bar-soap-vs-liquid-soap

Cotton is a thirsty plant and can drink up to 29,000 litres of water for every 1kg of cotton: assets.wwf.org.uk/downloads/thirstycrops.pdf

22 million cotton buds were found for every 100 metres of beach in the UK during a beach clean survey in 2018: cottonbudproject.org.uk/plastic-cotton-bud-sticks-in-marine-litter.html

1.5 million cotton buds are produced every day: wwf.org.au/news/blogs/10-worst-single-use-plastics-and-eco-friendly-alternatives

People flushing wet wipes down the toilet causes 93% of sewer blocks in the UK – and it costs around £100 million a year to unblock them: theguardian.com/environment/2017/dec/12/baby-wipes-93-percent-matter-causing-uk-sewer-blockages

In the UK alone, we use 11 billion wet wipes a year: water.org.uk/wp-content/uploads/2020/02/Environment-Bill-Water-UK-Recommendations-Feb-2020.pdf

The biggest ever fatberg found in the UK was 84 metres long and weighed 90 tonnes: independent.co.uk/news/uk/home-news/fatberg-liverpool-sewer-oil-grease-wet-wipes-fat-united-utilities-biofuel-a8790361.html

79% of people in the UK buy deodorant as part of their weekly shop – which equates to around 50 million people; About 600 million aerosol cans are used in the UK every year: zerowasted.co.uk/best-natural-and-eco-friendly-deodorant

One pack of sanitary towels can contain up to 4 plastic bags worth of plastic; Conventional sanitary towels are 90% plastic: friendsoftheearth.uk/sustainable-living/plastic-periods-menstrual-products-and-plastic-pollution

In 2013, the Marine Conservation Society found 428 tampons and applicators per 4.4kms of beach, and 1291 sanitary towels per 13.3km: bloomandnora.com/pages/why-switch

The average person uses 22 sanitary towels or tampons per period – 11,000 in a lifetime: ahpma.co.uk/menstruation_facts_and_figures

Tampons, pads and pant liners generate more than 200,000 tonnes of waste every year: globalcitizen.org/en/content/best-period-products-for-the-environment

Most of us will use around 300 toothbrushes in a lifetime: nationalgeographic.com/environment/article/story-of-plastic-toothbrushes.

300 million toothpaste tubes end up in landfill every year in the UK; Toothpaste tubes take up to 500 years to decompose: nature.com/articles/s41415-021-2926-y

An estimated 5.5 million people use disposable plastic razors in the UK: statista.com/statistics/303508/razors-and-razor-blades-and-electric-shavers-usage-by-type-in-the-uk

We use roughly 8-9 sheets of toilet paper per trip to the loo and an average of 57 sheets a day; You will use 384 trees worth of toilet roll in your life: toiletpaperhistory.net/toilet-paper-facts/toilet-paper-fun-facts

In the UK we cut down 7 million trees a year for toilet roll: independent.co.uk/climate-change/opinion/toilet-paper-environmental-impact-trees-b1847644.html

52% of people who flush items they shouldn't down the toilet said it was because they didn't know the consequences of doing so: @CleanCoasts on Twitter twitter.com/cleancoasts/status/1398313146369118210

SAVE WATER

62% of people in the UK admit they don't drink the recommended 2 litres of water a day: a survey by Britvic's family brand Robinsons, August 2019.

It's estimated that England will face water shortages by 2050 unless we save water fast: Speech by Sir James Bevan, Chief Executive of the Environment Agency Waterwise Conference, 19 March 2019

Our water usage is increasing at twice the rate of population growth: un.org/waterforlifedecade/scarcity.shtml

While 71% of the earth's surface is covered in water, only around 3% of it is fresh: nationalgeographic.org/media/earths-fresh-water/

One in three people in the world don't have access to safe, clean drinking water: who.int/news/item/18-06-2019-1-in-3-people-globally-do-not-have-access-to-safe-drinking-water-unicef-who

We use approximately 143 litres of water each a day in the UK: Preserving our water resources in a changing climate – industry and government tackle threat to future water supplies, March 2020, gov.uk/government/news/preserving-our-water-resources-in-a-changing-climate-industry-and-government-tackle-threat-to-future-water-supplies

A running tap uses up six litres every minute and it takes up to 13 litres of water per toilet flush: waterwise.org.uk/save-water/

You could save 22 litres a day by turning off the tap while you lather up your hands with soap: greenmatters.com/p/water-conservation-hand-washing

In developing countries, women and girls in developing countries walk an average of 6 kilometres a day just to get clean water: worldvision.org/clean-water-news-stories/walk-water-6k

A typical bath uses around 80-100 litres of water whereas the average shower uses

50 litres: savewatersavemoney.co.uk/water-efficiency-tips-advice/view/82/water-efficiency-showerheads.html

The average length of time people spend in the shower in the UK is 8 minutes: mirashowers.co.uk/blog/trends/revealed-what-brits-are-really-getting-up-to-in-the-bathroom-1

Reducing your shower time by one minute can save your household up to £120 a year: savewatersavemoney.co.uk/products/view/38872/four-min-showertimer-swsm.html

Two-minute shower songs for Cape Town: 2minuteshowersongs.com

Dual-flush toilets can save up to 67% of water compared to a toilet that has a single-handle: flushfamilyhandyman.com/article/heres-why-you-should-consider-installing-a-dual-flush-toilet

Modern dishwashers use 11-13 litres of water per cycle: money.co.uk/energy/guides/energy-efficiency-dishwashing-dishwasher-versus-hand-washing

Average sink holds 20 litres of water: saveenergynb.ca/en/save-energy/education-and-tips/energy-efficiency-articles/which-is-more-energy-efficient-dishwasher-vs-hand-washing/

Hand-washing (5,620kg of greenhouse gases) versus using the dishwasher (2,090 kg greenhouse gases): iopscience.iop.org/article/10.1088/2515-7620/ab716b

Pre-rinsing dishes can use up to 24 litres of water: finish.co.uk/our-values/save-water/

Using the eco setting saves around 20% less water and energy: currys.co.uk/gbuk/techtalk/how-to-pick-an-eco-friendly-dishwasher/

Average water a washing machine uses: inthewash.co.uk/washing-machines/how-much-water-does-a-washing-machine-use/

The average pipe uses 170 litres of water in 10 minutes: tameside.gov.uk/EnergyEfficiency/Top-Tips-%E2%80%93-July-Avoid-Using-Hosepipes

Sprinklers can use up to 1,000 litres an hour: southwestwater.co.uk/siteassets/documents/uwu-0618-web-version.pdf

On average, the annual rainfall in the UK is around 1.2 metres: statista.com/statistics/610602/annual-rainfall-uk/

DIGITAL

It's estimated that the carbon footprint of our gadgets, the internet and all the systems supporting them account for 3.7% of global greenhouse gas emissions: escp.eu/fr/node/81672

The cumulative emissions from internet usage amount to around 1.7 billion tonnes a year – 45% more than the aviation industry: green-clicks.com/digitally-eco-friendly

When Cristiano Ronaldo posts an image on instagram 36 megawatt hours of power are needed to show it to his 240million followers. That's enough electricity to power 10 UK homes for a year: twitter.com/c4dispatches/status/1328413419649851392

It's estimated that data centres are responsible for 1-1.5% of global electricity usage: davidmytton.blog/how-much-energy-do-data-centers-use

The energy needed for a single internet search is around 1 KJ – enough to power a 60W light bulb for 17 seconds: business.directenergy.com/blog/2017/november/powering-a-google-search

There are now 4.1 billion people using the internet (53.6% of the world's population): itu.int/en/mediacentre/Pages/2019-PR19.aspx

The number of data centres around the world has grown from 500,000 in 2012 to more than 7 million today: datacenterknowledge.com/industry-perspectives/data-center-dilemma-our-data-destroying-environment

The amount of energy used by data centres continues to double every four years: https://www.workspace-technology.com/is-it-possible-to-sustain-energy-guzzling-data-centres-whilst-trying-to-save-the-planet

40% of the energy used in data centres is to keep the tech equipment cool: nature.com/articles/d41586-018-06610-y

It's estimated that the average person in the UK spends 6.4 hours a day online: uswitch.com/mobiles/screentime-report

Globally, the world's email usage generates as much CO_2 as having an extra seven million cars on the roads; The average email (with no picture attachment) uses about 4g of CO_2; The average person (in the developed world) adds 136kg of CO_2 to their carbon footprint from the emails they send and receive – the equivalent of driving 230 miles; Sending 65 emails is roughly equivalent to driving 1km in a car: sciencefocus.com/planet-earth/the-thought-experiment-what-is-the-carbon-footprint-of-an-email/

Brits send 64 million unnecessary emails every day, with 'thank you' and 'thanks' coming in at the top; If every adult in the UK sent one less 'thank you' email, it could save 16,433 tonnes of carbon a year – the equivalent of cancelling 81,152 flights from the UK to Madrid: ovoenergy.com/blog/ovo-news/think-before-you-thank

300 billions emails are sent every day: statista.com/statistics/456500/daily-number-of-e-mails-worldwide

Using your phone for an hour a day produces the equivalent of 63kg CO_2 a year – about the same as driving 158 miles in an average car: reboxed.co/blogs/outsidethebox/the-carbon-footprint-of-your-phone-and-how-you-can-reduce-it

Streaming videos account for 60% of internet traffic: ncta.com/whats-new/report-where-does-the-majority-of-internet-traffic-come

4G mobile networks consume four times the amount of electricity as WiFi; One study estimates that video streaming generates up to 300 million tonnes of carbon dioxide – approximately 1% of global emissions – but it has been disputed: theshiftproject.org/wp-content/uploads/2020/06/2020-06_Did-TSP-overestimate-the-carbon-footprint-of-online-video_EN.pdf

Netflix consumes 15% of that traffic, and uses 451,000 megawatts hours per year – enough to power 37,000 homes: safetydetectives.com/blog/how-to-reduce-digital-carbon-footprint

12.6 million households in the UK now have at least one streaming subscription: finder.com/uk/tv-streaming-statistics

The smaller the device, the less energy needed to watch something. A 50-inch LED TV used 100 times the energy of a smart phone to watch the same show: iea.org/commentaries/the-carbon-footprint-of-streaming-video-fact-checking-the-headlines

A study found that 4.6 billion streams of Luis Fonsi and Daddy Yankee's song Despacito used as much energy as the annual electricity consumption of Chad, Guinea-Bissau, Somalia, Sierra Leone and the Central African Republic: aljazeera.com/economy/2020/2/28/emissions-possible-streaming-music-swells-carbon-footprints

Leaving one computer on overnight for a year creates enough CO_2 to fill a double decker bus: re-limited.co.uk/media/87144/green-week-stickers.pdf

Electricity used by "sleeping devices" can make up 10% of household energy use; The average house has 40 products that are constantly drawing power, even when they are not in active use: money.howstuffworks.com/personal-finance/budgeting/how-much-save-unplugging-appliances.htm

The average UK household spends £30 per year leaving devices on standby: money.co.uk/energy/guides/why-you-should-not-leave-devices-on-standby-mode

76% of households leave electrical items on standby with 38% admitting to doing so all the time: current-news.co.uk/news/leaving-appliances-on-standby-cost-uk-households-227-million-a-year-764

80% of the carbon emissions associated with a mobile phone are generated during manufacturing: mobilemuster.com.au/how-do-you-reduce-the-impact-of-your-mobile

In the UK, around 1 million tonnes of electrical waste is disposed of each year: recyclenow.com/recycling-knowledge/how-is-it-recycled/electricals

Globally, we create 53 million tonnes of electrical waste: itu.int/en/ITU-D/Environment/Documents/Toolbox/GEM_2020_def.pdf

BUY LESS

It's estimated that we are exposed to between 6,000 and 10,000 adverts a day: ppcprotect.com/blog/strategy/how-many-ads-do-we-see-a-day/

The UN says that by 2050 the equivalent of almost three planets could be required to provide the natural resources needed to sustain current lifestyles given the growth in global population: un.org/sustainabledevelopment/sustainable-consumption-production

It's estimated that by 2030 we could run out of landfill space in the UK: groundsure.com/resources/the-reducing-landfill-capacity-in-the-uk

The average drill is used for only 13 minutes during its lifetime, yet most households have one: greenallianceblog.org.uk/2017/05/26/why-hasnt-the-sharing-revolution-taken-off

UK households spend an average of £371.30 on household tools every year: propertywire.com/how-many-brits-buy-household-tools-and-never-use-them

Data shows that there has been a 404% increase in pre-loved sales since 2018: ebayinc.com/stories/press-room/uk/second-hand-sales-skyrocket-in-2020-as-fashionistas-shift-to-thrift/

FASHION

The fashion industry is also the second-largest consumer of water in the world: weforum.org/agenda/2020/01/fashion-industry-carbon-unsustainable-environment-pollution

The fashion industry pollutes water with microplastics, chemicals and clothing dye: forbes.com/sites/mikescott/2020/09/19/out-of-fashionthe-hidden-cost-of-clothing-is-a-water-pollution-crisis/?sh=2f5ffb4589ce

The fashion industry accounts for 10% of all emissions; The fashion industry uses 93 billion cubic meters of water every year – enough to meet the consumption needs of five million people: worldbank.org/en/news/feature/2019/09/23/costo-moda-medio-ambiente

Global emissions from textile production are equivalent to 1.2 billion tonnes of CO_2 – more than the carbon footprint of international flights & shipping combined: climatecouncil.org.au/resources/fast-fashion-climate-change

150 million trees are cut down every year to make our clothes: eco-age.com/resources/is-your-clothing-destroying-the-rainforest

The average life of an item of clothes these days is 2.2 years in the UK: wrap.org.uk/resources/guide/textiles/clothing

Around 350,000 tonnes of clothes, with an estimated value of £140 million, go to landfill every year in the UK: clothesaid.co.uk/about-us/facts-on-clothes-recycling

It's thought that we now own five times the amount of clothes that our grandparents did and that clothing production has roughly doubled since 2000: sustainyourstyle.org/en/whats-wrong-with-the-fashion-industry

British people buy more clothes per person than any other nationality in Europe: publications.parliament.uk/pa/cm201719/cmselect/cmenvaud/1952/full-report.html

If we carry on as we are, it is estimated that by 2030 clothing consumption will have increased globally by 63% (from 62 million tonnes to 102 million tonnes): cleanclothes.org/climate-change

We wear 20% of our clothes 80% of the time: thecut.com/2013/04/you-only-wear-20-percent-of-your-wardrobe.html

33% of women consider an outfit old after only three wears: nytimes.com/2021/10/27/business/rent-the-runway-ipo.html

85% of our unwanted clothes end up in landfill: bbc.com/future/article/20200710-why-clothes-are-so-hard-to-recycle

Half of clothes sold by online fashion brands are made from 'virgin plastic' such as polyester, nylon and acrylic: nationalobserver.com/2021/06/14/news/half-clothes-sold-online-fashion-brands-made-virgin-plastic

Washing clothes releases 500,000 tons of microfibres into the ocean each year, the equivalent of 50 billion plastic bags: lifelabs.design/journal/microfibers-dont-have-to-end-up-in-the-ocean

It takes over 2,700 litres of water to make a cotton shirt – the amount you'd drink in three years: worldwildlife.org/stories/the-impact-of-a-cotton-t-shirt

Cotton also uses more pesticides and insecticides to grow than any other single major crop in the world: pan-uk.org/cotton.

In the UK, 70 million pairs are sold every year; It takes about 10,000 litres of water to produce a pair of jeans: standard.co.uk/insider/fashion/sustainable-denim-a3810546.html

Producing one pair also creates as much greenhouse gas as driving a car for 80 miles: wri.org/insights/numbers-economic-social-and-environmental-impacts-fast-fashion

Textile dyeing and 'finishing' is one of the biggest water polluters on our planet: nrdc.org/issues/encourage-textile-manufacturers-reduce-pollution

Organic cotton uses 71% less water to grow than conventional cotton: sustainyourstyle. org/en/organic-cotton

Lengthening the life of your clothes by one year can decrease their carbon footprint by 24%: refinery29.com/en-gb/clothing-repair-alteration-sustainability

Nine out of 10 items of clothing end up in landfill long before they should; 70% of clothing waste is preventable with better care habits: vanish.co.uk/press-centre/oxwash/

Washing laundry at 60°C and drying it in the tumble-dryer produces the equivalent of 3.3kg of CO_2. If you switch to washing at 30°C and line-drying, that amount goes down to 0.6kg: bbc.com/future/article/20200326-the-hidden-impact-of-your-daily-water-use

CELEBRATIONS

An extra 30% of rubbish is produced and discarded over the festive period: businesswaste. co.uk/christmas-waste-facts-its-not-very-jolly

The average British adult spends £500 on Christmas gifts: finder.com/uk/christmas-shopping-statistics

At Christmas, 54 million platefuls of food are wasted: cleanstreets.westminster.gov.uk/ christmas2021

A party for 30 people can send more than 100 single-use items to a landfill: partykitnetwork.org

It is estimated we use 4.7 billion plastic straws in England every year: gov.uk/government/ news/start-of-ban-on-plastic-straws-stirrers-and-cotton-buds

One in five unwanted Christmas gifts ends up in landfill – that's 23 million presents worth approximately £42million: Research by the UK Gift Card and Voucher Association.

A third of people in the UK don't even think about the negative aspects of the gifting process: rajapack.co.uk/blog-uk/gifting-brits-gift-giving-habits/

80% of kids' plastic toys end up in landfill or incinerators, while 90% have a lifespan of just 6 months: Research by ecoBirdy, stylus.com/recycled-plastic-toys-transformed-into-kids-furniture

227,000 miles of wrapping paper is thrown away each year – enough to stretch to the moon: gwp.co.uk/guides/christmas-packaging-facts/

Each year, a forest the size of Wales is required to provide all the paper used in Britain: wragwrap.com/wrapping-paper-facts

TRANSPORT

Transport accounts for 27% of the UK's total emissions. Of this 91% came from road transport vehicles: https://www.gov.uk/government/statistics/transport-and-environment-statistics-autumn-2021/transport-and-environment-statistics-autumn-2021

Carbon dioxide emissions from transport in the UK totalled 97.2 million metric tons in 2020: assets.publishing.service.gov.uk/government/uploads/system/uploads/attachment_data/file/984685/transport-and-environment-statistics-2021.pdf

77% of households in Great Britain have a car: racfoundation.org/wp-content/uploads/2017/11/car-ownership-in-great-britain-leibling-171008-report.pdf

Four out of every five miles travelled in the UK happens in a car: greenpeace.org.uk/news/electric-cars-greener-petrol-cars

Just under half the population of England and Wales travel less than 3.1 miles to work; 20% of all journeys in the UK are less than one mile; cycling-embassy.org.uk/wiki/cycling-is-not-practical-for-the-transportation-or-commuting-needs-of-most-people

56% of car journeys in the UK are under five miles: assets.publishing.service.gov.uk/government/uploads/system/uploads/attachment_data/file/729521/national-travel-survey-2017.pdf.

Nine out of 10 people breathe polluted air that exceeds WHO guidelines: who.int/news/item/02-05-2018-9-out-of-10-people-worldwide-breathe-polluted-air-but-more-countries-are-taking-action

In the UK, between 28,000 and 36,000 deaths a year are linked to air pollution: gov.uk/government/news/public-health-england-publishes-air-pollution-evidence-review

In 2019, 84% of journeys were made by car, van or taxi: assets.publishing.service.gov.uk/government/uploads/system/uploads/attachment_data/file/945829/tsgb-2020.pdf

In 2002, cars produced 78 million metric tons of carbon dioxide equivalent; cars in the UK emitted 67.7 million metric tons of carbon dioxide equivalent in 2019: statista.com/statistics/509066/greenhouse-gas-emissionspassenger-cars-in-the-united-kingdom-uk/

All greenhouse gas equivalent calculations made using: epa.gov/energy/greenhouse-gas-equivalences-calculator

The introduction of E10 petrol at UK forecourts could cut transport emissions by 750,000 tonnes a year – the equivalent of taking 350,000 cars off the road, or all the cars in North Yorkshire: gov.uk/guidance/e10-petrol-explained

Research suggests that one in five car journeys we make are unnecessary: bewiser.co.uk/news/car-insurance/research-claims-one-five-car-journeys-unnecessary

An average car emits approximately 228g of CO_2e per mile: https://www.nimblefins.co.uk/average-co2-emissions-car-uk

20% of journeys under one mile are made by car: cycling-embassy.org.uk/wiki/cycling-is-not-practical-for-the-transportation-or-commuting-needs-of-most-people

The average distance travelled to school is 2.5 miles (1.6 miles for primary, 3.4 for secondary): assets.publishing.service.gov.uk/government/uploads/system/uploads/attachment_data/file/476635/travel-to-school.pdf

3.2 million people die every year from physical inactivity: who.int/data/gho/indicator-metadata-registry/imr-details/3416

It's recommended that we do a minimum of 150 minutes of moderate intensity (such as walking) exercise a week: nhs.uk/live-well/exercise/

This will reduce the risk of dementia, depression and stroke by 30%, breast cancer by 25%, bowel cancer by 45% and type 2 diabetes by a whopping 50%: aomrc.org.uk/wp-content/uploads/2016/05/Exercise_the_Miracle_Cure_0215.pdf

Walking 1km more, along with eating less meat and insulating more homes, is also one of the ways that could save the NHS up to £17 billion pounds a year: acmedsci.ac.uk/file-download/11365167

During the height of the pandemic, bike sales rose by 22%: mintel.com/press-centre/leisure/the-great-british-bike-boom-brits-bought-over-3-million-bikes-in-2020

Taking the train rather than driving can cut your emissions by 75%; A journey via bus emits 40% less carbon dioxide than driving the same route in the car: https://ourworldindata.org/travel-carbon-footprint

A 15% increase in coach journeys each year could lead to approximately 47 million fewer cars on the road, saving over a quarter of a million tonnes of carbon dioxide; The average emissions per passenger per coach journey are around five times lower than travelling by car: cpt-uk.org/media/5qiagic1/coach-strategy-full-strategy-document.pdf

On average, cars cost 14.6p per mile for fuel, so in terms of price per mile: nimblefins. co.uk/largest-car-insurance-companies/average-cost-petrol-car

There are 11,000 miles of train lines in the UK, 2,500 stations and 1,500 trains each day: projectbritain.com/transport.html

An idling engine can produce up to twice the emissions of a car in motion: staffordshire. gov.uk/DoingOurBit/Get-Inspired/Clean-green-and-safe/Air-aware/Turning-your-car-off.aspx

The average cost of owning a car in the UK is £256 per month: nimblefins.co.uk/cheap-car-insurance/average-cost-run-car-uk

English households have an average of 1.3 cars at their disposal: nimblefins.co.uk/cheap-car-insurance/number-cars-great-britain

It will cost you around 25% more in fuel to drive at 70mph than 50mph: ageas.co.uk/solved/your-car/how-to-maximise-your-fuel-efficiency

11.6% of new car sales in 2021 were electric; As of December 2021, there were an estimated 370,000 electric cars on the road in the UK and 710,000 plug-in hybrids: heycar.co.uk/blog/electric-cars-statistics-and-projections

From 2030, the government has banned the sale of new petrol and diesel cars in the UK. And hybrid cars will be phased out by 2035. ft.com/content/6c112691-fa2f-491a-85b2-b03fc2e38a30

Many car manufacturers are aiming to beat this target, with Peugeot saying they'll be fully electric by 2025 and Vauxhall by 2028: carscoops.com/2021/07/peugeot-will-electrify-its-whole-range-in-europe-by-2025; vauxhall.co.uk/experience/vauxhall-news/2021/07/vauxhall-all-electric-in-2028.html

Even the most efficient petrol cars use only 12-30% of the fuel's energy to create movement (and other useful functions). The rest is wasted in heat and noise; Electric cars use around 77% of the energy they produce to move the car; An electric car has about half the climate impact over its lifetime compared to an average petrol or diesel car; Electric cars get more than twice as many miles out of the same amount of energy than conventional cars: greenpeace.org.uk/news/electric-cars-greener-petrol-cars

Electric cars cost more than £1,300 less to run each year than an equivalent car with a petrol or diesel engine: thisismoney.co.uk/money/cars/article-9811055/EVs-cheaper-petrol-diesel-cars-7-year-period.html

There are now more than 42,000 (and counting!) charge point connectors across the UK in more than 15,500 locations: edfenergy.com/electric-cars/charging-points

The average price of a new electric car in the UK is £44,000, but they range from around £17,000 to upwards of £138,000; It can range from around £2.36 up to £15.49 to fully charge: nimblefins.co.uk/average-cost-electric-car-uk

On average, these cost between £800 and £1,100, but the government is currently offering grants to cover up to 75% of the cost of new chargers being installed, with a maximum contribution of £350: theecoexperts.co.uk/electric-vehicles/charging-point-installation-cost; gov.uk/government/publications/customer-guidance-electric-vehicle-homecharge-scheme/electric-vehicle-homecharge-scheme-guidance-for-customers

Aviation alone is responsible for 2.5% of global emissions: ourworldindata.org/co2-emissions-from-aviation

Short-haul flights emit more CO_2e per person per mile than long haul: robeco.com/uk/insights/2020/02/short-haul-flights-are-the-worst-offenders-for-co2.html

A single journey from London to Paris by plane costs from £64, and takes on average a total time of 4 hours 40 minutes and emits 59kg equivalent of carbon dioxide. By train, the same journey will cost from £49, take an average of 2 hours 55 minutes and emit 2kg equivalent carbon dioxide: granthaminstitute.com/gicj7413-plane-vs-train-infographic-01/

One return flight from London to Sydney will use around 40% of the average person's annual carbon footprint: wanderlust.co.uk/content/to-fly-or-not-to-fly

Travelling by coach instead of plane can cut your carbon emissions by 90%, while a train journey can reduce your emissions by 75%: bbc.co.uk/news/science-environment-49349566

If every passenger who took a flight from Heathrow to Frankfurt in a typical year (pre-Covid) packed one fewer pairs of jeans, they would have saved 59 tonnes of CO_2: flyaware.com/your-journey/pack-lighter/how-packing-lighter-can-reduce-emissions/

A cruise liner such as Queen Mary 2 emits 0.43kg of CO_2 per passenger mile compared to 0.257kg on a long-haul flight: innovate-eco.com/are-cruise-ships-more-polluting-than-planes/

Norway was the first country to launch the first hybrid electric-powered cruise liner, which lowers CO_2 emissions by 20%: reuters.com/article/us-shipping-electric-idUSKCN1TW27E

RECYCLE RIGHT

All facts: recyclingbins.co.uk/recycling-facts and recyclenow.com.

THIS BOOK'S JOURNEY

Before becoming the book that you are holding in your hands now, *Everyday Ways To Save The Planet* started its life in forests from a variety of locations – from Brazil to Belgium, Sweden to Spain – and always from a sustainably chosen forest and an audited, controlled source. It was then transported over to Poland, for arrival at the Arctic Paper Kostrzyn mill, which has recently reduced its CO_2 emissions from paper production by more than 50%. Here it made its second transformation – this time into an FSC® and PEFC™ certified paper, falling under FSC Chain of Custody (CoC) certification.

The paper then caught the eye of renowned UK printers Bell & Bain Ltd in Glasgow, who purchased it transparently in accordance with their environmental policies. It was transported from Poland to Immingham, England, and stored along with all the other FSC® and PEFC™ certified paper, ready for Bell & Bain to use. After a (slightly shorter) journey up to Glasgow, it was here that it made its final (and most impressive) transformation, from paper into a first-class book of the highest environmental integrity. The book is printed using uncoated stock, meaning that it is almost entirely free of additional lamination or chemical coating.

Bell & Bain are a 190-year-old, ISO 14001 and FSC Chain of Custody-accredited, book and journal printer who work with many publishers in the UK to ensure that books are printed and distributed responsibly. At every step of the book printing and binding process, excess material trimmed off is extracted into their baling system, ready to be recycled in its totality by an equally highly environmentally-accredited contractor, Highlander International Recycling. From storeroom to printing press, printing press to folding machine, folding machine to binding line, this book has been subject to the care and expert craft of multiple individuals before being loaded onto the final delivery truck towards the book shop where it was bought by you!